PLATE I. THE RADIO TELESCOPE, JODRELL BANK
(*Husband & Co., Consulting Engineers*)

PLATE II. RECIRCULATING BALL NUT AND LEADSCREW

(*Bristol Siddeley Engines Ltd.*)

Applied Mechanics

Applied Mechanics

by

John HANNAH

B.Sc. (Eng.), A.M.I.Mech.E.

Senior Lecturer in the Department of Mechanical
Engineering, Enfield Technical College

and

M. J. HILLIER

M.Sc. (Eng.), D.I.C., B.Sc.

London:
SIR ISAAC PITMAN & SONS LTD.

First published 1962
Reprinted 1966

SIR ISAAC PITMAN & SONS LTD.
PITMAN HOUSE, PARKER STREET, KINGSWAY, LONDON, W.C.2
THE PITMAN PRESS, BATH
PITMAN HOUSE, BOUVERIE STREET, CARLTON, MELBOURNE
22–25 BECKETT'S BUILDINGS, PRESIDENT STREET, JOHANNESBURG

ASSOCIATED COMPANIES
PITMAN MEDICAL PUBLISHING COMPANY LTD.
46 CHARLOTTE STREET, LONDON, W.1

PITMAN PUBLISHING CORPORATION
20 EAST 46TH STREET, NEW YORK, N.Y. 10017

SIR ISAAC PITMAN & SONS (CANADA) LTD.
(INCORPORATING THE COMMERCIAL TEXT BOOK COMPANY)
PITMAN HOUSE, 381–383 CHURCH STREET. TORPNTO

MADE IN GREAT BRITAIN AT THE PITMAN PRESS, BATH
F6—(T.909)

Preface

THIS text covers the work in Applied Mechanics for the final year of the Ordinary National Certificate Course in Engineering. It should also be useful to those studying for the Joint Part I examination of the Engineering Institutions and for the first year examinations of Diploma in Technology and Degree Courses.

An attempt has been made to develop the theory so that the number of formulae to be memorized is kept to a minimum. Emphasis is placed on the relations between forces, and the diagrams have been designed to this end. Each major topic includes worked examples, and specially prepared problems to be attempted. These unworked problems are relevant to the immediately preceding text to simplify the selection of suitable exercises for practice. The examples are of examination standard except where introductory exercises are required.

The practical aspects of the subject have not been neglected. The nature of experimental error, graphical work, the practical aspects of friction, the properties of materials and of real fluids have each been discussed in rather more detail than is now usual at this level.

Work which is normally covered in previous years has been omitted or revised only briefly. For example, a knowledge of centres of gravity, uniform velocity and acceleration, and elementary statics is assumed. Important results are, however, restated for reference. Again, purely mathematical derivations, such as those for moments of inertia, are omitted, the results only being stated.

Finally, the engineer is often accustomed to solving dynamics problems using the idea of an "inertia force." The concept of inertia force is used consistently throughout this text.

The authors are indebted to their colleagues and students at Enfield Technical College for helpful criticism and suggestions. Grateful acknowledgments are due to the following for the supply of photographs and information: The French National Railways; The Institution of Mechanical Engineers; Husband and Co., Consulting Engineers; The Bristol Siddeley Engine Co., Ltd.

We would like also to thank Mr. W. G. Clouter, Technical Editor of Sir Isaac Pitman & Sons, Ltd., for his interest, forbearance and guidance during the preparation of this book.

JOHN HANNAH
M. J. HILLIER

Contents

List of Plates

1

Statics

THE following notes on some elementary principles and theorems of statics are intended as a reminder of work which the student should have already covered and which will be required in subsequent chapters.

1.1. Force

A *force* is simply a push or a pull and may be measured by its effect on a body. A force may change or tend to change the shape or size of a body; if applied to a body at rest the force will move or tend to move it; if applied to a body already moving the force will change the motion.

A force may be measured by the weight it will just support or by comparing its effect with that of a standard weight (Fig. 1.1). Thus

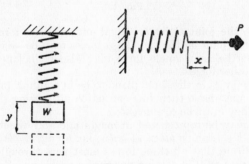

Fig. 1.1

if a standard weight W (pound weight, lb-wt or lb) is suspended from a spring the extension of the spring is said to be due to a force of W lb-wt. If y is the extension produced by W and a force P on the

1

same spring produces an extension x then the value of P is measured in terms of W by simple proportion: thus

$$\frac{P}{W} = \frac{x}{y}$$

providing the spring is not "overstretched."

Proper specification of a force requires knowledge of three quantities—

1. its magnitude
2. its point of application
3. its line of action.

Since a force has magnitude, direction and sense it is a *vector quantity* and may be represented by a straight line of definite length.

1.2. Forces in Equilibrium

Statics is the study of forces in *equilibrium* ("in balance"). A single force cannot exist alone and is unbalanced. For equilibrium it must be balanced by an equal and opposite force acting along the same straight line. Thus in Fig. 1.2 the load of 1 ton *on* the tie is

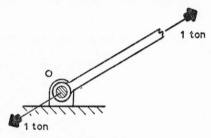

Fig. 1.2

balanced at the joint O by an equal and opposite force of 1 ton exerted *by* the joint *on* the tie. Thus forces may be said to exist in pairs. Nevertheless a single force may also be balanced by any number of other forces.

For three forces in the same plane to be in equilibrium—

(*a*) they must have their lines of action all passing through one point, i.e. they must be *concurrent*;

(*b*) they may be represented in magnitude and direction by the three sides of a triangle *taken in order*, i.e. by a *triangle of forces*.

The condition that all three forces must pass through one point is particularly useful in solving mechanics problems. For example, the light jib crane shown in Fig. 1.3 (*a*) is in equilibrium under the action of three forces. The jib carries a load W at A; the free end is supported by a cable in which the tension is T; the end C is pinned to the wall by a joint which allows free rotation of the jib at C. The reaction P of the joint on the jib is completely unknown;

the magnitude of T is unknown but its direction must be that of the cable. Since the three forces are in balance their lines of action must pass through one point, i.e. where the lines of action of W and T intersect (point Z, Fig. 1.3 (*a*)). The line of action of P is therefore found by joining C to Z.

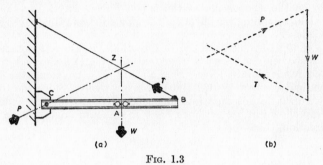

FIG. 1.3

Since the magnitude of W is known and the directions of the three forces have been determined the triangle of forces can now be drawn, Fig. 1.3 (*b*).

1.3. Resultant and Equilibrant: Parallelogram of Forces

The forces W and T of Fig. 1.3 may also be represented by the two sides **ab** and **ad**, respectively, of the parallelogram **abcd**, Fig. 1.4

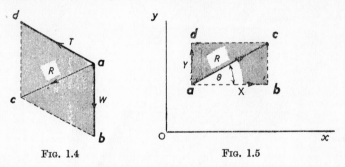

FIG. 1.4   FIG. 1.5

The diagonal **ac**, taken in the sense **a** to **c**, is the *resultant* R of the two forces W and T acting together. This resultant force is equivalent to, and may replace completely, these two forces. The resultant **ac** may be balanced by an equal and opposite force **ca** called the *equilibrant*. This is in fact the force P at the pin-joint, Fig. 1.3 (*a*). This construction, by which two forces are replaced by a single equivalent force, is known as the *parallelogram of forces*. It can only be used if the two forces are specified in both magnitude *and* direction.

1.4. Resolution of Forces

Since the forces represented by **ab** and **ad** in Fig. 1.4 may be replaced completely by a single force **ac**, it is often useful to carry out the reverse process, i.e. to replace a single force by two other forces in any two convenient directions. These two forces are then known as the *components* of the single force. Physically this is equivalent to finding the effects of the single force in the two chosen directions.

The most convenient choice of directions in which to *resolve* a force is in two directions at right angles. Fig. 1.5 shows a force $R = \mathbf{ac}$ resolved into forces $X = \mathbf{ab}$ and $Y = \mathbf{ad}$ along the two perpendicular directions Ox and Oy, respectively. Since the three forces shown do not represent independent forces the components of R are shown in broken lines. Let R make an angle θ with the Ox direction, then

$$\mathbf{ab} = \mathbf{ac} \cos \theta$$

i.e.

$$X = R \cos \theta$$

and

$$\mathbf{ad} = \mathbf{ac} \sin \theta$$

or

$$Y = R \sin \theta$$

1.5. Polygon of Forces

If more than three forces act at the same point and are in equilibrium, they may be represented in magnitude and direction by the

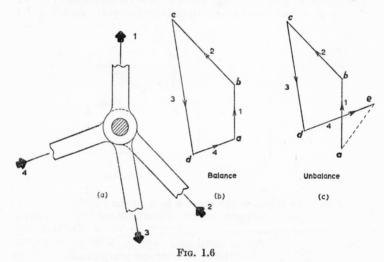

Fig. 1.6

sides of a polygon *taken in order*. "Taken in order" refers to the order of drawing the sides of the polygon and not to the order in which the forces are taken from the space diagram.

Suppose the four forces 1, 2, 3 and 4 acting at the joint shown in Fig. 1.6 (*a*) to be in balance; they may then be represented by the four sides of the polygon **abcd**, Fig. 1.6 (*b*). This is a closed polygon since the forces are in equilibrium. If the forces are not in balance the polygon will not close and the required closing line gives the equilibrant or the equal and opposite resultant force, depending on the sense in which it is taken. Fig. 1.6 (*c*) shows the force polygon assuming unbalance. The forces 1, 2, 3, 4 are represented by lines **ab**, **bc**, **cd** and **de**, respectively. To close the polygon and maintain a balance of forces requires the equilibrant **ea** taken in the sense **e** to **a**. The resultant of the original set of four unbalanced forces is given by the line **ae** and acts in the sense **a** to **e**.

1.6. Moment of a Force

The *moment* of a force P about a point O (Fig. 1.7) is the product of the force and the perpendicular distance x of its line of action from O, thus—

$$\text{moment of } P \text{ about } O = Px$$

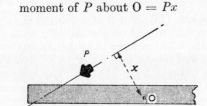

Fɪɢ. 1.7

1.7. Couple

A pair of equal and opposite parallel forces, which do not act in the same straight line, form a *couple*, Fig. 1.8. The total moment

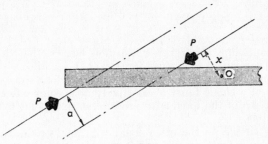

Fɪɢ. 1.8

M of the two forces P about any point O in the plane of the couple is

$$M = P(a + x) - Px$$
$$= Pa$$

This moment is independent of the distance x and is therefore *the same about any point in the same plane*. The turning effect of the couple is also the same wherever it may be placed in the plane.

The magnitude Pa of a couple is known as its *moment* or *torque*, although the term torque is usually restricted to a moment tending to twist a shaft.

1.8. Balance of Moments

Consider any system of forces which do not act at a point. Take moments about any arbitrary point and let clockwise moments be positive and anticlockwise moments be negative. Then for balance of moments we must have—

clockwise moments = anticlockwise moments

or *the algebraic sum of the moments of all the forces about the same point is zero*.

1.9. Resolution of a Force into a Force and a Couple

Consider the arm OA pivoted at a bearing at O and subjected to a force P at A which acts perpendicularly to OA (Fig. 1.9). We wish to know the effect of force P at the bearing O. Suppose therefore two equal and opposite forces P to be introduced at O acting parallel to the existing force P at A. The system of forces is not upset and the resultant force is unaltered since the two new forces

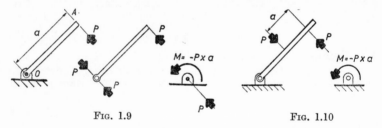

Fɪɢ. 1.9   Fɪɢ. 1.10

are self-cancelling. However, it can now be seen that the effect of P at A is equivalent to a single force P at O, together with a couple of moment Pa tending to turn the arm anticlockwise. The effect therefore of a single force P on a body at a point offset from the line of action of the force is to produce at that point both a force *and* a couple.

A pure couple on the other hand will not introduce this single out-of-balance force at any point. In Fig. 1.10 the two forces P form a pure couple; they are self-balancing and no force is produced at the bearing (unlike the previous case). The couple due to the two forces is of course out of balance and can only be balanced by an equal and opposite couple in the same plane. This result is independent of the position of the couple.

1.10. The General Conditions of Equilibrium

We now require to consider the balance of *any* system of forces, in a plane, which do *not* all act through the same point. Since any force may be replaced by a similar force at any other point, together with a couple, then each of the forces may be considered as acting at any one point, provided that allowance is made for all the couples produced. For complete equilibrium of the system, therefore, there must be no unbalanced force *or* couple. *For force balance a polygon of forces may be drawn and must close for equilibrium. For couple balance the algebraic sum of the moments of all the forces about any point must be zero.*

Alternatively it is often convenient to resolve all the forces in the same two mutually-perpendicular directions. Consider the force system shown in Fig. 1.11. The forces may be resolved in the two

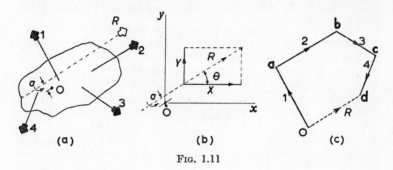

(a)   (b)   (c)

FIG. 1.11

directions parallel to Ox and Oy. Let X and Y be the algebraic sum of the components of all the forces in the Ox- and Oy-directions, respectively; and let M be the algebraic sum of the moments of all the forces about any chosen point O. Then the resultant force R is given by Fig. 1.11 (b)—

$$R^2 = X^2 + Y^2$$

and the line of action of the resultant is at an angle θ to Ox given by—

$$\tan \theta = \frac{Y}{X}$$

The resultant couple M is the same about any point in its plane hence it may be obtained by calculating the algebraic sum of the moments of all the forces about any point O.

The conditions of equilibrium are therefore—

$$R = 0 \quad (\text{i.e. } X = 0, \text{ and } Y = 0)$$

and $\qquad\qquad M = 0$

Otherwise, if R and M are not zero, to find the *position* of the resultant R we calculate the distance a of its line of action from any chosen point O, Fig. 1.11 (*a*). The resultant R may be replaced by a force acting at O, together with a couple of moment $R \times a$ about O. This couple is equal in magnitude and sense to the resultant couple M, i.e.—

$$R \times a = M$$

This determines the distance a from O of the line of action of R.

If $M = 0$, then $a = 0$ and the resultant R passes through the chosen point O.

If M is not zero, then as R becomes very small the distance a becomes very large so that $R \times a$ is always equal to M.

Note—If the force polygon is drawn, Fig. 1.11 (*c*), the closing line **od** gives the resultant R in magnitude, sense and direction but *not* in position. To obtain the position we must take moments about some point O.

Example. Fig. 1.12 shows the tensions in the tight and slack sides of a rope passing round a pulley of weight 80 lb. Calculate the resultant force on the bearings, and its direction.

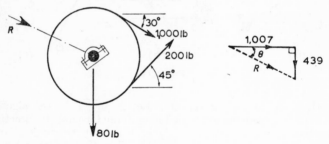

Fig. 1.12

Resolving horizontally—

unbalanced force, $X = 1{,}000 \cos 30° + 200 \cos 45°$
$$= 1{,}007 \text{ lb (to the right)}$$

Resolving vertically—

unbalanced force, $Y = 1{,}000 \sin 30° - 200 \sin 45° + 80$
$$= 439 \text{ lb (downwards)}$$

Resultant force R is given by

$$R^2 = X^2 + Y^2$$

i.e.
$$R = \sqrt{(1{,}007^2 + 439^2)}$$
$$= \textbf{1,098 lb}$$

The line of action of R makes an angle θ with the horizontal given by

$$\tan \theta = \frac{439}{1{,}007} = 0{\cdot}436$$

thus
$$\theta = 23° \ 34'$$

Fig. 1.12 shows the base of the bearing inclined to this resultant thrust in order that the cap bolts shall not carry any lifting load.

Example. Find the magnitude, direction and position of the resultant of the system of forces shown in Fig. 1.13. The forces act at the four corners of a square of 3 in. side.

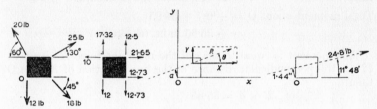

FIG. 1.13

Solution

Force (lb)	Vertical component (lb)	Moment of vertical component about O (lb-in.)
20	$+20 \sin 60° = \ \ 17{\cdot}32$	0
12	-12	0
18	$-18 \sin 45° = -12{\cdot}73$	$+12{\cdot}73 \times 3 = \ \ \ 38{\cdot}2$
25	$+25 \sin 30° = \ \ 12{\cdot}5$	$-12{\cdot}5 \times 3 = -37{\cdot}5$
Totals	$Y = \ +5{\cdot}09$	$+0{\cdot}7$

Force (lb)	Horizontal component (lb)	Moment of horizontal component about O (lb-in.)
20	$-20 \cos 60° = -10$	$-10 \times 3 = -30$
12	0	0
18	$+18 \cos 45° = +12{\cdot}73$	0
25	$+25 \cos 30° = +21{\cdot}65$	$+21{\cdot}65 \times 3 = \ \ 64{\cdot}95$
Totals	$X = +24{\cdot}38$	$+34{\cdot}95$

The horizontal and vertical components of each force together with the moments of these components about point O are shown in the above table. Upward vertical forces and horizontal forces to the right are positive, clockwise moments are positive.

$$R^2 = X^2 + Y^2$$

therefore

$$R = \sqrt{(24 \cdot 38^2 + 5 \cdot 09^2)}$$

$$= \mathbf{24 \cdot 8\ lb}$$

$$\tan \theta = \frac{5 \cdot 09}{24 \cdot 38} = 0 \cdot 209$$

thus

$$\theta = \mathbf{11° \ 48'} \text{ above the horizontal}$$

Total moment about O $= + 0 \cdot 7 + 34 \cdot 95$

$$= + 35 \cdot 65 \text{ lb-in. (clockwise)}$$

This moment is equal to that of the resultant force R about O. If a is the perpendicular distance of the line of action of R from O then

$$R \times a = 35 \cdot 65$$

$$a = \frac{35 \cdot 65}{24 \cdot 8} = \mathbf{1 \cdot 44\ in.}$$

Therefore R must act along a line 1·44 in. from O as shown in Fig. 1.13, such that it produces a *clockwise* moment about O and is inclined at 11° 48' to the horizontal. This solution may be checked by drawing the force polygon to obtain the magnitude and direction of R. To find the total moment about O, measure from a scale drawing the perpendicular distance of the line of action of each force from O.

PROBLEMS

1. Fig. 1.14 shows a link AB which is maintained in equilibrium by three forces at A, G and B. The force at A acts along line XX. The force at G is

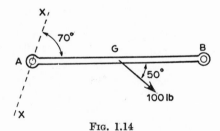

Fig. 1.14

100 lb and acts at 50° to the link as shown. Find the magnitude and sense of the force at A and the magnitude, direction and sense of the force at B. AG = GB = 20 in.

(40·8 lb upwards; 87·5 lb, 26° to horizontal, upwards in direction B to A)

2. The jib of a crane, Fig. 1.15, is 100 ft long and weighs 7 tons. It is pin-jointed at one end and supported at the other end by a cable which

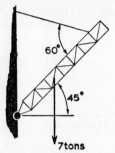

60°

45°

7tons

FIG. 1.15

maintains the jib in the position shown. The centre of gravity of the jib is 40 ft from the pinned end. Find the pull in the cable and the reaction at the pin joint.

(6·83 tons; 2·27 tons)

3. Calculate the resultant force on the gusset plate shown, Fig. 1.16, and the angle made by its line of action with the vertical.

(22·7 tons, 5° 11′)

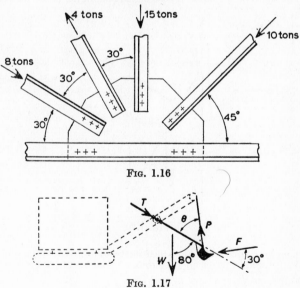

4 tons   15tons

10 tons

8 tons

30°

30°

+ +
+ +

+
+
+

30°

+ + +

45°

+ + +   + + +

FIG. 1.16

T

θ

P

F

W 80°   30°

FIG. 1.17

4. Fig. 1.17 shows the forces acting on the handle and dipper of a power shovel. T = thrust in handle = 50,000 lb, W = weight of handle and dipper = 4,000 lb, F = cutting force at rock face = 48,500 lb. Find the rope pull P and the angle θ.

(29,500 lb, 72° 51′)

5. Calculate the magnitude and direction of the resultant of the force system shown in Fig. 1.18. Check by drawing the polygon of forces.

(0·586 lb at 45° to, and below, AB)

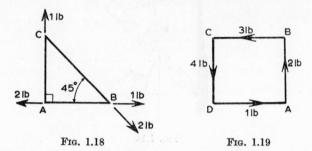

Fɪɢ. 1.18   Fɪɢ. 1.19

7. Calculate the magnitude and direction of the resultant of the forces shown in Fig. 1.19. Where does the line of action of the resultant force cut line DA? The forces act round the sides of a square of 1 ft side.

(2·83 lb at 45° to DA; 2·5 ft to left of D on AD produced)

8. The link AB shown in Fig. 1.20 is 4 ft long and pinned at both ends to blocks free to move in guides. At the instant shown the link is maintained in

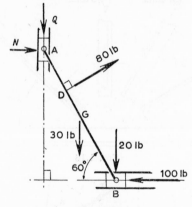

Fɪɢ. 1.20

equilibrium by a force system in which the two forces N and Q are unknown. Draw the polygon of forces and determine N and Q. Check by resolution of forces.

(N, 30·7 lb; Q, −10 lb, upwards)

9. The pulley and shaft shown in Fig. 1.21 weigh 200 lb and the tensions in the sides of the belt passing round the pulley are 400 lb and 100 lb. Find the magnitude and direction of the resultant force on the bearing.

(508 lb, 17° 8′ to horizontal)

10. For the force system shown in Fig. 1.22 calculate: (*a*) the resultant force; (*b*) the angle which the line of action of the resultant makes with the

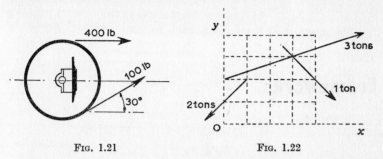

FIG. 1.21   FIG. 1.22

O*x* axis; (*c*) the total moment about O; (*d*) the point at which the resultant cuts the O*x* axis. The figure is marked off in 1 ft squares.

(2·44 lb; 28° 36′; 8·52 ton-ft, 7·3 ft to right of O)

11. The equilateral triangle shown in Fig. 1.23 has a side of 10 in. Find (*a*) the magnitude and direction of the resultant force; (*b*) the point at which the resultant cuts QR.

(5·3 lb, 41° to QR, 15 in. to right of R on QR produced)

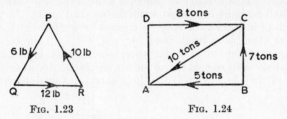

FIG. 1.23   FIG. 1.24

12. The rectangle shown, Fig. 1.24, has AB = 2 ft and BC = 1·5 ft. Calculate the magnitude, direction, and position of the resultant force.

(5·1 tons, 11° 19′ to BA; cuts at 0·4 ft from A on DA)

2

Frameworks

A FRAMEWORK is an assembly of bars connected by hinged or pinned joints and intended to carry loads at the joints only. Each hinge joint is assumed to rotate freely without friction, hence all the bars in the frame exert direct forces only and are therefore in tension or compression. A tensile load is taken as positive and a member carrying tension is called a *tie*. A compressive load is negative and a member in compression is called a *strut*. The bars are usually assumed to be light compared with the applied loads. In practice the joints of a framework may be riveted or welded but the direct forces are often calculated assuming pin joints. This assumption gives values of tension or compression which are on the safe side.

Fig. 2.1 shows a simple frame for a wall crane. In order that the framework shall be *stiff* and capable of carrying a load, each portion

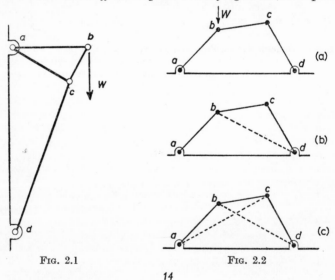

Fig. 2.1   Fig. 2.2

14

such as *abc* forms a triangle, the whole frame being built up of triangles. Note that the wall *ad* forms the third side of the triangle *acd*. The four bars shown in Fig. 2.2 (*a*) on the other hand, do not form a stiff frame since they would collapse under load. This latter arrangement may be converted into a frame by adding a fifth bar *bd* as shown, Fig. 2.2 (*b*); then both *abd* and *bdc* form complete triangles. However, if both *bd* and *ac* are joined by bars the result, Fig. 2.2 (*c*), remains a frame but is said to be *overstiff*. The forces in the members cannot then be obtained by the methods of statics alone.

2.1. Forces in Frameworks

The forces in a stiff or perfect frame can be found by using a force diagram, since the forces in each bar are simply tensile or compressive. Fig. 2.3 shows a tie and a strut under load. The

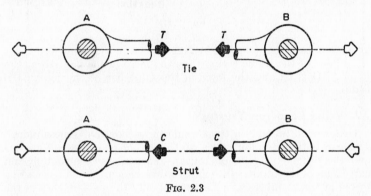

FIG. 2.3

tensile forces acting *on* the tie at each joint are each balanced by equal and opposite internal forces exerted by the tie on the pin joint. Thus the tie appears to be pulling inwards on the two pins at A and B. Similarly the strut appears to be pushing outwards on the pin ends with a force *C* to resist the compressive loads.

When constructing a force diagram for a framework we are concerned with the polygon of forces acting at each pin *exerted by* each member of the framework connected at that joint, i.e. the forces required are *T* and *C* of Fig. 2.3.

The force diagram is started at any joint at which at least one force is known in magnitude and direction, and where there are not more than *two* unknown forces. The complete diagram is then built up of the force polygons for each joint in succession. The forces are described using *Bow's notation* in which each space between two forces is lettered separately. A force is thus denoted by the two space letters on either side of the force. A joint is conveniently described by using the letters of the spaces meeting at the joint.

Thus in Fig. 2.4 the load of 1 ton is described as a force **ab** taken in the sense of the load. The joint at which this force acts is called the joint ABD. It is also necessary to consider the forces at a joint

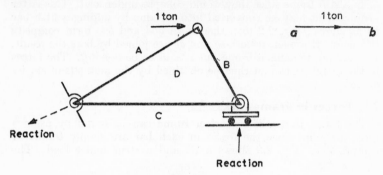

Fig. 2.4

in a definite order (clockwise) and maintain the same order for *every* joint of the framework. Thus the force in the bar DB at the joint ABD is **bd** and the force in the same bar at the joint CDB is **db**.

2.2. Wind Loads on Trusses

Under wind pressure a truss would move sideways unless pinned at one or both ends. For long span trusses one end is usually pinned and the other end rests on rollers. This allows contraction and expansion of the frame with temperature change. When calculating forces in the members of a frame it is only the components of the wind load perpendicular to the face of the truss which are usually considered, together with any vertical or other "dead loads."

An unusual structure, which is particularly subject to wind loading, is the Jodrell Bank Radio Telescope shown in Plate I.

Example. The framework shown Fig. 2.5 (*a*) is loaded by a 1 ton horizontal force at the apex. The frame is pinned at the left-hand support and rests on rollers at the right-hand support. The rollers may be assumed frictionless. Find the magnitude and nature of the force in each bar.

Solution

The load of 1 ton is known in magnitude and direction at the joint ABD. Hence the forces in bars DA and BD may be obtained from the force diagram for this joint. The force diagram is then continued for the forces at the other joints as shown below. Note that at the roller support the reaction must be vertical whereas at the pinned support the reaction is completely unknown.

JOINT ABD, FIG. 2.5 (b)

Draw **ab** to represent the 1 ton load.

From **b** draw a line **bd** of unknown length parallel to the bar BD to represent the force in BD.

From **a** draw a line **ad** to represent the unknown force in DA. The lines **bd** and **ad** intersect at **d** to complete the triangle of forces for the joint.

The force directions at the joint are determined:

(1) by the direction of the 1 ton load **ab**;

(2) by following the sides of the triangle **abd** *in order* as shown, Fig. 2.5 (b).

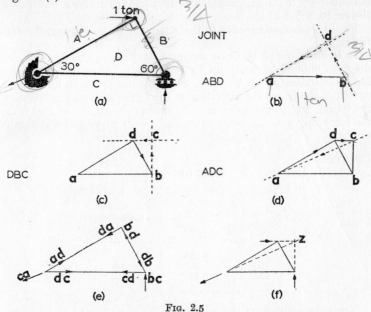

FIG. 2.5

These force directions are inserted in the sketch of the frame, Fig. 2.5 (e). The arrows in this sketch represent the internal forces in the bars at the joint ABD.

The arrowhead representing the force in AD at joint ADC can now be added also, and is drawn away from this joint. Similarly at joint DBC the arrowhead representing the force in bar BD is drawn towards the joint. In each bar the pair of arrowheads should now be pointing in opposite directions.

JOINT DBC, FIG. 2.5 (c)

For clarity triangle **abd** is redrawn.

At this joint the known force is **db** drawn in a direction opposite to that at the top joint.

Reaction **bc** is vertical and is so drawn from point **b**.

The force in bar CD is represented by a horizontal line **cd** through **d**.

The intersection of lines **bc** and **cd** at point **c** completes the triangle of forces.

The directions of the forces at the joint follow the sequence **db**, **bc** and **cd** as shown, Fig. 2.5 (c).

These directions are now inserted in the frame sketch, Fig. 2.5 (e). The only unknown force is now the reaction at joint ADC.

JOINT ADC, FIG. 2.5 (d)

The known forces at this joint are **ad** and **dc** in the directions indicated by the arrowheads. The line joining **c** and **a** represents the reaction CA at the hinge support.

Fig. 2.5 (d) now represents the complete force diagram for the frame.

It is unnecessary to draw separate diagrams. The whole force diagram should be built up in one picture while following the sequence indicated above. It is advisable, however, to fill in on a sketch of the frame the directions of the forces at each joint as they are found, and to prevent confusion arrows should be omitted from the force diagram. Those shown in Fig. 2.5 (d) are given for guidance only.

RESULTS

Reaction *BC*   **0·433** ton vertical.

Reaction *CA*   **1·09** ton at **23°** to horizontal.

Member	Tension (ton)	Compression (ton)
AD	**0·866**	—
BD	—	**0·5**
CD	**0·25**	—

Note—As a check on the results the reactions may also be found as follows. Since the frame is right-angled let the sides be: DB = 1 ft, DC = 2 ft. Then, taking moments about the pinned support, and remembering that the reaction *BC* at the roller support is vertical,

$$BC \times 2 = 1 \times 1 \cos 30°$$
$$BC = 0·433 \text{ ton}$$

Further, since the whole frame is subject to three external forces only, i.e. the applied load of 1 ton and the two reactions, then the lines of action of these forces must meet in the same point. This point is Z, Fig. 2.5 (f). A line joining the pinned support to Z gives the line of action of the reaction at this support. Thus the triangle of forces can now be drawn and the reaction *CA* found.

If the right-hand support had not been on rollers the direction of the reaction there would have been indefinite unless the 1 ton load were vertical. This may be verified by finding the reactions for a 1 ton vertical load at the joint ABD. When the load is vertical the support reactions will be vertical also, and may be found by taking moments about each support in turn. However, when the load is not vertical it will be found that this cannot be done. Such a problem is said to be statically indeterminate and cannot be solved by the methods of statics alone.

Example. The sloping sides of the symmetrical roof truss shown, Fig. 2.6 (*a*), are at 30° to the horizontal and the bars BG, CH are of equal length. The reaction at joint KEF is vertical. For the loading shown find the magnitude and nature of the force in each member. All loads are in tons.

Solution

It is convenient to begin by calculating the reaction EF at joint KEF and then with this information draw the force triangle for joint KEF. Assuming each sloping bar to be of unit length then each horizontal bar is of length 2 cos 30°. Taking moments about joint ABGF—

$$EF \times 4 \cos 30° = (2 \times 1) + (1 \times 2) + (2 \times 2 \cos 30°)$$
thus $\qquad EF = \textbf{2·155 tons}$

JOINT EFK, FIG. 2.6 (*b*)

Draw **ef** = 2·155 tons vertically upward. Complete the triangle of forces by drawing **fk** horizontally and **ek** parallel to EK to meet **fk** in **k**. The directions of the forces at the joint follow the sequence **ef, fk, ke** and the directions of the internal forces in the bars are now shown in the diagram of the truss, Fig. 2.6 (*a*).

JOINT EKJ, FIG. 2.6 (*c*)

Draw **ej** from **e** parallel to JE and **kj** from **k** parallel to KJ. The intersection point **j** is found to coincide with **k**. Hence the force in KJ is zero. (This result could have been seen by inspection. Since no load acts at joint EKJ and the forces in JE and EK are in line, these two forces must be equal and opposite.)

JOINT CDEJH, FIG. 2.6 (*d*)

The known triangle of forces **efk** is redrawn for clarity. **de** is drawn to represent the known downward load DE of 2 tons. The known load **cd** of 1 ton is drawn parallel to CD to end at **d**. The line **jh** is drawn vertically through **j** parallel to JH. The line **hc** is drawn through **c** parallel to HC to cut **jh** in **h**, thus completing the polygon. The directions of the forces at the joint follow the closed sequence **cd**, **de**, **ej**, **jh** and **hc** as shown. These directions are now inserted in the diagram of the truss, Fig. 2.6 (*a*).

JOINT HJKFG, FIG. 2.6 (*e*)

The known force at this joint is **hj** vertically upwards, **fg** is drawn horizontally through **f** and **hg** drawn parallel to HG to cut **fg** in **g**.

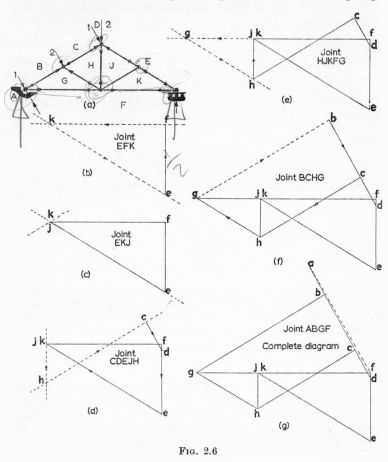

FIG. 2.6

The force diagram **hjkfg** is then complete, the force directions shown on this diagram now being inserted in the diagram of the truss.

JOINT BCHG, FIG. 2.6 (*f*)

At this joint **bc**, **ch** and **hg** taken in that order, are the known forces. The polygon is completed at **b** by joining **g** to **b**.

Joint ABGF, Fig. 2.6 (g)

ab is drawn towards **b** to represent the 1 ton load at this joint. Joining **f** to **a** gives the reaction FA and completes the force diagram for the truss.

RESULTS

Reaction $EF = $ **2·155** tons vertical.

Reaction $FA = $ **3·89** tons at 29° to vertical.

Member	BG	CH	EJ	EK	FK	FG	GH	HJ	JK
Tension (tons)	—	—	—	—	**3·73**	**5·7**	—	**1·12**	—
Compression (tons)	**4·9**	**3·7**	**4·3**	**4·3**	—	—	**2·3**	—	—

Note—Fig. 2.6 (g) is all that is required for the solution. However, in commencing the diagram it would be possible, and more accurate, to draw the *load-line* **ab, bc, cd, de** and **ef** representing the known loads and reaction. The solution then follows the steps set out above. This method is illustrated in the next example.

Example. Fig. 2.7 shows a loaded roof truss. The truss is symmetrical, each bar in the sloping sides being of equal length. Each sloping side is at 30° to the horizontal. The span is 40 ft and the horizontal member NK is 10 ft below the apex. Calculate the magnitude and nature of the force in each member if the right-hand reaction is vertical. All loads are in tons.

Solution

Since reaction JK is vertical its magnitude may be found by taking moments about the left-hand support. Assuming sloping bars of unit length—

$$JK \times 4 \cos 30° = (2 \times 1) + (1 \times 2) + (1 \times 1 \times \cos 30°) +$$
$$(1 \times 2 \times \cos 30°) + (1 \times 3 \times \cos 30°) +$$
$$(1 \times 4 \times \cos 30°)$$

thus $JK = $ **3·65 tons.**

Load Line

Draw the load line **abcdefghj** to represent the known loading in magnitude and direction. Draw **jk** upward from **j** to represent the vertical reaction of 3·65 tons. Then line **ka** represents the reaction KA.

Joint HJKQ

The polygon for this joint is completed by drawing **kq** parallel to KQ and **hq** parallel to HQ to meet in **q**. The force directions follow the sequence **hj, jk, kq** and **qh**.

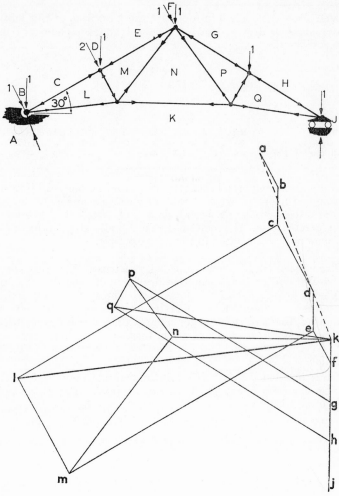

FIG. 2.7

JOINT GHQP

Draw **qp** and **gp** to meet in **p**. The force directions follow the sequence **gh**, **hq**, **qp** and **pg**.

JOINT PQKN

Draw **kn** and **pn** to meet in **n**. The force directions follow the sequence **pq**, **qk**, **kn** and **np**.

JOINT EFGPNM

Draw **em** and **nm** to meet in **m**. The force directions follow the sequence **ef, fg, gp, pn** and **nm**.

JOINT CDEML

Draw **ml** and **cl** to meet in **l**. The force directions follow the sequence **cd, de, em, ml** and **lc**.

JOINT LMNK

The force directions follow the sequence **lm, mn** and **nk**.

JOINT ABCLK

Join **k** to **a** to represent the left-hand reaction. The force directions follow the sequence **ab, bc, cl** and **lk**.

RESULTS

Reaction $JK = 3{\cdot}65$ tons vertical.

Reaction $KA = 5{\cdot}25$ tons at $22\frac{1}{2}°$ to vertical.

Member	CL	EM	GP	HQ	KQ	KN	KL	LM	MN	NP	PQ
Tension (tons)	—	—	—	—	5·94	4·32	3·57	—	4·52	1·88	—
Compression (tons)	8·1	7·56	6·3	6·8	—	—	—	2·84	—	—	0·86

PROBLEMS

1. Fig. 2.8 shows a simple roof truss. A wind load normal to the longer sloping side is assumed to be equivalent to a 1 ton load at each pin joint. The

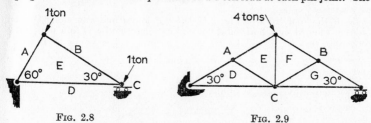

FIG. 2.8 $\qquad\qquad$ FIG. 2.9

reaction at the right-hand joint may be taken vertical. Determine the reactions and the nature and magnitude of the force in each member.

(Members: AE, -1; BE, 0; DE, $-0{\cdot}5$; reactions: CD, $0{\cdot}866$; DA, $1{\cdot}325$ at 41° to, and above, the horizontal. *Note*—a negative sign denotes compression, otherwise the member is in tension)

2. In the symmetrical truss shown, Fig. 2.9, a load of 4 tons at the vertex acts normal to one sloping side. The reaction at the right-hand support may be assumed vertical. Find the magnitude of the support reactions, and the magnitude and nature of the force in each member.

(Reactions: BC, 23·1; CA, 2·31 tons; members: AD, $-2{\cdot}31$; AE, $-2{\cdot}31$; DE, 0; DC, 4; EF, 0; BF, 4·62; FG, 0; BG, $-4{\cdot}62$; GC, 4 tons)

3. The truss shown, Fig. 2.10, is made up of three equilateral triangles loaded at each of the two lower panel pins. It is supported by a pin joint at

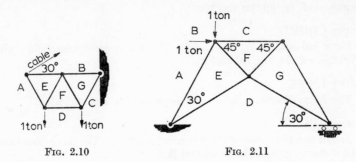

FIG. 2.10   FIG. 2.11

the wall on the right-hand side and by the tension in the cable on the left. Determine: (*a*) the tension in the cable; (*b*) the reaction at the wall; (*c*) the nature and magnitude of the force in each bar.

((*a*) 2 tons; (*b*) 2 tons; (*c*) EB = BG, = − 2·31; EF = FG = 0; DF, 0·578; EA, 1·15; GC, 1·15 tons)

4. The framework shown, Fig. 2.11, is loaded by 1 ton horizontal and vertical loads at the top left-hand joint. The reaction at the right-hand support is vertical. Find: (*a*) the magnitude and direction of each support reaction; (*b*) the nature and magnitude of the force in each bar of the framework.

((*a*) 0·79 ton vertically upward; 1·02 ton at 12° to, and above, the horizontal; (*b*) AE, − 1·37; ED, 1·95; EF, 0·28; FC, − 1·9; FG, 1·7; GC, − 1·37; GD, 0·79)

5. In the roof truss of Fig. 2.12 the pin joints mid-way along the long sides are joined by a horizontal bar and are connected also to a pin joint at

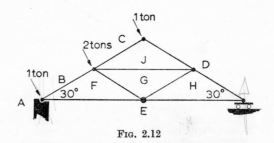

FIG. 2.12

the mid-point of the horizontal link spanning the points of support. The right-hand reaction is vertical. Find: (*a*) the magnitude and direction of the support reactions; (*b*) the nature and magnitude of the force in each member.

(Reactions: 1·16 ton vertical; 3·05 tons at 49° to, and above, the horizontal; members: BF, − 2·88; EF, 3·95; FG, − 1·14; GJ, − 2·04; CJ, − 0·58; JD, − 1·18; DH, − 2·32; GH, 1·14; HE, 2·0 tons)

6. In the roof truss shown, Fig. 2.13, the longer sloping sides are at 30° to the horizontal; the span is 35 ft and the horizontal member is $8\frac{3}{4}$ ft below the

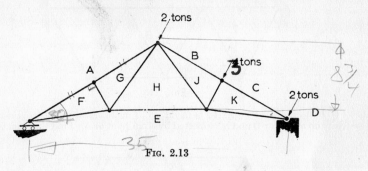

FIG. 2.13

apex. The two shortest sloping bars are mid-way between each long side and are at right angles to it. The wind load is assumed concentrated at the pin joints of one long side. The left-hand support reaction is vertical. Find the reactions at the supports and the force in each member, stating whether it is in tension or compression.

(Reactions: *DE*, 6·13; *EA*, 2·31 tons; members: EF, 5·15; AF, − 5·9; FG, 0; AG, − 5·9; GH, 0·79; EH, 4·65; HJ, 5·9; JB, − 8·3; JK, − 4; KC, − 8·3; KE, 10·4 tons)

8. The symmetrical roof truss shown (Fig. 2.14) is of 30 ft span and 10 ft high. The horizontal member MJ is 8 ft below the top joint. The longer

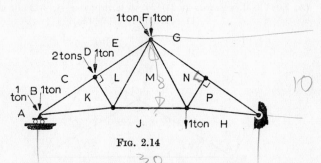

FIG. 2.14

sloping sides are pin-jointed at their mid-spans and the members LK and PN are each normal to these sides, as are the wind loads shown. All other loads are vertical. Determine the magnitude and nature of the loads in each member and state the magnitude of each reaction.

(Reactions: *AJ*, 4·73; *GH*, 3·48 tons; members: CK, − 7·35; EL, − 6·8; GN, − 5·7; GP, − 5·7; HP, 2·5; JM, 1·53; JK, 5·5; KL, − 2·83; LM, 4·16; MN, 1·85; NP, 0 tons)

9. In the Warren girder shown in Fig. 2.15 all bars are of equal length and the loads are vertical. Find the magnitude and nature of the forces in the members A, B and C. Both reactions are vertical.

(A, 4·62; B, − 2·31; C, − 6·93 tons)

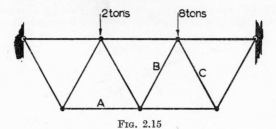

Fɪɢ. 2.15

10) The frame of Fig. 2.16 is made up of members of equal length, rests freely on rollers at B and is supported by a pin-joint at A. Find the magnitude

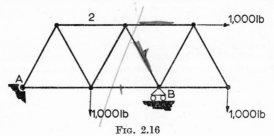

Fɪɢ. 2.16

and direction of the reactions at A and B and the nature and magnitude of the forces in the members marked 1 and 2.

(A, 1,093 lb downwards at 23° 25′ to horizontal; B, 2,433 lb upwards; (1) − 1,660 lb; (2) 500 lb)

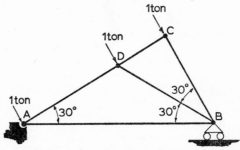

Fɪɢ. 2.17

11. Find the nature and magnitude of the forces in the framework of Fig. 2.17. The 1 ton loads are normal to the longer sloping side. State the magnitude and direction of the reactions at the joints A and B.

(Members: CB, − 1; CD, 0; DB, − 1·155; DA, − 0·577; BA, 1·5; reactions: at A, 1·895 tons at 37° 36′ to the horizontal, upwards; at B, 1·443 tons upward)

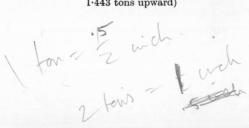

3

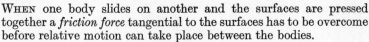

Friction

WHEN one body slides on another and the surfaces are pressed together a *friction force* tangential to the surfaces has to be overcome before relative motion can take place between the bodies.

Friction conditions may fall into one of the following categories—

dry and clean;
greasy or boundary;
fluid or viscous;
pure rolling.

Dry friction is mainly dealt with here but a discussion of the mechanism and types of friction is given in paragraph 3.5.

Calculations involving friction between two dry and clean surfaces in contact are based upon the following experimental facts—

1. If a force is applied tending to move one body over another the opposing friction force brought into play is tangential to the surfaces in contact and is just sufficient to balance the applied force.

2. There is a limit beyond which the friction force cannot increase. When this limit is reached sliding is about to start and the corresponding friction force is termed the *limiting* value.

3. The limiting friction force is proportional to the *normal* load pressing the two surfaces together and is independent of the area of contact.

4. The ratio of the limiting friction force F and normal reaction N is a constant which depends only on the nature of the pair of surfaces in contact.

Thus

$$\frac{F}{N} = \mu, \text{ a constant}$$

or $$F = \mu N$$

μ is called the *coefficient of static or limiting friction*.

721

In Fig. 3.1 when sliding is about to start the pull P is equal to the limiting friction force F, i.e.

$$P = F = \mu N$$

Before sliding starts P is equal to the friction force which is less than the limiting value μN.

5. After sliding starts the direction of the friction force is *opposite* to that of the *resultant* motion. The friction force is again given by $F = \mu N$, where μ is now called the *coefficient of sliding* or *kinetic friction*. The kinetic value is usually slightly less than the static or limiting value. It is also approximately independent of the speed of sliding. Otherwise sliding friction obeys the same laws as limiting friction.

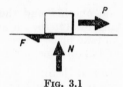

Fig. 3.1

When the pull P remains equal to μN during sliding the body moves at a steady speed. When P is greater than μN the body is accelerated and this particular case is dealt with in Chapter 5.

These laws of friction are approximately true and are sufficient for most engineering purposes. Their limitations are discussed in paragraph 3.5.

3.1. Friction on the Inclined Plane

(a) MOTION UP THE PLANE; PULL P PARALLEL TO PLANE (FIG. 3.2)

The friction force F opposes the motion of the body up the plane, N is the normal reaction of the plane on the body, and the weight

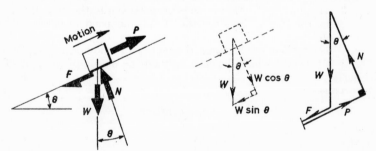

Fig. 3.2

W acts vertically downwards. The angle between W and N is θ, the angle of the plane.

Resolving perpendicular to the plane

$$N = W \cos \theta$$

Resolving parallel to the plane,

$$P = F + W \sin \theta$$

and for limiting friction,

$$F = \mu N$$

The pull P must overcome both the friction force and the resolved part of the weight down the slope. This is shown clearly in the force diagram.

(b) MOTION DOWN THE PLANE; PULL P PARALLEL TO PLANE

When the body is pulled down the plane by the force P (Fig. 3.3) the component of the weight down the slope assists the pull.

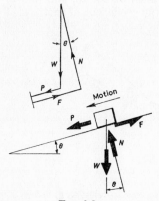

FIG. 3.3

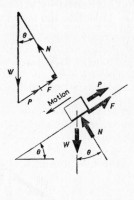

FIG. 3.4

Resolving parallel and perpendicular to the plane—

$$P + W \sin \theta = F = \mu N$$

and
$$N = W \cos \theta$$

If the force P is acting up the plane (Fig. 3.4), resisting the downward motion of the body, then when the body is just about to move down, we have—

$$P + F = W \sin \theta$$
$$N = W \cos \theta$$

and
$$F = \mu N$$

When $P = 0$, the component of the weight down the slope is just able to overcome the friction force F, i.e.

$$F = W \sin \theta$$

and since $\qquad\qquad N = W \cos \theta$

therefore $\qquad\qquad \dfrac{F}{N} = \dfrac{W \sin \theta}{W \cos \theta} = \tan \theta$

but $\qquad\qquad\qquad \dfrac{F}{N} = \mu$

thus $\qquad\qquad\qquad \tan \theta = \mu$

This particular angle of inclination of the plane is known as the *angle of repose*. If the plane is inclined at an angle greater than the angle of repose the body will slide down; if the inclination is less than the angle of repose the body will remain at rest.

Example. A 1 ton load is to be pulled up a track inclined at 30° to the horizontal by a force P inclined at 20° to, and above, the track. Calculate the value of P if the coefficient of friction is 0·15.

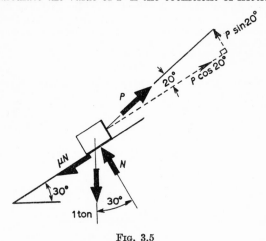

Fig. 3.5

Solution

Pull P has components $P \cos 20°$ and $P \sin 20°$ parallel and perpendicular to the track, respectively.

Resolving forces parallel to the track—

$$P \cos 20° = 0{\cdot}15\, N + 2{,}240 \sin 30°$$
$$P \times 0{\cdot}9397 = 0{\cdot}15\, N + 2{,}240 \times 0{\cdot}5$$
$$P = 0{\cdot}16\, N + 1{,}193 \qquad . \qquad . \qquad . \quad (3.1)$$

Resolving perpendicular to the track—

$$N = 2,240 \cos 30° - P \sin 20°$$
$$= 2,240 \times 0.866 - P \times 0.342$$
$$= 1,940 - 0.342 P$$

substituting for N in equation (3.1)

$$P = 0.16(1,940 - 0.342 P) + 1,193$$

hence $P = \textbf{1,425 lb}$

PROBLEMS

1. A load weighing 3,000 lb lies on a gradient inclined at 60° to the horizontal. For static friction $\mu = 0.5$, for kinetic friction, $\mu = 0.4$. Calculate: (a) the pull parallel to the gradient required to prevent the load sliding down; (b) the pull required to haul the load up the gradient at uniform speed.

(1,848, 3,198 lb)

2. The force required to haul a load of 800 lb along a horizontal surface is 240 lb. Find (a) the force parallel to a track of slope 20° required to haul the load up the incline; (b) the force required to lower it down the incline at steady speed. Assume the coefficient of friction to be the same in all cases.

(500, 48 lb)

3. Two castings weigh 300 and 200 lb, respectively, and are connected by a towing cable. They are hauled at uniform speed up a ramp of 30° slope. If the coefficient of kinetic friction is 0.1 for the heavier casting and 0.4 for the lighter find the total hauling pull required.

(345 lb)

4. A shaft transmits 300 h.p. at 120 rev/min. Calculate the torque transmitted. If a gear is splined to the shaft as shown (Fig. 3.6), what is the load

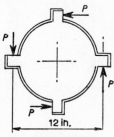

Fig. 3.6

P on each spline? If the coefficient of sliding friction between gear and splines is 0.1 what force would be required to move the gear axially when transmitting the above torque?

(13,125 lb-ft, 6,560 lb, 2,624 lb)

3.2. The Angle of Friction and Total Reaction

In all the cases considered so far the body is in equilibrium under the action of the four forces P, W, N and F. The method of resolution of forces will solve all problems of this type but two equations are required for a solution. However, a simpler method of calculation exists for certain problems. This makes use of the resultant reaction R of the friction force F and the normal reaction N, together with the angle ϕ between R and N. This angle ϕ is known as the *angle of friction*.

Consider a body about to move to the right (Fig. 3.7). The force

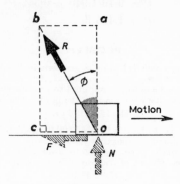

FIG. 3.7

R is the resultant of N and F. Since the latter are at right angles the angle ϕ between R and N is given by

$$\tan \phi = \frac{\mathbf{ab}}{\mathbf{oa}}$$

$$= \frac{F}{N}$$

$$= \frac{\mu N}{N} \text{ for limiting friction}$$

$$= \mu$$

The direction in which R must be drawn is determined by the fact that its tangential component F must oppose the motion of the body, that is, R is always drawn backwards to the direction of motion. R acts only at angle ϕ to N for limiting friction; if R lies inside the angle of friction the force of friction is less than the limiting value and *slipping cannot take place*.

When N and F are replaced by one force R, the forces P, W and R form *three* forces in equilibrium and the triangle of forces can then be drawn.

It should be noted particularly that in the *absence of friction* the only force between two surfaces is *normal* to the surfaces.

3.3. Application of Angle of Friction to Motion on the Inclined Plane

Fig. 3.8 shows a body being moved up a plane by means of a horizontal force P. R is the resultant force exerted by the plane

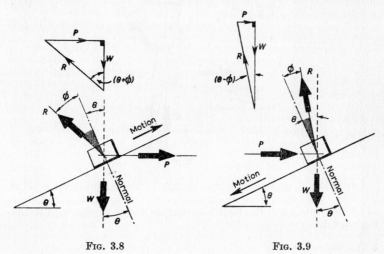

FIG. 3.8   FIG. 3.9

on the body. It acts at an angle ϕ to the normal and, when slipping is just about to start, $\tan \phi = \mu$. Since motion is up the plane, R must have a component down the plane to provide the resisting friction force and is therefore directed as shown. The pull P, weight W and resultant R form a triangle of forces and, since P and W are at right angles—

$$P = W \tan (\theta + \phi)$$

Fig. 3.9 shows the case when the body is just about to move down the plane against a resisting horizontal force P. R now has a component up the plane and is directed backwards to the direction of motion at angle ϕ to the normal. From the triangle of forces

$$P = W \tan (\theta - \phi)$$

In this case the angle of the plane θ is greater than the angle of friction ϕ.

When the body is about to move down the plane and force P assists the motion (Fig. 3.10), R is directed backwards to the normal as before, and hence

$$P = W \tan (\phi - \theta)$$

The angle of inclination of the plane θ is in this case less than the angle of friction ϕ.

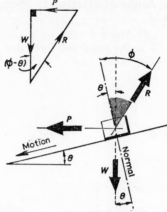

Fig. 3.10

Example. A casting weighing 2 tons is to be pulled up a slope inclined at 30° by a force at an angle to the slope. If the coefficient of friction is 0·3 find the *least* force required and its direction to the horizontal.

Solution

In the triangle of forces, Fig. 3.11, **oa** represents the known weight, and **ax** the direction of the total reaction R at $(30° + \phi)$ to the vertical. Pull P is represented by **bo** which, for equilibrium,

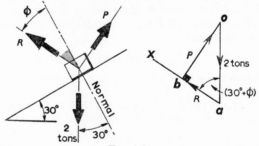

Fig. 3.11

must close the triangle. For P to be the least force required **bo** must be perpendicular to **ax**. Hence the minimum value of P is given by

$$P = 2 \sin (30° + \phi)$$

where $\tan \phi = 0·3$ or $\phi = 16° 42'$; hence

$$P = 2 \sin 46° 42'$$

$$= \mathbf{1·456 \ ton}$$

From triangle **oba** it can be seen that the minimum value of the force must be at angle $(30° + \phi)$, i.e. **46° 42'** to the horizontal.

Example. A wood block is split by a horizontal force P of 30 lb on the wedge shown (Fig. 3.12). Calculate the vertical force tending to force the wood apart. $\mu = 0.4$.

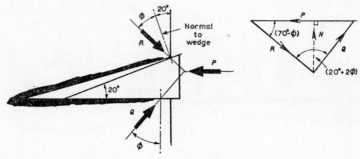

FIG. 3.12

Solution

The three forces acting on the wedge are: horizontal force P, total reaction Q of the lower half of the block, total reaction R of the upper half. Both Q and R act at angle ϕ to the respective normal so as to oppose motion of the wedge.

$$\tan \phi = \mu = 0.4$$
thus
$$\phi = 21° 49'$$

From the triangle of forces, using the sine rule,

$$\frac{Q}{\sin (70° - \phi)} = \frac{P}{\sin (20° + 2\phi)}$$

therefore
$$Q = \frac{P \sin (70° - 21° 49')}{\sin (20° + 43° 38')}$$

$$= \frac{30 \sin 48° 11'}{\sin 63° 38'}$$

$$= \frac{30 \times 0.7453}{0.896}$$

$$= 25 \text{ lb}$$

The force N tending to separate the two halves of the block is the vertical component of Q (or R), i.e.

$$N = Q \cos \phi$$
$$= 25 \times \cos 21° 49'$$
$$= \textbf{23.2 lb}$$

3.4. Rolling Resistance

A cylinder rolling on a flat plane encounters no frictional resistance to motion providing there is no sliding and that neither cylinder nor plane deform under load. In practice, of course, both surfaces will deform to some extent. Assuming the cylinder to be hard and the plane soft, the deformation is as shown

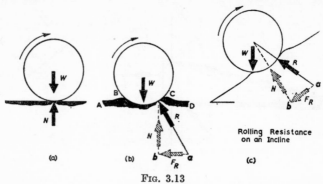

(a)   (b)   (c)

Fig. 3.13

in Fig. 3.13 (b). For example, a rotating cylinder pressed into a rubber surface travels forward in one revolution a distance which may be 10 per cent less than its circumference. Negligible slip occurs between cylinder and surface, but energy is lost due to the stretching of the surface of the rubber along the line ABCD. Owing to the deformation of the surface the reaction R has a horizontal component ab opposing the motion. This horizontal component is an apparent friction force, F_R.

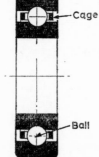

Fig. 3.14

The rolling resistance is very little affected by lubricant films. Lubricant may reduce wear but does not reduce the rolling resistance since there is no sliding friction. The coefficient of "friction" for rolling is about 0·001 or less, depending on the hardness of the surfaces in contact. Rolling resistance F_R may be assumed to be directly proportional to the normal load N, i.e.

$$F_R = \mu_R N$$

where μ_R is the *coefficient of rolling resistance*.

In designing machines the attempt is made to replace sliding by rolling friction wherever possible. Hence the use of ball or roller bearings in place of plain bearings, although in roller bearings sliding friction may occur owing to their method of construction. For example, it is usually necessary to enclose the rollers in a cage. The effect is probably small since the cage carries little load. Again with ball bearings it is often necessary to allow the balls to run in a groove in the ball race (Fig. 3.14). Sliding now takes place between the ball and the sides of the groove and this contact between the surfaces may be heavily loaded. Lubrication may therefore be necessary to reduce sliding friction as well as wear and to protect the bearing against corrosion.

PROBLEMS

1. A load of 2,000 lb is to be hauled slowly at constant speed up an incline of 1 in 2 (sine). If the coefficient of sliding friction is 0·6 what pull parallel to the incline would be required?
If the load is placed on a trolley weighing 400 lb what would then be the pull? The coefficient of rolling resistance is 0·12 and friction at the bearing journals may be neglected.
If the trolley is given rubber tyres increasing the coefficient of rolling resistance to 0·5 what is then the pull?

(2,039, 1,449, 2,239 lb)

2. A load of 600 lb will just start to slide down a 25° slope. What horizontal force will be required to haul the load up the slope at constant speed?
What is the *least* force required to haul the load up the incline?

(715, 459·6 lb)

3. The catch shown in Fig. 3.15 acts through the wedge forcing apart two steel balls against the springs S. If the coefficient of friction between wedge

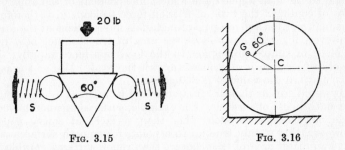

Fig. 3.15   Fig. 3.16

and balls is 0·3, calculate the force on each spring when the vertical load on the wedge is 20 lb.
What would be the spring force if friction were negligible?

(9·424, 17·32 lb)

4. A circular roller of 20 in. diameter rests against a vertical wall as shown in Fig. 3.16. The centre of gravity of the roller is at G, 6 in. from the centre C of the roller. In the position shown the roller is just about to rotate. Assuming the friction coefficient to be the same for both contact surfaces what is its value?

(0·432)

3.5. Further Notes on Friction and Lubrication

DRY FRICTION

The simplest explanation of the friction effect when dry clean surfaces rub together is that it is due to surface roughness. When studied closely even the most apparently smooth surfaces consist of "hills" and "valleys." There is a tendency for each surface to shear the tips of the irregularities of the other. Since it is only the projecting "hills" or high spots which are actually bearing on one another the area of true contact is very much less than the apparent area of contact; this is shown in Fig. 3.17. At average loads the

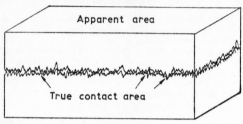

FIG. 3.17

area of true contact is proportional to the load applied and is almost independent of the apparent area of contact. Hence the friction force, which is determined by the area of true contact, is proportional to the load applied and almost independent of the apparent area of contact: the ratio of friction force to load, μ, is therefore constant and for a given pair of materials independent of the load. However, for very great loads the area of true contact may not increase in simple proportion to the load but more rapidly. In practice therefore μ may increase with the load. Also as surfaces become worn the value of μ changes.

It would appear that dry friction would be reduced by improving the smoothness of surfaces. For example, surfaces of smooth wood slide more easily on each other than surfaces of emery paper. However, this is only true up to a point, for smooth surfaces will have a greater area of true contact than rough surfaces. Owing to the attraction between the surface molecules of the materials there tends to be cohesion or binding together of the surfaces and the greater the area of true contact the greater is this tendency for cohesion. This condition ultimately leads to the surfaces seizing together. For example, two highly-polished dry-metal surfaces will tend to seize together very rapidly under load.

FLUID FRICTION (VISCOUS FRICTION)

When there is an excess of lubricant present two solid surfaces may be separated by a film of fluid so that friction depends wholly upon the lubricant and not on the nature of the surfaces. The force necessary to produce relative motion is that required to shear the lubricant film. The friction force in fluid friction increases with the velocity of sliding. In contrast to dry friction the friction force is proportional to the total or apparent area of contact.

$A \propto W \propto F$ high load area

increases more

Fluid friction only exists when there is motion, otherwise the lubricant is squeezed out by the load. In practice all bearings running under design conditions should have full fluid-film lubrication.

BOUNDARY FRICTION (GREASY FRICTION)

It should be realized that for perfectly clean and dry surfaces the coefficient of static friction is often greater than unity and may be very high indeed. However, such conditions are not usually met with in engineering practice. Unless specially cleaned all surfaces possess a very thin film of grease and this may only be an "adsorbed" film; a film of lubricant perhaps 0·00001 in. thick. This attaches itself to the bearing surface and may prevent metal-to-metal contact. Cohesion, therefore, between smooth surfaces occurs between relatively weak grease molecules rather than strong metal ones. The coefficient of friction now depends upon the nature of both the lubricant and of the metal surfaces, but is very much lower than for dry surfaces. For greasy friction μ may be between 0·01 and 0·5.

The laws of friction for greasy friction are the same as those for dry friction.

Under heavy loads, or at low speeds of sliding, bearings which appear profusely lubricated may in fact be operating with boundary lubrication. The engineer seeks to maintain the maximum thickness of the oily boundary layer.

Under excessive load the boundary layer itself may break down. Contact takes place between high spots on the metal surfaces and the high rubbing temperatures which occur may result in local melting and seizure.

3.6. The Square-threaded Screw

Fig. 3.18 shows a single-start thread. The development of a thread is an inclined plane ABC, the thread being formed in effect by wrapping the plane around the core of the screw in the form of a helix or spiral. The height of the plane BC is the distance moved axially in one revolution of the screw in its nut, i.e. the *pitch p*. The base of the plane AC is the circumference of the thread at the mean radius, i.e. πD where D is the mean thread diameter. The angle θ of the plane is therefore given by

$$\tan \theta = \frac{p}{\pi D}$$

For a double-start thread the distance moved axially by the screw in its nut in one revolution is the *lead l*, which is twice the pitch. Thus for a double-start thread.

$$\tan \theta = \frac{l}{\pi D} = \frac{2p}{\pi D}$$

Let W be the axial load on the screw or nut and P the tangential force required at the *mean thread radius* to turn the screw.

Turning the screw is equivalent to moving the load W along the inclined plane by a horizontal force P. The forces acting on the screw are: the axial load W, the horizontal force P and the total reaction R of the inclined plane formed by the thread of the nut.

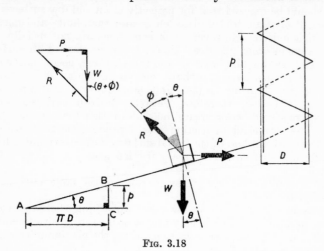

Fig. 3.18

The reaction R acts at an angle ϕ to the normal where ϕ is the angle of friction and $\tan \phi = \mu$, the coefficient of friction between screw and nut.

Consider two cases according as the load is being raised or lowered.

(*a*) RAISING LOAD

When the load is raised by the force P the motion is up the plane and the reaction R acts to the left of the normal as shown (Fig. 3.18). From the triangle of forces

$$P = W \tan (\phi + \theta)$$

The *torque* T required to rotate the screw against the load is

$$T = P \times \tfrac{1}{2}D$$
$$= \tfrac{1}{2}WD \tan (\phi + \theta)$$

The *efficiency* of the screw is equal to—

$$\frac{\text{work done on load } W \text{ in 1 revolution}}{\text{work done by } P \text{ in 1 revolution}} = \frac{W \times \text{lead } (l)}{P \times \pi D}$$

But $\qquad \dfrac{W}{P} = \tan (\phi + \theta) \quad \text{and} \quad \dfrac{l}{\pi D} = \tan \theta$

Hence

$$\text{efficiency} = \frac{\tan \theta}{\tan (\phi + \theta)}$$

Alternatively

$$\text{efficiency} = \frac{\text{force } P \text{ required without friction } (\phi = 0)}{\text{force } P \text{ required with friction}}$$

$$= \frac{W \tan \theta}{W \tan (\phi + \theta)}$$

$$= \frac{\tan \theta}{\tan (\phi + \theta)}$$

Note that this efficiency is *independent of the load.* However, the above theory has neglected the weight of the screw itself. If the constant weight of the screw were to be taken into account it would be found that the efficiency would increase with the load as in other load lifting machines.

(b) LOAD BEING LOWERED

When the load is being lowered the reaction R must lie to the right of the normal (Fig. 3.19). If the angle of friction ϕ is greater

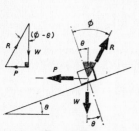

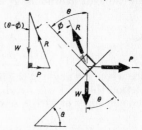

FIG. 3.19   FIG. 3.20

than the angle of the plane θ (the usual condition) then it can be seen from the triangle of forces that the force P must be applied to *help* lower the load. The angle between R and W in the triangle of forces is now $(\phi - \theta)$ so that

$$P = W \tan (\phi - \theta)$$

and the torque required is

$$T = P \times \tfrac{1}{2}D$$
$$= \tfrac{1}{2}WD \tan (\phi - \theta)$$

When ϕ is less than θ, R is still to the right of the normal, opposing the motion, but the triangle of forces must now be as shown in Fig. 3.20, with force P applied to *resist* the downward movement of the load. Under this condition the load would just be about to move downwards. If P were not applied in this direction the load would *overhaul*, that is, move down under its own weight.

From the triangle of forces (Fig. 3.20) when P is resisting—

$$P = W \tan (\theta - \phi)$$

and $$T = \tfrac{1}{2}WD \tan (\theta - \phi)$$

When the load is lowered or falling, the efficiency of the screw has little physical significance. When it overhauls, the load is the effort. When the load is lowered by a force P it assists the effort. When the load falls against a restraining force P, this force is, in effect, a resistance. The term *reversed efficiency* is sometimes used in this latter case; it is the ratio of the work done against P in one revolution of the screw to the corresponding work done by the load W.

3.7. Overhauling of a Screw

When the load moves down and overcomes the thread friction by its own weight it is said to overhaul. When it moved down against a resisting force P we found that

$$P = W \tan (\theta - \phi)$$

When the load overhauls, $P = 0$, therefore

$$\tan (\theta - \phi) = 0$$

or $$\theta - \phi = 0$$

i.e. $$\theta = \phi$$

Hence when the angle of the inclined plane is just equal to the angle of friction the load will overhaul.

The efficiency of such a screw when *raising* a load is given by

$$\eta = \frac{\tan \theta}{\tan (\theta + \phi)}$$

but $\theta = \phi$; hence

$$\eta = \frac{\tan \phi}{\tan 2\phi}$$

Table 3.1 gives the efficiency of the screw which will just overhaul in this manner for various values of the angle of friction ϕ and coefficient of friction μ. It is seen that as the angle ϕ tends to zero, as for a frictionless screw, the efficiency tends to a limiting value of 50 per cent. Note, however, that this is *not* the greatest efficiency a screw may have; for if $\phi = 0$ and θ is *not* equal to the angle of friction, the efficiency is

$$\eta = \frac{\tan \theta}{\tan (\theta + \phi)}$$

$$= 1 \text{ or } 100 \text{ per cent}$$

In general, if the angle of the inclined plane is greater than the angle of friction the load will accelerate downwards.

TABLE 3.1

ϕ (degrees)	$\mu = \tan \phi$	Efficiency (%)
1	0·0175	50 approx.
5	0·0875	49·6
10	0·1763	48·4
20	0·364	43·4
30	0·5774	33·3
40	0·839	14·8
45	1·000	0

The efficiency of a screw is often only about 25 per cent but may be increased by separating the sliding surfaces between screw and nut by steel balls. Thus sliding friction is replaced by rolling friction, as in a recirculating ball nut.

Plate II shows a ball screw manufactured by Bristol Siddeley Engines, Ltd. This screw has a minimum efficiency of ninety per cent. The re-circulating balls and the screw threads in which they move are precision ground. This ball screw finds many present-day applications in the aircraft, machine-tool and nuclear-power industries.

Example. A screw-jack carries a load of 400 lb. It has a square-thread single-start screw of 1 in. pitch and $2\frac{1}{2}$ in. mean diameter. The coefficient of friction between screw and nut is 0·22. Calculate the torque to raise the load and the efficiency of the screw. What is the torque to lower the load?

Solution

Helix angle θ of the thread is given by

$$\tan \theta = \frac{p}{\pi D}$$

$$= \frac{1}{\pi \times 2\cdot5}$$

$$= 0\cdot1275$$

hence $\theta = 7° 16'$

The angle of friction ϕ is given by

$$\tan \phi = \mu = 0\cdot22$$

hence $\phi = 12° 24'$

Torque to raise load $= \frac{1}{2}WD \tan (\phi + \theta)$
$$= \frac{1}{2} \times 400 \times 2 \cdot 5 \times \tan 19° \, 40'$$
$$= \textbf{179 lb-in.}$$

Efficiency $= \dfrac{\tan \theta}{\tan (\phi + \theta)}$

$$= \frac{0 \cdot 1275}{0 \cdot 3574}$$

$$= 0 \cdot 357 \text{ or } \textbf{35·7 per cent}$$

Torque to lower load $= \frac{1}{2}WD \tan (\phi - \theta)$
$$= \frac{1}{2} \times 400 \times 2 \cdot 5 \times \tan 5° \, 8'$$
$$= \textbf{44·9 lb-in.}$$

Example. A turnbuckle has right- and left-hand square threads of $\frac{1}{2}$ in. pitch, mean diameter 2 in., $\mu = 0 \cdot 16$. The turnbuckle is

Turnbuckle

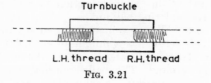

L.H. thread   R.H. thread

Fig. 3.21

used to tighten a wire rope, Fig. 3.21. If the tension in the rope is constant at 2,400 lb find the turning moment required.

Solution

For *each* thread, $\tan \phi = \mu = 0 \cdot 16$; hence $\phi = 9° \, 5'$

$$\tan \theta = \frac{p}{\pi D}$$

$$= \frac{\frac{1}{2}}{\pi \times 2}$$

$$= 0 \cdot 0796$$

hence $\qquad\qquad \theta = 4° \, 33'$

Torque to overcome friction on each thread

$$= \frac{1}{2}WD \tan (\phi + \theta)$$
$$= \frac{1}{2} \times 2,400 \times 2 \tan 13° \, 38'$$
$$= 2,400 \times 0 \cdot 2421$$
$$= 582 \text{ lb-in.}$$

Total torque for two threads $= 2 \times 582$
$$= \textbf{1,164 lb-in.}$$

PROBLEMS

1. The helix angle of a screw thread is 10°. If the coefficient of friction is 0·3 and the mean diameter of the square thread is 4 in., calculate (a) the pitch of the thread, (b) the efficiency when raising a load of 200 lb, (c) the torque required.

(2·215 in., 35 per cent, 16·8 lb-ft)

2. Find the torque to raise a load of 1,200 lb by a screw jack having a double-start square thread with four threads per inch and a mean diameter of 3 in. $\mu = 0·12$. What is the torque required to lower the load?

(314 lb-in., 120 lb-in.)

3. A nut on a single-start square-thread bolt is locked tight by a torque of 60 lb-in. The thread pitch is ¼ in. and the mean diameter 3 in. Calculate (a) the axial load on the screw, (b) the torque required to loosen the nut. $\mu = 0·1$.

(315 lb, 34·7 lb-in.)

4. Calculate the pitch of a single-start square-thread screw of a jack which will just allow the load to fall uniformly under its own weight. The mean diameter of the thread is 4 in. and $\mu = 0·08$. If the pitch is ¾ in. what is the torque required to lower a load of 600 lb?

(1 in.; 24 lb-in.)

5. A double-start square-thread screw has a pitch of 1 in. and a mean diameter of 5 in.; $\mu = 0·03$. Calculate its efficiency when raising a load.

(80·5 per cent)

6. A lathe saddle weighs 60 lb and is traversed by a single-start square-thread screw of ½ in. pitch and mean diameter 2 in. If the vertical force on the cutting tool is 50 lb find the torque at the screw required to traverse the saddle. The coefficient of friction between saddle and lathe bed, and for the screw thread is 0·15.

(3·84 lb-in.)

7. A stop valve in a horizontal pipeline consists of a plate of 6 in. diameter which moves in vertical guides. If the coefficient of friction between valve and guides is 0·3 and the pressure upstream of the valve is 300 lb/in.², calculate the vertical force required just to move the valve when fully closed.

If the valve is raised by a screw having a square thread, ½ in. pitch and mean diameter 2 in., calculate the torque on the screw. The coefficient of friction between screw and nut is 0·2.

(2,545 lb, 60·2 lb-ft)

8. A wire rope is tightened by means of a turnbuckle having right- and left-hand square threads of ⅜ in. pitch. The mean diameter of the thread is

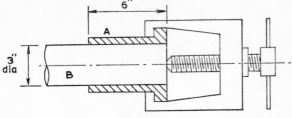

FIG. 3.22

1⅜ in. Find the turning moment to tighten the rope at the instant the pull in the rope is 1,500 lb. $\mu = 0.12$.

(432 lb-in.)

9. The bush A is drawn from the shaft B by the screw operated extractor shown in Fig. 3.22. If the radial pressure between bush and shaft is 250 lb/in.^{2} and the coefficient of friction is 0.2 what is the force required to draw the bush? If the screw pitch is ¼ in. and the mean diameter of the square thread is 1 in. what is the torque required on the screw? For screw and nut $\mu = 0.15$.

(2,830 lb, 330 lb-in.)

4

Velocity and Acceleration

4.1. Average Speed

THE *average speed*, v_{av}, of a body is defined as the distance travelled s divided by the time taken t; thus

$$v_{av} = \frac{s}{t}$$

4.2. Constant Speed

If the distance travelled is the same in successive intervals of time then the speed is said to be *constant*.

4.3. Varying Speed

When the speed is not constant but changes continuously we require to state exactly what we mean by the *speed at a point*. Consider therefore a body which travels a distance s ft after a time t sec given by the equation

$$s = 2t + t^2$$

Table 4.1 gives the values of s and of the average speed v_{av} corresponding to time intervals $t = 0, 1, 2, 3, 4$ sec.

TABLE 4.1

Time t (sec) . . .	0	1	2	3	4
Distance s ft travelled from time $t = 0$ . . .	0	3	8	15	24
Average speed (ft/sec) $v_{av} = s/t$	?	3	4	5	6

When $t = 0$, the average speed given by the formula s/t would appear to be $0/0$, which has no meaning. However, if the average speed be plotted against the *time interval* a smooth curve (in this case a straight line) is obtained which cuts the speed axis at a speed of 2 ft/sec (Fig. 4.1). Thus at point A when the time interval is zero the *average* speed is 2 ft/sec.

The ratio (distance travelled)/(time taken) therefore has a real meaning even when the time interval is zero. It is then known as

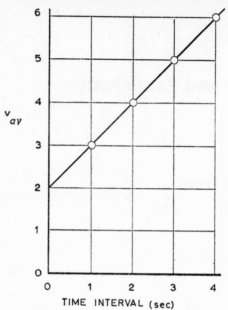

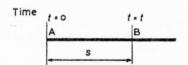

FIG. 4.1. AVERAGE SPEED–TIME GRAPH

the speed at a point A. Thus, speed at a point, v, = limiting value of the ratio

$$\frac{\text{distance travelled}}{\text{time taken}}$$

when the time interval is zero and is the *rate of change* of distance with respect to time, i.e. ds/dt in the notation of the calculus.

The speed at time $t = 0$ is therefore obtained by first differentiating the expression $s = 2t + t^2$ and then setting $t = 0$. Thus—

$$v = \frac{ds}{dt} = \frac{d}{dt}(2t + t^2)$$

$$= 2 + 2t$$

$$= 2 \text{ ft/sec} \qquad \text{when } t = 0$$

4.4. Velocity

The *velocity* of a body is defined as a vector quantity, of magnitude equal to its speed, and direction tangent to the path of motion of the body. Velocity therefore is completely specified only by stating both magnitude *and* direction.

The distinction between speed and velocity and changes in those quantities is illustrated in Fig. 4.2. This shows the speed and

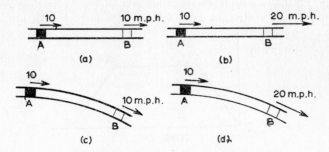

FIG. 4.2. (*a*) CONSTANT SPEED; UNIFORM VELOCITY
(*b*) CHANGE IN SPEED AND VELOCITY.
(*c*) CONSTANT SPEED; VECTOR CHANGE IN VELOCITY.
(*d*) CHANGE IN SPEED AND VELOCITY

velocity of a body at successive points A and B on a track AB. It should be noted that if the speed changes then the magnitude of the velocity changes accordingly, Fig. 4.2 (*b*), but that velocity may be altered by a change in direction without change in speed, Fig. 4.2 (*c*).

Uniform velocity is motion along a straight line at constant speed.

4.5. Motion in a Straight Line

AVERAGE AND UNIFORM ACCELERATION

The *average acceleration* f_{av} of a body moving in a straight line is defined as the change in speed or velocity divided by the time taken. If u is the initial velocity, v, the final velocity, and t, the time taken, then

$$f_{av} = \frac{\text{change in velocity}}{\text{time taken}}$$

$$= \frac{v - u}{t}$$

If the velocity increases by equal amounts in equal intervals of time then the acceleration f is said to be *constant*.

Uniform acceleration is motion in a straight line with constant acceleration. Thus

$$f = f_{av}$$

$$= \frac{v - u}{t}$$

or $$v = u + ft$$

Fig. 4.3 shows a typical speed-time graph (or velocity-time graph for motion in a straight line) for a body moving with uniform

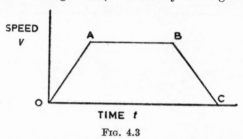

FIG. 4.3

acceleration. Uniform acceleration from rest to a maximum speed is shown by OA; the speed is maintained constant at the maximum value, shown by AB; finally the body decelerates uniformly to rest, BC. Note that provided the acceleration is uniform the v–t graph is made up of straight lines. Note also that the area under the graph OABC represents the total distance travelled.

As a reminder of work which the student should have already covered we now state the formulae for motion with uniform acceleration.

4.6. Summary of Formulae for Uniform Acceleration

$$v = u + ft$$
$$v^2 = u^2 + 2fs$$
$$s = ut + \tfrac{1}{2}ft^2$$
$$s = v_{av}t$$
$$v_{av} = \frac{u + v}{2}$$

When the speed is increasing the acceleration is positive.

When the speed is decreasing the acceleration is negative, i.e. a retardation or deceleration.

PROBLEMS

1. The cutting stroke of a planing machine is 2 ft and it is completed in 1·2 sec. For the first and last quarters of the stroke the table is uniformly accelerated and retarded, the speed remaining constant during the remainder

of the stroke. Using a speed–time graph, or otherwise, determine the maximum cutting speed.

$$(2 \cdot 5 \text{ ft/sec})$$

2. A diesel train accelerates uniformly from rest to reach 60 m.p.h. in 6 min, after which the speed is kept constant. Calculate the total time taken to travel 6 miles.

$$(9 \text{ min})$$

3. A train travelling at 30 m.p.h. is slowed by a "distant" signal at A, and comes uniformly to rest between A and B to stop at B, 300 yd from A. After 1 min at rest the "stop" signal at B allows the train to accelerate uniformly to C, 500 yd from B, where it is again travelling at 30 m.p.h. Calculate the total time lost between A and C due to signals.

$$(1 \text{ min}, 54 \cdot 6 \text{ sec})$$

4. The driver of a train shuts off the power and the train is then uniformly retarded. In the first 30 sec the train covers 110 yd, and it then comes to rest in a further 30 sec. Determine (a) the initial speed of the train before power is cut off, (b) the total distance travelled in coming to rest.

$$(14 \cdot 67 \text{ ft/sec}; \quad 440 \text{ ft})$$

5. A car A starts from rest with a uniform acceleration of 2 ft/sec². A second car B starts from the same point, 4 sec later and follows the same path with an acceleration of 3 ft/sec². How far will the cars have travelled when B passes A?

$$(475 \text{ ft})$$

4.7. Relative Velocity

In dealing with speed and velocity it has been assumed so far that the earth's surface has been "fixed." Yet it is known that the earth rotates around its axis and that the earth's centre is in motion around the sun. In fact, therefore, there is no point completely at rest and all velocities have been measured *relative to the surface of the earth*. In a similar way any moving point A may be regarded as "fixed" and the velocity of any other point B measured relative to the point A; that is, the velocity of B is obtained as it would appear to an observer moving with point A. The velocity of B relative to the earth, v_B (or just "velocity of B") is then made up of two parts:

1. v_{BA}, the velocity of B relative to A (as if A were at rest).
2. v_A, the velocity of A relative to earth, i.e. the "velocity of A."

4.8. Velocity Diagram

If A and B are moving in the *same straight line* the velocity of B

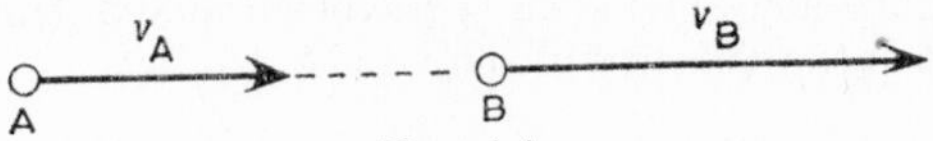

Fig. 4.4

is the algebraic sum of the velocity of B relative to A and the velocity of A. Thus from Fig. 4.4—

$$v_B = v_{BA} + v_A$$

or

$$v_{BA} = v_B - v_A$$

If A and B are not moving in the same straight line, then account must be taken of *direction* as well as magnitude, i.e. speed. Then v_A, v_{BA} and v_B are each vectors and are added or subtracted in the same way as other vectors such as force vectors are added or subtracted.

Let A and B be bodies having velocities v_A, v_B, respectively (Fig. 4.5). These velocities are represented in magnitude and direction in a *velocity diagram* as follows—

Choose a point o to represent a point at rest relative to earth.

From o draw a line oa to represent v_A in magnitude and direction.

Similarly from the same point o draw a line ob to represent v_B.

Then the line ab, taken in the sense a to b, represents v_{BA}, the velocity of B relative to A, i.e. it is as if A were the fixed point and a represented a point at rest.

Similarly ba, taken in the sense b to a, represents v_{AB}, the velocity of A relative to B, in both magnitude and direction.

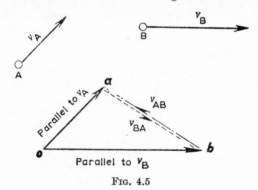

Fig. 4.5

Note that an absolute velocity, i.e. a velocity relative to earth, is always measured *from* point o in the velocity diagram.

Note also that the velocity of B is found by *adding vectorially* vector oa representing v_A and vector ab representing v_{BA}.

Example. A tool is traversed across a lathe bed at 0·2 ft/min relative to the slide. The slide is traversed at 0·5 ft/min along the lathe. What is the velocity of the tool?

Solution

Draw oa horizontal to represent the velocity of the slide, 0·5 ft/min (Fig. 4.6).

From a draw ab perpendicular to oa to represent the velocity of the tool across the bed, relative to the slide, 0·2 ft/min.

Then ob represents the velocity of the tool.

By measurement from the velocity diagram—

velocity of tool = **ob** = **0·54 ft/min**

Its direction of motion is that corresponding to **ob** which makes an angle of 21° 48′ with **oa**, i.e. with the axis of the lathe.

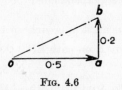

Fig. 4.6

Example. Two ships are steadily steaming towards each other. When 1,000 yd apart ship B takes avoiding action by turning through 30° to port. The speed of ship A is 20 ft/sec and that of B is 30 ft/sec. Calculate their nearest distance apart and how long before this distance is reached after B takes avoiding action. Neglect the time taken to alter course.

Solution

Fig. 4.7 (*a*) shows a diagram to scale of the paths of the two ships. The motion of B is at 30° to the line BA and AB = 1,000 yd. The velocity diagram is drawn as follows (Fig. 4.7 (*b*)):

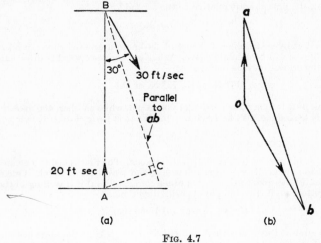

(a)   (b)

Fig. 4.7

Draw **oa** parallel to AB to represent the velocity of A, 20 ft/sec.
Draw **ob**, 30° to BA, to represent the velocity of B, 30 ft/sec.

Then **ab** represents in magnitude and direction the velocity of B relative to A, i.e. the motion of B as seen from A.

In Fig. 4.7 (*a*) BC is drawn from B parallel to **ab** to represent the *path* of B relative to A. The shortest distance between A and B is found by drawing the perpendicular AC from A on BC. By measurement—

$$\text{nearest approach} = AC = 932 \text{ ft or } \textbf{311 yd}$$

distance travelled by B on path BC = length BC

$$= 2{,}850 \text{ ft}$$

velocity of B relative to A on this path = **ab**

$$= 48 \cdot 5 \text{ ft/sec}$$

therefore　　　　　time taken to reach $C = \dfrac{BC}{\textbf{ab}}$

$$= \frac{2{,}850}{48 \cdot 5}$$

$$= \textbf{58·7 sec}$$

PROBLEMS

1. An aircraft travelling due west at 600 m.p.h. just passes over another aircraft travelling due north at the same speed. What is the velocity and direction of the first aircraft relative to the second?

(850 m.p.h., SW.)

2. To a destroyer steaming due east at 30 knots a cruiser whose speed is 24 knots appears to be steaming NW. What are the two possible directions in which the cruiser may be moving?

(17° N. of E., 73° N. of E.)

3. An aircraft is flying due north at 1,000 m.p.h. while another, 400 miles to the east, is travelling NW. at 1,800 m.p.h. What is their closest distance of approach?

(84 miles)

4. Two trains pass each other on parallel tracks. The first is 600 ft long and travels at 30 m.p.h., the second is 400 ft long and travels at 20 m.p.h. Calculate the total time taken to pass each other completely (*a*) if travelling in the same direction, (*b*) if travelling in opposite directions.

((*a*) 68·25 sec; (*b*) 13·65 sec)

5. Two aircraft leave airports A and B 100 miles apart at the same instant. The first flies directly from A to B at 200 m.p.h., the second flies on a course inclined at 60° to the line joining B to A at 300 m.p.h. Find (*a*) the nearest distance of approach of the two aircraft, (*b*) the time taken to reach the nearest distance. Neglect the curvature of the earth.

(60 miles, 0·183 hr)

4.9. Angular Velocity of a Line

Let a line AB of fixed length move in the plane of the paper in any manner whatsoever (Fig. 4.8). After a small interval of time

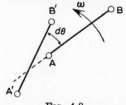

FIG. 4.8

dt let the line AB move to A'B' and let AB make with A'B' a small angle dθ rad. Then the *angular velocity* ω of the line AB is defined as—

$$\omega = \frac{d\theta}{dt}$$

and is measured in radians per second (rad/sec).

4.10. Motion of a Body in a Plane

A rigid body forming part of a mechanism will always be of fixed length whatever its motion. Any two points A and B on the body will therefore remain at a fixed distance apart. Since there is no stretch along the line AB, there will be no velocity of B relative to A along AB, Fig. 4.9. However, since the body may rotate, B may

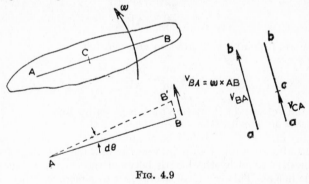

FIG. 4.9

have a velocity relative to A by rotation about A, as if A were fixed. The motion of B relative to A *can occur only in a direction perpendicular to the line* AB. This must be so whatever the motion of A. If B rotates about A with angular velocity ω then, after a small time dt, let AB' be the position of AB, where $\angle BAB' = d\theta$ (Fig. 4.9).

3—(T.909)

Distance travelled by B = BB′

therefore velocity of B normal to AB = $v_{BA} = \dfrac{BB'}{dt}$

since $d\theta$ is small, BB′ = AB × $d\theta$

therefore $\qquad v_{BA} = AB \times \dfrac{d\theta}{dt}$

$\qquad\qquad\qquad = AB \times \omega$, since $\omega = \dfrac{d\theta}{dt}$

hence $\qquad\qquad \omega = \dfrac{v_{BA}}{AB}$

$\qquad\qquad\qquad = \dfrac{\text{velocity of B relative to A}}{\text{length AB}}$

The relative velocity v_{BA} would be represented by a vector **ab**, of length ωAB, drawn perpendicular to AB, the sense of the vector corresponding to the motion of B relative to A (Fig. 4.9). In the same way for any point C on the line AB we may write

$$v_{CA} = \omega \, . \, AC$$

thus $\qquad\qquad \dfrac{v_{CA}}{v_{BA}} = \dfrac{\omega AC}{\omega AB}$

i.e. $\qquad\qquad \dfrac{\mathbf{ac}}{\mathbf{ab}} = \dfrac{AC}{AB}$

Therefore, if point **c** is located on **ab** such that

$$\frac{\mathbf{ac}}{\mathbf{ab}} = \frac{AC}{AB}$$

then the velocity of C relative to A is given by **ac**.

Vector **ab** is called the *velocity image* of the line AB. When the velocity image of a link has been obtained, therefore, the relative velocity between any two points on the link (or on an extension of the link) is given by the length between the corresponding points on the image. This is a most useful fact to remember when dealing with mechanisms.

4.11. Velocity Triangle for a Rigid Link. Application to Mechanisms

Suppose now that AB represents a link in a mechanism and that v_A, the velocity of A, is known completely whereas v_B the velocity

of B is known only in direction (Fig. 4.10). The problem is to find
the magnitude of v_B and the angular velocity of the link. To do
this we draw a *velocity triangle* for the link, thus—

Draw **oa** to represent v_A in magnitude direction and sense.
Through **o** draw a line **ox** parallel to the given direction of v_B.
Through **a** draw a line *perpendicular to the link* to cut **ox** in **b**.
Then **ob** represents v_B and **ab** is the velocity image of AB.
oab is the velocity triangle for link AB.

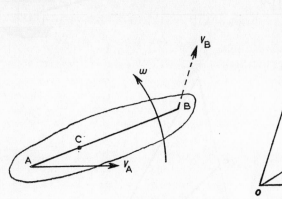

FIG. 4.10

To find the velocity of any point C on AB first locate point **c** on
the velocity image **ab** such that

$$\frac{\mathbf{ac}}{\mathbf{ab}} = \frac{AC}{AB}$$

then $$v_C = \mathbf{oc}$$

The angular velocity of the link is

$$\omega = \frac{v_{BA}}{AB} = \frac{\mathbf{ab}}{AB}$$

Note that (*a*) **oac** is the velocity triangle for link AC and

$$\omega = \frac{v_{CA}}{AC} = \frac{\mathbf{ac}}{AC}$$

and (*b*) all absolute velocities are measured from **o**.

The velocity triangle is most useful when dealing with the problem
of finding the velocities of points in mechanisms. Each link is taken
in turn and the velocity diagram obtained before proceeding to the
next link in the chain. The method is shown in the following
examples.

Example. The crank OA of the engine mechanism shown (Fig. 4.11) rotates at 3,600 rev/min anticlockwise. OA = 4 in., and the connecting-rod AB is 8 in. long. Find (*a*) the piston velocity; (*b*)

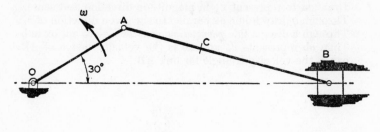

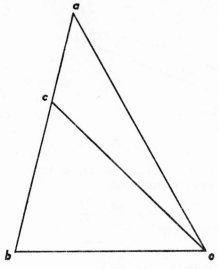

Fig. 4.11

the angular velocity of AB; (*c*) the velocity of point C on the rod 2 in. from A.

Solution

Angular velocity of crank OA

$$\omega = \frac{2\pi \times 3,600}{60} = 376{\cdot}8 \text{ rad/sec}$$

velocity of A

$$v_A = \omega OA = 376{\cdot}8 \times \tfrac{4}{12}$$
$$= 125{\cdot}6 \text{ ft/sec}$$

Point A is moving in a circular path and **oa** is therefore drawn at right angles to OA to represent v_A. The velocity of B is unknown but its *direction* is horizontal. Hence in the velocity diagram a line of indefinite length is drawn horizontally through **o**. The velocity of B *relative* to A must be *perpendicular* to AB; therefore the velocity triangle for the link AB is completed by drawing a line **ab** perpendicular to AB. The lines **ab**, **ob** cut at point **b** which determines the magnitude of the velocity v_B of the piston B. From the diagram

$$v_B = ob = \textbf{90 ft/sec}$$

$$v_{BA} = ab = 112 \text{ ft/sec}$$

$$\text{Angular velocity of AB} = \frac{\text{velocity of B relative to A}}{\text{length of AB}}$$

$$= \frac{112}{8/12}$$

$$= \textbf{168 rad/sec}$$

To find velocity of C: since C is on AB mark off **ac** on the velocity image **ab** such that

$$\frac{ac}{ab} = \frac{AC}{AB}$$

Then **oc** represents in magnitude and direction the velocity of C, the sense being from **o** to **c**. Thus

$$v_C = oc = \textbf{108 ft/sec}$$

Example. Fig. 4.12 shows a four-bar mechanism OABQ for a wrapping machine. OA and QB rotate about fixed points O and Q 16 in. apart. OA = 3 in., AB = 12 in., BQ = 4 in. At the instant considered OA is at 30° to OQ and is rotating clockwise at 720 rev/min. Find (*a*) the velocity and direction of motion of point C on AB, 4 in. from A; (*b*) the angular velocity of the link AB.

Solution

Angular velocity of OA

$$\omega = \frac{2\pi \times 720}{60} = 75 \cdot 4 \text{ rad/sec}$$

velocity of A

$$v_A = 75 \cdot 4 \times \tfrac{3}{12} = 18 \cdot 85 \text{ ft/sec}$$

First draw the mechanism to scale.
Set off **oa** to represent the velocity of A, 18·85 ft/sec. Note the sense of **oa** since OA rotates clockwise.

Draw **ab** of indefinite length perpendicular to AB, and draw **ob** perpendicular to QB; these two lines meet in point **b**.

ob represents the velocity of B.

(*a*) Divide **ab** at **c** such that

$$\frac{\mathbf{ac}}{\mathbf{ab}} = \frac{AC}{AB} = \frac{4}{12}$$

Then **oc** represents the velocity of C in magnitude and direction. From the diagram, $v_C = \mathbf{oc} = \mathbf{17 \cdot 5}$ **ft/sec** at **53°** to the horizontal in the sense **o** to **c**.

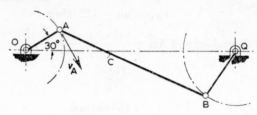

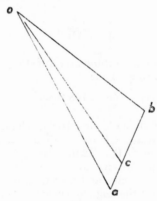

FIG. 4.12

(*b*) The velocity of B relative to A

$$v_{BA} = \mathbf{ab}$$
$$= 8 \text{ ft/sec, from the diagram}$$

$$\text{angular velocity of AB} = \frac{\mathbf{ab}}{AB}$$

$$= \frac{8}{1}$$

$$= \mathbf{8 \ rad/sec}$$

Example. Fig. 4.13 shows a four-bar mechanism OABQ with a link CD attached to C the mid-point of AB. The end D of link CD is constrained to move vertically. OA = 2·5 ft, AB = 4 ft, QB = 3 ft, OQ = 6 ft, and CD = 5 ft. For the position shown the angular velocity of crank OA is 60 rev/min clockwise; find (a) the velocity of D; (b) the angular velocity of CD; (c) the angular velocity of BQ.

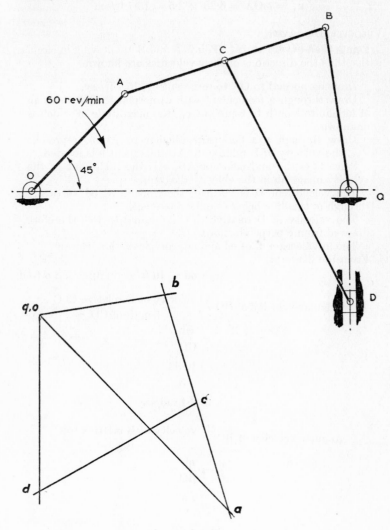

Fig. 4.13

Solution

Angular velocity of OA

$$\omega = \frac{2\pi \times 60}{60} = 6 \cdot 28 \text{ rad/sec}$$

velocity of A

$$v_A = \omega OA = 6 \cdot 28 \times 2 \cdot 5 = 15 \cdot 7 \text{ ft/sec}$$

VELOCITY DIAGRAM

Points O and Q are at rest. Points A and B are moving in circular paths, thus the directions of their velocities are known.

Draw **oa** normal to OA to represent v_A, 15·7 ft/sec.

Draw through **q** (coincident with **o**) normal to QB a line **qb** of indefinite length to represent v_B, the magnitude of which is unknown.

Draw through **a** a line perpendicular to AB to represent v_{BA}, the velocity of B relative to A; thus point **b** is located.

Since C is the mid-point of AB, **c** is the mid-point of the velocity image **ab** in the velocity diagram.

The velocity of D is vertical, therefore draw **od** vertically through **o**, this line being of indefinite length.

The velocity of D relative to C is normal to DC, therefore draw **cd** from **c** perpendicular to CD.

The intersection **d**, of **od** and **cd**, completes the diagram.

From the diagram,

$$v_D = \mathbf{od} = \mathbf{10 \text{ ft/sec}} \text{ in direction } \mathbf{o} \text{ to } \mathbf{d}$$

$$\text{Angular velocity of CD} = \frac{\text{velocity of D relative to C}}{\text{length of CD}}$$

$$= \frac{\mathbf{cd}}{CD}$$

$$= \frac{10 \cdot 52}{5}$$

$$= \mathbf{2 \cdot 1 \text{ rad/sec}}$$

$$\text{Angular velocity of BQ} = \frac{\text{velocity of B relative to Q}}{BQ}$$

$$= \frac{\mathbf{qb}}{BQ}$$

$$= \frac{7 \cdot 54}{3}$$

$$= \mathbf{2 \cdot 51 \text{ rad/sec}}$$

PROBLEMS

1. The engine mechanism of Fig. 4.14 has a crank 8 in. long and connecting rod 20 in. long. If the crank speed is 3,000 rev/min clockwise, find for the

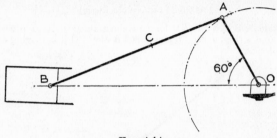

Fig. 4.14

position shown: (*a*) the piston velocity; (*b*) the angular velocity of the connecting rod; (*c*) the velocity of a point C on the rod 8 in. from the crankpin.

(220 ft/sec; 66 rad/sec anticlockwise; 206 ft/sec)

2. The crank OA in the mechanism shown, Fig. 4.15, rotates anticlockwise at 300 rev/min and is 1 ft long. The link AB is 2 ft long and the end B moves

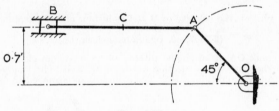

Fig. 4.15

in horizontal guides. Find for the position shown: (*a*) the velocity of B; (*b*) the velocity of point C, the mid-point of AB; (*c*) the angular velocity of AB.

(22·3 ft/sec; 25 ft/sec; 11·1 rad/sec clockwise)

3. In the mechanism shown, Fig. 4.16, crank OA rotates at 100 rev/min clockwise. Links AB and AC are pin-jointed at A and the pin ends B and C

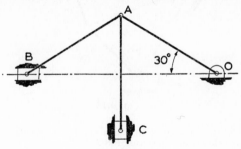

Fig. 4.16

are attached to blocks sliding in horizontal and vertical guides, respectively. For the position shown when C is vertically below A find the velocity of B and C and the angular velocity of links AB and AC. OA = AB = AC = 6 in.

    (B, 5·24 ft/sec; C, 4·53 ft/sec; AB, 10·48 rad/sec anticlockwise;

    AC, 5·24 rad/sec clockwise)

4. The ends A, B of a link 5 ft long are constrained to move in vertical and horizontal guides (Fig. 4.17). When A is 3 ft above O it is moving at 5 ft/sec

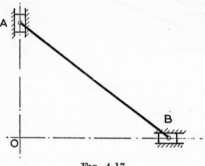

FIG. 4.17

upwards. What is the velocity of B at this instant and the angular velocity of the link?

    (3·75 ft/sec, 1·25 rad/sec clockwise)

5. The crank OA of an engine rotates at 1,800 rev/min clockwise and is 1 ft long. There are two connecting rods AB, AC each 18 in. long, connected to the single crankpin (Fig. 4.18). The cylinders are arranged to form a 60°

FIG. 4.18

"vee." Find for the configuration shown: (a) the velocity of each piston; (b) the angular velocity of connecting rod AC.

    (B, 224 ft/sec; C, 80 ft/sec; 124 rad/sec anticlockwise)

6. The mechanism shown in Fig. 4.19 has the following dimensions: OA = 2 ft, AB = 4 ft, QB = 3 ft, centre distance OQ = 4 ft. When in the

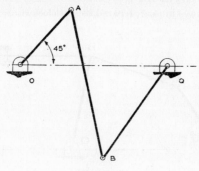

FIG. 4.19

position shown, OA rotates at 60 rev/min clockwise. Find the velocity of pin B and the angular velocity of the link AB.

(14·4 ft/sec; 0·8 rad/sec anticlockwise)

7. The cranked lever AOB shown in Fig. 4.20 drives a block C through a link BC. The lever is pivoted at O and the block moves in vertical guides.

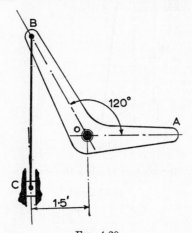

FIG. 4.20

At the instant considered when OA is horizontal the end A has a velocity of 10 ft/sec vertically upwards. OA = 2·5 ft, OB = 3 ft, BC = 4 ft. Find (a) the velocity of B; (b) the velocity of C; (c) the velocity of C relative to B.

(12 ft/sec; 6 ft/sec; 10·4 ft/sec)

8. The four-bar mechanism OABQ shown, Fig. 4.21, is pivoted at O and Q and has the following dimensions: OA = 4 in., AB = 5 in., BQ = 5 in., OQ = 8 in. Attached to the pin at B is a link BC, 5 in. long, which carries a

block at end C constrained to move in horizontal guides. When OA rotates at 30 rev/min clockwise, find for the position shown: (*a*) the velocity of C; (*b*) the angular velocity of AB.

(8·5 in./sec; 1·76 rad/sec anticlockwise)

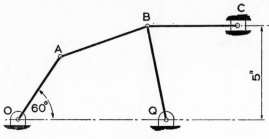

FIG. 4.21

9. Fig. 4.22 shows a crank press for impact extrusion. Crank OA rotates at 60 rev/min clockwise. OA = 5 in., AB = 20 in., CB = 12 in., BD = 15 in.

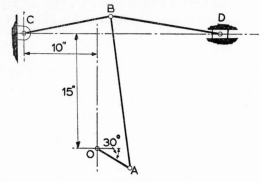

FIG. 4.22

Find the velocity of the plunger D when the crank makes an angle of 30° with the horizontal.

(8·5 in./sec)

5

Inertia and Change of Motion

5.1. Inertia and Mass

A CHANGE in motion of a body (treated simply as a particle, without rotation) can occur both by a change in speed and in direction, i.e. by a change in its velocity. The rate of change of velocity is its acceleration and is determined by circumstances external to the body itself. Consider, for example, two spring connected bodies A and B, Fig. 5.1. Imagine A and B to be drawn apart and then allowed

FIG. 5.1

to move *freely* in a horizontal plane. At an instant when A is moving from left to right with acceleration f_A, B is moving from right to left with acceleration f_B. Neither f_A nor f_B will remain constant but we are concerned only with their values at any instant.

One body is said to act upon or influence the motion of the other. Further, it is a fundamental idea or proposition, and might be verified experimentally, that the ratio of the accelerations f_A/f_B is constant for these two bodies throughout the motion. Moreover, the ratio f_A/f_B is independent of the type of "connexion" between them. For example, they may influence each other by virtue of gravitational or magnetic attraction, electrically and so on. The ratio of the accelerations depends solely upon the bodies themselves; upon an inherent property which determines the ratio f_A/f_B. This property we call *inertia*. Each body has this property, which is measured by a quantity called its *mass*.

Let the body A have mass M_A and the body B have mass M_B. Then the *ratio of the masses* is defined by the proportion

$$\frac{M_A}{M_B} = \frac{f_B}{f_A} \qquad . \qquad . \qquad . \qquad . \qquad (5.1)$$

If B be a standard *unit mass*, then $M_B = 1$, and we may define the mass of A by the relation

$$\frac{M_A}{1} = \frac{f_B}{f_A}$$

or
$$M_A = \frac{f_B}{f_A} \qquad . \qquad . \qquad . \qquad . \qquad (5.2)$$

It is unnecessary to define mass as a *quantity of matter*, or inertia as a *reluctance to accelerate*, nevertheless these are sometimes useful and more familiar terms. The ideas of mass and inertia are important whenever changes of motion are considered.

5.2. Force

We may rewrite equation (5.1) in the form

$$M_A f_A = M_B f_B \qquad . \qquad . \qquad . \qquad . \qquad (5.3)$$

Thus, the product **mass** × **acceleration** for the body A is of the same magnitude as the corresponding product for body B. This product is called a *force*, and it should be noted that it may vary from instant to instant. A force P is therefore defined by the product

$$P = Mf \qquad \text{(Newton's second law of motion)*}$$

and it is regarded as that which changes the motion of a particular body. We say that force causes acceleration.

A force P is further defined to be a *vector quantity*, of magnitude Mf, which has the same direction and sense as the acceleration f. Thus the force on body A is from left to right and that on body B is from right to left. The action, or force exerted by body B upon A, is, therefore, equal and opposite to that of A upon B (Newton's third law of motion). This force is the same as that encountered in statics. When the acceleration f of a body is zero then force P must be zero; conversely, we say that if there is no force acting on a body it will have no acceleration and its motion will remain

---

* The fundamental facts concerning the science of dynamics were discovered by Galileo in the seventeenth century. He was among the first to carry out experiments in dynamics. Subsequently Sir Isaac Newton made the first formal presentation of all the then known facts in the form of three laws of motion. Law 1: Every body continues in its state of rest or of uniform motion in a straight line, except in so far as it is compelled by impressed forces to change that state. Law 2: Change of motion (momentum) is proportional to the impressed force, and takes place in the direction of the straight line in which the force acts. Law 3: To every action there is an equal and opposite reaction.

unchanged (Newton's first law of motion). If more than one force acts on a body the acceleration is in the direction of the *resultant* force and proportional to the magnitude of the resultant force.

5.3. Weight

Consider a body A falling "freely" near the earth's surface (Fig. 5.2). The acceleration of A is $f_A = g$, vertically downwards

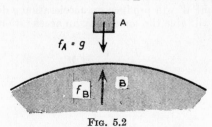

FIG. 5.2

towards the centre of the earth, where g is the acceleration due to gravity. (The reader will recall the experiments of Galileo by which he proved that all bodies dropped at the same place fell to earth with the same acceleration g.) As before, if suffix B denotes the earth

$$M_A f_A = M_B f_B$$

or

$$M_A g = M_B f_B$$

i.e.

$$f_B = \frac{M_A g}{M_B}$$

But the mass M_B of the earth is very large indeed compared with falling bodies, so that the acceleration f_B of the earth towards the moving body is negligibly small. Nevertheless, the force $M_A g$ is a finite quantity, known as the weight W of the mass M_A. Thus

$$W = M_A g$$

This quantity W is the same "weight" as measured in statics. For example, to prevent the downward acceleration g of a falling

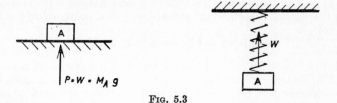

FIG. 5.3

body A we may imagine an equal and opposite upward acceleration $-g$ to be added to the motion of A. That is, the net acceleration

$= g - g = 0$, and the body is then at rest or in uniform motion. This would require a force $P = M_A g$ upwards. Thus, if A were at rest on a table (Fig. 5.3), then $W = M_A \, g$, is the force exerted by the table on the body. Or, if A is a body suspended from a spring, W is the upward force exerted by the spring on A.

5.4. The Equation of Motion

Since a weight W will produce an acceleration g downwards, any other force P will give the *same* body an acceleration f according to the proportion:

$$\frac{P}{f} = \frac{W}{g} = M$$

or
$$P = Mf \quad . \qquad . \qquad . \qquad . \quad (5.4)$$

$$= \frac{W}{g} f$$

This is the *equation of motion* of a body of weight W acted upon by a force P.

5.5. Units of Mass, Weight and Force

The standard of mass is the *pound mass*. Engineers, however, use a standard of force, the *standard pound weight*. But the weight of a standard mass varies with position on the earth's surface. An internationally accepted *standard pound weight* (lb-wt or lb) is therefore chosen as the weight of a standard pound mass at a point where the acceleration due to gravity is $32 \cdot 1741$ ft/sec². The pound weight therefore is the force which will give a standard pound-mass an acceleration of $32 \cdot 1741$ ft/sec², i.e. from equation (5.4)—

$$P = Mf$$

or   1 lb-wt = 1 lb-mass $\times$ $32 \cdot 1741$ (ft/sec²)

However, the variation in g, and therefore in the weight of the standard mass, is only about $\pm \frac{1}{4}$ per cent on the surface of the earth; for practical purposes therefore g is taken as $32 \cdot 2$ ft/sec². Hence a subsidiary, or practical, standard pound weight may be defined as the weight of a standard pound-mass at a point where g is $32 \cdot 2$ ft/sec², i.e.

1 lb-wt = 1 lb-mass $\times$ $32 \cdot 2$ (ft/sec²)

This is sometimes referred to as a gravitational system of units.

The British aeronautical engineer's absolute system of units uses this standard of force, together with a derived standard of mass, the *slug*, defined as follows. Let unit force (1 lb-wt) produce unit acceleration (1 ft/sec²) in unit mass (1 slug). Then—

1 lb-wt = 1 slug $\times$ 1 ft/sec²

A force of 1 lb-wt produces on a body of mass 1 lb an acceleration of 32·2 ft/sec²; therefore, a force of 1 lb-wt produces on a body of mass 32·2 lb an acceleration of 1 ft/sec². But the mass of a body which is given an acceleration of 1 ft/sec² by a force of 1 lb is 1 slug. Therefore 1 slug is equivalent to a mass of 32·2 lb, i.e. the ratio of the units is—

$$\frac{1 \text{ slug}}{1 \text{ lb-mass}} = 32\cdot2$$

The mass of a body in slugs is found from the ratio W/g when W is in pounds (lb) and g in feet per second per second (ft/sec²). Fig. 5.4 gives a summary of the unit systems.

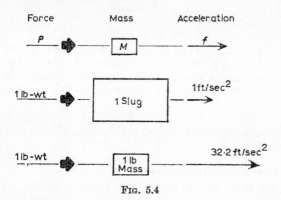

FIG. 5.4

5.6. Inertia Force

The ideas of force met with in dynamics are similar to those used in statics. Hence it would be useful if we could use the methods of statics to solve problems in dynamics. To do this we imagine a body existing free from all actions or influences from other bodies. We say that no force acts upon it, hence its motion is unchanged; in particular if it is "at rest" it will remain at rest. Let a force P act upon an otherwise free body of mass M (Fig. 5.5). We have seen that there is a direct connexion between the ideas of force, mass and acceleration, such that the body will accelerate in the direction of the force with an acceleration f given by the equation of motion—

$$P = Mf$$

In order to treat this problem as one of statics, it is useful to think of the body as being in "equilibrium," even though accelerated, i.e. it is necessary to consider the accelerating force P as being balanced by an equal and opposite force of magnitude Mf, Fig. 5.5. This force is known as an *inertia force* and always "acts" to balance the resultant force on the body, i.e. in a direction opposite to that of the acceleration f.

It is useful to consider the inertia force as a resistance to change of motion, or a reluctance to being accelerated. Similarly we sometimes think of a tractive resistance or friction force as a resistance to be overcome in order to *maintain* steady motion. Such resisting forces are of a similar nature to the accelerating force P but act in a direction opposite to that of the velocity, so as to tend to slow down or

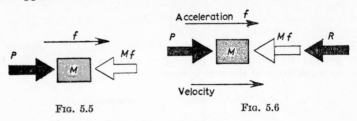

FIG. 5.5   FIG. 5.6

decelerate the body. Thus if R is the resistance to steady motion without acceleration, and P the accelerating force, the forces acting on the body are as shown in Fig. 5.6. For "static" balance in accelerated motion we may equate forces, thus—

$$P = Mf + R$$

The nature of tractive resistance will be investigated more fully in a later section.

5.7. Active and Reactive Forces

A useful distinction is often made between active and reactive forces. An *active force* is one which can itself cause or tend to cause a change in motion; for example a push, a weight or the tractive effort of a vehicle. A *reactive force* is called into play by the action of an active force, and cannot of itself cause appreciable change of motion. Examples of reactive forces include the upward reaction of a support upon which a load rests, a bearing reaction, an inertia force, and some friction forces. For example, let a package A (Fig. 5.7) be carried by the trolley B. When B is set in motion (accelerated)

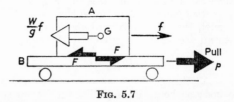

FIG. 5.7

A will slide off the end unless the friction force between A and B is large enough to cause A to move with the trolley. A moves with B due to the friction force F acting from left to right and exerted by B upon A. This force is an active force since it causes a change in motion. The equal and opposite friction force on B is reactive since it does not cause a change in motion.

5.8. Tractive Resistance

On a level track the resistances to steady motion of a vehicle are due to (a) rolling resistance, (b) air resistance. The *rolling resistance* arises from the deformation of the tyres (Chapter 3) or of the track. In a car it is increased by too low an air pressure in the tyres. In a rail wagon further effects arise from the sliding friction in bearing journals, friction at wheel flanges—particularly on rounding a curve —and friction due to misalignment of axles or inadvertent rubbing of brake blocks on tyre rims. The rolling resistance of a wagon is measured by the *coefficient of rolling resistance* μ_r. The force required just to move the wagon without acceleration on a level track is equal to the rolling resistance R_r. If the weight of the wagon is W, the coefficient of rolling resistance is defined by the ratio

$$\mu_r = \frac{R_r}{W}$$

For freight wagons a typical value of μ_r is 0·004.

On rail track the *track resistance* will depend upon the condition of the rails and rail joints. In still air the resistance to motion is dependent upon the shape of the vehicle and the frontal area; the resistance arises mainly from the disturbance of the air flow at the front, the underside and the rear of the vehicle. *Air resistance* is proportional to the square of the speed of the vehicle. *Wind resistance* depends upon both vehicle and wind speed: the effect of wind may be either to assist or retard the vehicle. The *total resistance to motion* R at a given speed is usually expressed as so many pounds per ton weight of the vehicle. For example, for a train of coaches in good condition the total resistance may be about 10 lb/ton. For goods wagons the figure might be about 20 lb/ton depending upon the speed.

5.9. Tractive Effort and Driving Torque

The *tractive effort* E required to provide motion of a vehicle is the pull in a cable or tow rope, Fig. 5.8 (a). If the weight of the vehicle is W then the effort required to give it an acceleration f is given by:

$$E = \frac{W}{g} f$$

In practice a vehicle is usually driven by an engine *torque* at the driving axle. A wheeled vehicle will be driven forward by this torque only if there is a friction force F at the road surface, Fig. 5.8. (b). This friction force does *not* form a resistance to motion and only prevents slipping of the wheel.

The force F is equivalent to a couple $F \times r$, where r is the wheel radius, together with a force F at the axle bearing, Fig. 5.8. (c). Then the driving torque T must balance the couple Fr, i.e.

$$T = Fr \qquad . \qquad . \qquad . \qquad . \qquad (5.5)$$

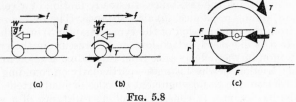

FIG. 5.8

(this is strictly true only if the rotational inertia of the wheels is neglected). Also, the force F acting on the bearing from left to right, Fig. 5.8. (c), is the effort which accelerates the vehicle; thus—

$$F = \frac{W}{g} f$$
$$= E$$

(again, this is strictly true only if the wheel inertia is negligible). The relation between driving torque and tractive effort is—

$$T = Fr$$
$$= Er$$

or
$$E = \frac{T}{r}$$

5.10. Maximum Possible Driving Torque

It may be recalled that in pure rolling motion no slip occurs between wheel and road. Nevertheless on a perfectly smooth surface the wheels would always slip and no effort could be exerted at the driving wheels. The maximum possible tractive effort is limited by the greatest force F which can be exerted at the track surface. This limiting force depends on the load N normal to the track at the driving wheels and on the *limiting coefficient of adhesion* μ_a. Thus—

$$F = \mu_a N$$

The coefficient of adhesion μ_a may be thought of as a limiting coefficient of friction. It may also take account of wheel flattening.

For a vehicle of weight W driven on all its wheels up a slope inclined at angle θ to the horizontal—

$$N = W \cos \theta$$

and on the level

$$N = W, \text{ the weight of the vehicle}$$

A similar argument applies for the maximum possible braking effort.

We consider only problems in which the vehicle is driven or braked at all wheels since, owing to acceleration or retardation, there is a redistribution of load on the wheels. It is the total load on the driving wheels which governs the maximum possible effort which can be exerted. The problem of a vehicle driven at one axle only is complex and is not considered.

5.11. Horse-power

If the tractive effort exerted by a vehicle is E lb and the speed v ft/sec, the horse power (h.p.) developed is—

$$\text{h.p.} = \frac{\text{work done/sec}}{550} = \frac{\text{force} \times \text{speed}}{550} = \frac{Ev}{550}$$

If the total resistance to motion at constant speed is R and the tractive effort E then, since there is no acceleration and no inertia force, the tractive effort required on the level is just equal in magnitude to the resistance; thus $E = R$. The horse power developed is then equal to the rate of working against the resistance.

If the tractive effort is increased above that required to maintain constant speed the vehicle accelerates and the power required will increase due to both the increase in effort and the resulting increase in speed. The horse power developed is then equal to the rate of working against both the resistance to motion and the inertia force. On ascending a gradient the tractive effort and horse power are increased to provide the force required to overcome the component of the weight down the gradient. For motion down the incline this additional term must of course be subtracted from the total effort, since the weight is assisting motion down the incline. The power is decreased accordingly.

Since the tractive resistance generally increases with speed, in practice the acceleration due to an increase in tractive effort will usually diminish until the higher resistance again equals the effort exerted, and the vehicle again continues to move at constant speed. In general, if the tractive effort is constant, the horse power developed is proportional to the speed; when starting from rest the power is initially zero even though the effort may be large. The maximum horse power is developed, of course, at the greatest speed attained (at constant effort).

5.12. Horse Power Developed by a Torque

If a torque T (lb-ft), exerted at an axle, rotates the axle at angular speed ω (rad/sec) the rate of working is—

$$T\omega \text{ ft-lb/sec}$$

and

$$\text{h.p.} = \frac{T\omega}{550}$$

Example. Determine the tractive effort required to accelerate a car at 0·1 ft/sec² down an incline of 1 in 100. The car weighs 1½ tons and the resistance to motion is 40 lb.

Solution

The forces acting down the incline are the tractive effort E and the resolved part of the weight $W \sin \theta$. The resistance to motion R acts up the plane and a "static" balance of forces is obtained by adding to this the inertia force $(W/g)f$, acting in the direction opposite to that of the acceleration f.

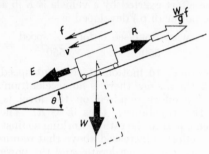

FIG. 5.9

For "static" equilibrium

$$E + W \sin \theta = R + \frac{W}{g}f$$

hence

$$E = R + \frac{W}{g}f - W \sin \theta$$

$$= 40 + \frac{1·5 \times 2,240}{32·2} \times 0·1 - \frac{1·5 \times 2,240}{100}$$

$$= \mathbf{16·8 \ lb}$$

Example. A locomotive and train weigh 100 and 500 tons, respectively. The coefficient of adhesion between wheel and track is 0·5. If 80 per cent of the weight of the locomotive is carried by the driving wheels and the tractive resistance to motion is 20 lb/ton find the maximum possible starting acceleration.

Solution

The tractive effort of a locomotive is limited to the greatest friction force which can be exerted at the wheels before slip occurs.

Tractive effort E = coefficient of adhesion $\times$ load on *driving* wheels

$$= 0·5 \times 0·8 \times 100$$

$$= 40 \ tons$$

Total resistance to motion,

$$R = 20 \times (100 + 500)$$
$$= 12,000 \text{ lb}$$

The tractive effort must balance both the tractive resistance and the inertia force.

Therefore $\qquad E = R + \dfrac{W}{g} f$

i.e. $\qquad 40 \times 2{,}240 = 12{,}000 + \dfrac{600 \times 2{,}240}{32 \cdot 2} f$

since the total weight of the train being accelerated is 600 tons. Hence

$$f = 1 \cdot 86 \text{ ft/sec}^2$$

Example. A car weighs 2,000 lb and is driven on all four wheels. The coefficient of friction between wheels and road surface is 0·65. Calculate the maximum tractive effort when ascending a gradient of 1 in 6 and find also the corresponding acceleration.

Solution

$$\sin \theta = \frac{1}{6}$$
$$= 0 \cdot 1667$$
therefore $\qquad \theta = 9° \ 36'$
and $\qquad \cos \theta = 0 \cdot 986$

Maximum tractive effort = maximum friction force
$$= \mu N$$
$$= \mu W \cos \theta$$
$$= 0 \cdot 65 \times 2{,}000 \times 0 \cdot 986$$
$$= 1{,}282 \text{ lb}$$

For balance of forces,

tractive effort = inertia force + component of weight down slope

therefore $\quad 1{,}282 = \dfrac{W}{g} f + W \sin \theta$

$$= \frac{2{,}000}{32 \cdot 2} \times f + 2{,}000 \times \frac{1}{6}$$

hence $\qquad f = 15 \cdot 3 \text{ ft/sec}^2$

If the car were driven at the rear axle only, as is usually the case, the effect of acceleration would be to increase the load on the driving wheels, and the maximum tractive effort would be increased accordingly.

Example. A lorry weighing 4 tons accelerates uniformly from 30 to 45 m.p.h. in 11 sec. If the tractive effort is constant during this time at 650 lb find the average resistance to motion. Also calculate (a) the average horse power developed during this time, (b) the maximum horse power, (c) the horse power developed if the lorry continues at a constant speed of 45 m.p.h.

Solution

$$\text{Initial speed} = 30 \text{ m.p.h.} = 44 \text{ ft/sec}$$

$$\text{Final speed} = 45 \text{ m.p.h.} = 66 \text{ ft/sec}$$

$$\text{Acceleration, } f = \frac{66 - 44}{11} = 2 \text{ ft/sec}^2$$

The tractive effort must balance both the tractive resistance and the inertia force. Thus

$$E = R + \frac{W}{g} f$$

or

$$650 = R + \frac{4 \times 2,240}{32 \cdot 2} \times 2$$

thus   average resistance, $R = \textbf{94 lb}$

(a) The distance travelled in 11 sec, is obtained from—

$$v^2 = u^2 + 2fs$$

$$66^2 = 44^2 + 2 \times 2 \times s$$

hence $s = 605 \text{ ft}$

$$\text{work done} = E \times s = 650 \times 605 = 393,250 \text{ ft-lb}$$

$$\text{rate of working} = \frac{393,250}{11} = 35,750 \text{ ft-lb/sec}$$

$$\text{average h.p.} = \frac{35,750}{550} = \textbf{65}$$

Alternatively, since f is uniform—

$$\text{average speed} = \frac{66 + 44}{2} = 55 \text{ ft/sec}$$

$$\text{average h.p.} = \frac{E \times \text{average speed}}{550} = \frac{650 \times 55}{550} = 65$$

(b) The maximum horse power is developed when the speed is a maximum. Thus

$$\text{maximum h.p.} = \frac{E \times v}{550} = \frac{650 \times 66}{550} = \textbf{78 h.p.}$$

(c) At a uniform speed of 45 m.p.h., since there is no acceleration,

tractive effort, E = resistance, R

$$= 94 \text{ lb}$$

$$\text{rate of working} = \frac{E \times v}{550} = \frac{R \times v}{550}$$

$$= \frac{94 \times 66}{550}$$

$$= \mathbf{11 \cdot 3 \text{ h.p.}}$$

PROBLEMS

1. A weight of 1 lb is hung from a spring balance in a lift. What is the spring balance reading when the lift is (a) at rest; (b) accelerating upwards at 10 ft/sec²; (c) accelerating downwards at 10 ft/sec²; (d) moving downwards and retarding at 10 ft/sec²?

(1 lb; 1·31 lb; 0·689 lb; 1·31 lb)

2. The total weight of a small diesel locomotive is 50 tons and the whole of this weight is carried on the driving wheels. The limiting coefficient of adhesion between wheels and rails is 0·1, and the tractive resistance to motion is 20 lb/ton. The locomotive pulls a train of wagons totalling 300 tons having a tractive resistance of 10 lb/ton. Calculate (a) the maximum tractive effort exerted by the locomotive; (b) the starting acceleration on the level.

(11,200 lb; 0·296 ft/sec²)

3. A planing machine table weighs 1,000 lb and attains a speed of 120 ft/min at a distance of 2 ft from rest. The coefficient of friction between table and bed is 0·1. Calculate the average and maximum horse power exerted during this period.

If during the cutting stroke the force on the tool is 200 lb and the speed is held constant at the maximum value attained, calculate the horse power required to maintain the cutting stroke.

(0·239; 0·478; 1·09 h.p.)

4. The tool force on a shaping machine during the cutting stroke is 40 lb and the reciprocating parts are equivalent to a moving mass of 100 lb. If power is suddenly shut off what would be the further distance cut by the tool if the cutting speed were initially 4 ft/sec? Assume the cutting force to be independent of the speed.

(7·45 in.)

5. A train increases its speed uniformly from 30 to 60 m.p.h. while travelling 1,600 yd up an incline of 1 in 120. The total weight of the train is 200 tons and the resistance to motion is 12 lb/ton. Calculate the tractive effort exerted by the locomotive and the maximum horse power exerted.

(14,560 lb; 2,330 h.p.)

6. A jet aircraft climbs in a straight line at an attitude of 60° to the horizontal. The jet thrust amounts to 20,000 lb, the weight of the aircraft is 8 tons and the average air resistance amounts to 2,500 lb. Calculate the time taken to reach a height of 10,000 ft if the speed at the start of the climb is 100 m.p.h.

(49·3 sec)

7. A train of total weight 500 tons is hauled by two locomotives up an incline of 1 in 75, increasing its speed from 10 to 30 m.p.h. in 1 min, 40 sec. The tractive resistance to motion is 10 lb/ton and the leading locomotive develops 1,000 h.p. at the maximum speed attained. Calculate the horse power exerted by the second locomotive at this speed.

(1,415 h.p.)

8. An electric locomotive together with its train weighs 200 tons. The average tractive resistance to motion is 12 lb/ton while starting from rest up a gradient of 1 in 100. Calculate the time taken to travel the first mile if the average tractive effort exerted by the locomotive is 8,000 lb.

(6 min, 3 sec)

9. Four coal wagons are lowered 100 ft from rest down an incline of 1 in 10 with uniform acceleration, by means of a cable attached to a rope brake. The weight of each wagon is 12 tons and the resistance to motion is 30 lb/ton. At the end of the incline the wagons are travelling at 10 m.p.h. Calculate the maximum power dissipated as heat at the rope brake.

(152·5 h.p.)

10. A diesel locomotive weighing 60 tons hauls a train of wagons weighing 200 tons up an incline of 1 in 200. The tractive resistance is 24 lb/ton weight. Calculate the maximum retardation (a) if the brakes are applied at the locomotive only; (b) if the brakes are applied at every wagon and the locomotive. The coefficient of adhesion is 0·65.

(5·3 ft/sec²; 21·4 ft/sec²)

11. A racing car of weight 1 ton is driven on all four wheels and has a limiting coefficient of adhesion between tyres and road of 0·6. (a) Calculate its maximum starting acceleration; (b) what is the time and distance required to come to rest from 60 m.p.h. with the brakes locked? It may be assumed that the car does not skid sideways.

(19·3 ft/sec²; 4·56 sec; 200 ft)

12. A car of weight 4,000 lb travels down an incline of 1 in 8. Calculate the *maximum* braking torque which could be applied to all wheels before slipping occurs. The coefficient of static friction is 0·55 and the wheel diameter 2 ft 6 in.

(273 lb-ft)

5.13. Application of Inertia Force to Connected Bodies

Consider a load A, of weight W_2 lb, being pulled along a level plane by a cord passing over a light frictionless pulley, and attached to the freely hanging load B, of weight W_1 lb, shown in Fig. 5.10. If we assume no resistance to motion, B will accelerate downwards at f and, provided there is no stretch in the cord, A will have the same acceleration horizontally.

Let T lb be the tension in the cord. If there is no friction at the pulley this will produce an upward force T on B and a horizontal force T from left to right on A. The acceleration f and the tension T will be calculated by reducing the problem to a "static" one by the use of the idea of an inertia force. The forces acting on B are its weight W_1 downwards and the tension T upwards. For balance an inertia force $(W_1/g)f$ must be added in a direction opposite to

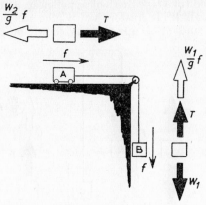

FIG. 5.10

that of f, i.e. vertically upwards (Fig. 5.10). For "static" balance of the vertical forces on B

$$W_1 = T + \frac{W_1}{g}f. \qquad \cdot \qquad \cdot \qquad \cdot \qquad (5.6)$$

The only horizontal force on A is the tension T from left to right. For balance an inertia force $(W_2/g)f$ must be added in the direction opposite to that of f, i.e. from right to left. Hence

$$T = \frac{W_2}{g}f \qquad \cdot \qquad \cdot \qquad \cdot \qquad \cdot \qquad (5.7)$$

Substituting this value of T in equation (5.6)—

$$W_1 = \frac{W_1}{g}f + \frac{W_2}{g}f$$

$$= \frac{W_1 + W_2}{g}f. \qquad \cdot \qquad \cdot \qquad \cdot \qquad (5.8)$$

This corresponds to

$$P = Mf$$

where $P = W_1$, the accelerating force on the *two* bodies and $M = (W_1 + W_2)/g$, the total mass of the two bodies. From equations (5.6) and (5.7) T and f can be found, or by considering the two bodies together f may be found directly from equation (5.8).

It should be noted that if there is friction at the pulley the tension in the cord is greater in the vertical portion than in the horizontal portion.

5.14. The Simple Hoist

Consider two loads A and B, of weight W_2 and W_1 lb, respectively, hanging either side of a *light* frictionless pulley system and connected by a light cord. If W_1 is greater than W_2 the acceleration of B will be downwards and of A upwards, as shown in Fig. 5.11. The

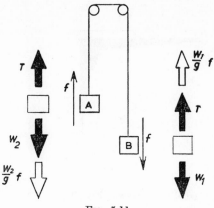

FIG. 5.11

tension T lb in the cord will be the same on both sides of the pulley. There is therefore a force T upwards on B and an upward force T at A.

Consider load B. The downward force due to the weight W_1 is balanced by the tension T, together with an inertia force $(W_1/g)f$ acting in the opposite direction to that of f, i.e. upwards. For balance, therefore

$$W_1 = T + \frac{W_1}{g}f. \qquad . \qquad . \qquad . \qquad (5.9)$$

For load A the tension T acting upwards is balanced by the weight W_2, together with the inertia force $(W_2/g)f$, both acting downwards. Thus—

$$T = W_2 + \frac{W_2}{g}f. \qquad . \qquad . \qquad . \qquad (5.10)$$

Substituting for T from equation (5.10) in equation (5.9) gives

$$W_1 = \left(W_2 + \frac{W_2}{g}f \right) + \frac{W_1}{g}f$$

$$= W_2 + \frac{W_1 + W_2}{g}f$$

or $$W_1 - W_2 = \frac{W_1 + W_2}{g}f \qquad . \qquad . \qquad . \qquad . \qquad (5.11)$$

By comparison with $P = Mf$, it is seen that the net accelerating force on the system is $P = W_1 - W_2$, and the total mass being accelerated is

$$M = \frac{W_1 + W_2}{g}$$

Example. A car of weight 1 ton hauls a trailer of weight $\frac{1}{2}$ ton with a common acceleration of 0·5 ft/sec². Calculate the pull in the horizontal tow rope and the tractive effort required.

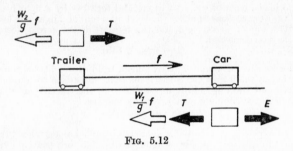

FIG. 5.12

Solution

Let E lb be the tractive effort and T lb be the tension in the tow rope. The external forces acting on the car alone are E and T.

The *inertia force* on the car $= \dfrac{W_1}{g} f = \dfrac{2,240 \times 0.5}{32.2} = 34.8$ lb

This force acts in the direction opposite to that of the acceleration. E, T and the inertia force together form a system of forces in equilibrium. For equilibrium of the car,

$$E = T + 34.8$$

Similarly, since the trailer has the same acceleration the inertia force is

$$\frac{1,120}{32.2} \times 0.5 = 17.4 \text{ lb}$$

The forces on the trailer are the tension T and the inertia force, hence for balance

$$T = 17.4 \text{ lb}$$

thus
$$E = T + 34.8$$
$$= 17.4 + 34.8$$
$$= \mathbf{52.2 \text{ lb}}$$

Alternatively, in this simple problem, the tractive effort can be obtained as the force required to accelerate the car and trailer together. Since the total weight is $1\frac{1}{2}$ tons this force is

$$\frac{1\cdot 5 \times 2{,}240}{32\cdot 2} \times 0\cdot 5 = 52\cdot 2 \text{ lb}$$

The idea of inertia force can, however, be used when this simple approach fails.

PROBLEMS

1. Two loads, each of weight 2 lb are tied together by a light inextensible cord. They are accelerated along the level by a pull of 2 lb at one load. Find the acceleration of the system and the tension in the cord. Resistance to motion may be neglected.

(16·1 ft/sec², 1 lb)

2. A locomotive of weight 80 tons pulls a train of weight 200 tons with an acceleration of 0·5 ft/sec² along the level. The resistance to motion of both locomotive and train is 10 lb/ton. Calculate (*a*) the tractive effort required, (*b*) the pull in the coupling hook at the locomotive.

(12,540; 8,950 lb)

3. In an experiment a load of weight 9 lb is pulled along a level track by a weight of 1 lb attached to it by a light inextensible cord passing over a light frictionless pulley and hanging vertically. Calculate the distance travelled from rest in 2 sec.

(6·44 ft)

4. A mine cage weighing $\frac{1}{2}$ ton is returned to the surface by a wire cable passing over a loose pulley at the pit head. The cable is fastened to a counterweight of 1,300 lb. Find the acceleration of the empty cage if allowed to move freely.

(2·4 ft/sec²)

5. A motor car develops 20 h.p. at a speed of 20 m.p.h. on the level, when towing another exactly similar car whose engine is out of action. Find the tension in the tow rope. The resistance to motion is 150 lb on each car.

(187·5 lb)

6

Motion in a Circle

6.1. Motion in a Circle

A LINEAR acceleration can be caused by a change in direction without a change in speed, that is, by a *vector* change in velocity.

Consider a point A moving in a circular path of radius r with constant angular velocity ω about a fixed point O (Fig. 6.1 (a)).

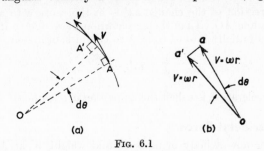

(a)   (b)

FIG. 6.1

Let the line OA move to OA' in a small time dt, and let angle AOA' $= d\theta$ rad. The initial vector velocity of A

$$v = \mathbf{oa}$$
$$= \omega \times \text{OA}$$
$$= \omega r$$

perpendicular to the line OA (Fig. 6.1 (b)). After time dt the vector velocity of A

$$v = \mathbf{oa}'$$
$$= \omega r$$

perpendicular to OA'.

The vector *change* in velocity of A in time dt

$$= \mathbf{aa}'$$
$$= \omega r \times d\theta, \text{ since } d\theta \text{ is small}$$

85

Therefore the acceleration of A,

$$f = \text{rate of vector change in velocity}$$

$$= \frac{\mathbf{aa'}}{\mathrm{d}t}$$

$$= \frac{\omega r\,\mathrm{d}\theta}{\mathrm{d}t}$$

$$= \omega^2 r,\ \text{since } \frac{\mathrm{d}\theta}{\mathrm{d}t} = \omega$$

Also since

$$\omega = \frac{v}{r}$$

then

$$f = \left(\frac{v}{r}\right)^2 \times r$$

i.e.

$$f = \frac{v^2}{r}$$

The direction of the change **aa'** is in the sense **a** to **a'**, that is, along the line AO. Thus the acceleration of A due to its rotation is directed radially inward from A to O and is of amount

$$\boldsymbol{f = \omega^2 r = \frac{v^2}{r}}$$

This acceleration is called the *centripetal acceleration*.

6.2. Centripetal Force

Consider now a body of mass M and weight W at A, rotating about O. The centripetal acceleration f can only take place if there is a force acting in the direction A to O. The magnitude of this force P is given by

$$P = Mf$$

$$= \frac{W}{g} \times \omega^2 r$$

$$= \frac{W}{g} \times \frac{v^2}{r}$$

and its direction is that of f, i.e. radially *inwards*. It is an active force since it is the force causing the body to move in a circular path and is known as the *centripetal force*. For example a body whirled in a horizontal circle at the end of a light cord is maintained in its circular path by the tension in the cord acting radially inwards at its connexion with the body at A, Fig. 6.2 (*a*).

6.3. The Inertia Force in Rotation

For balance of forces at the body A the centripetal force P may be considered as being in equilibrium with an equal and opposite inertia force of magnitude $(W/g)\omega^2 r$, Fig. 6.2 (c). This inertia force is a reactive force, since it cannot of itself cause motion. For

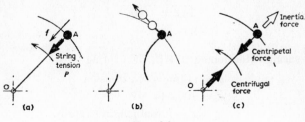

FIG. 6.2

example, if the cord is cut the active force P disappears and the body A moves in a straight line tangential to the circular path, Fig. 6.2 (b). It does not fly radially outwards.

6.4. Centrifugal Force

Now consider the tension in the cord at O. This is equal and opposite to the centripetal force at A and therefore acts radially outward. This force at O is called the *centrifugal force* and may be thought of as due to the cord tension required to provide the motion in a circle, or the action of A upon the point O due to the rotation of A.

Example. A body of weight 1·2 lb is whirled in a horizontal circle at the end of a spring. The spring stiffness is 100 lb/ft. The natural

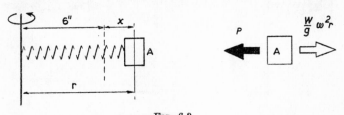

FIG. 6.3

unstretched length of the spring is 6 in. Calculate the radius of rotation of the weight and the stretch in the spring when the speed of rotation is 360 rev/min.

Solution

The radial forces acting on the body A are: the spring force P inwards and the inertia force $(W/g)\omega^2 r$ outwards. Hence

$$P = \frac{W}{g}\,\omega^2 r$$

$$= \frac{1 \cdot 2}{32 \cdot 2}\left(\frac{2\pi \times 360}{60}\right)^2 \times r$$

$$= 53\,r\,\text{lb} \qquad . \qquad . \qquad . \qquad . \qquad . \qquad (6.1)$$

where r is in feet.

Let spring extension equal x ft, then spring force

$$P = \text{stiffness} \times \text{extension}$$

$$= 100\,x\,\text{lb}$$

but $x = r - $ initial length of spring

$$= r - 0 \cdot 5\,\text{ft}$$

therefore $P = 100\,(r - 0 \cdot 5)\,\text{lb}$

From equation (6.1)

$$53\,r = 100\,(r - 0 \cdot 5)$$

hence $r = \mathbf{1 \cdot 065\ ft}$

thus extension $x = 1 \cdot 065 - 0 \cdot 5 = \mathbf{0 \cdot 565\ ft}$

Example. A centrifugal clutch is shown at the rest position with its axis mounted vertically, Fig. 6.4. The rotating weights are each

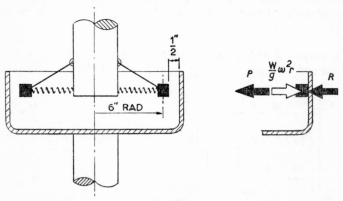

Fig. 6.4

$\frac{1}{2}$ lb and the spring strength is 500 lb/ft. The centre of mass of each weight is at 6 in. radius in the rest position. Calculate the radial force on the clutch face when the shaft rotates at 720 rev/min.

As the shaft speed rises the weights fly out until they engage the inside face of the clutch cylinder. The forces on each rotating weight are then—

spring force P, radially inwards

inertia force $\dfrac{W}{g}\,\omega^2 r$, radially outwards

reaction R of the clutch face on the weight, radially inwards

For balance of forces—

$$P + R = \frac{W}{g}\,\omega^2 r$$

At engagement, the spring force

$$P = \text{stiffness} \times \text{extension}$$

$$= 500 \times \frac{\frac{1}{2}}{12}$$

$$= 20 \cdot 8\,\text{lb}$$

radius of rotation $r = 6 + \frac{1}{2} = 6 \cdot 5$ in., or $0 \cdot 542$ ft

$$\text{inertia force} = \frac{W}{g}\,\omega^2 r = \frac{0 \cdot 5}{32 \cdot 2}\left(\frac{2\pi \times 720}{60}\right)^2 \times 0 \cdot 542$$

$$= 47 \cdot 8\,\text{lb}$$

hence $\qquad\qquad 20 \cdot 8 + R = 47 \cdot 8$

therefore $\qquad\qquad R = \mathbf{27\ lb}$

The force *on* the clutch face is equal and opposite to this.

Note—As the speed rises from rest there is a particular speed at which engagement just commences. At this speed the spring force is equal to the inertia force. As the speed rises above the engagement speed the spring force remains constant but the inertia force increases in value, thus increasing R. The value of R governs the friction force between weight and rim surfaces and hence determines the horse power transmitted.

PROBLEMS

1. What is the minimum speed at which a car may travel over a hump-backed bridge of radius 40 ft without leaving the ground?

(24·5 m.p.h.)

2. A 3-lb mass is attached at the end of a cord 3 ft long and whirled in the vertical plane. Find the greatest speed at which the tension in the cord just

disappears. What would be the maximum tension in the cord at a speed of 3 rev/sec?

(0·52 rev/sec; 102·4 lb)

3. A trolley travels at 20 m.p.h. round the inside of a vertical track. Calculate the maximum force on the track if the trolley weighs 30 lb and the track radius is 8 ft. What is the least velocity the trolley must have in order not to fall at the highest point?

(130 lb; 10·95 m.p.h.)

4. A rotor in a gyro instrument consists essentially of a flat disk of 4 in. diameter and 1 in. thick. It is mounted accurately on a spindle so that the central axis of the spindle coincides with the centre of the disk. What is the maximum out-of-balance force on the spindle at a gyro speed of 12,000 rev/min if the centre of mass of the disk is 0·001 in. out of alignment? Steel weighs 0·282 lb/in³.

(14·5 lb)

5. A body of weight 4 lb is whirled round at the end of a spring of stiffness 10 lb/in. extension at a speed of 60 rev/min. If the unstretched length of the spring is 6 in. find the radius of rotation of the body.

(6·26 in.)

6. A centrifugal clutch is designed just to engage when the centres of gravity of the rotating weights are 9 in. from the centre of rotation. The speed at engagement is 1,440 rev/min. If the revolving weights are each 1 lb weight, calculate the spring stiffness required for an extension of 1 in. at engagement.

(529 lb/in.)

7. The centrifugal clutch shown at rest in Fig. 6.5 has springs of stiffness 80 lb/in. and is designed to just engage at 600 rev/min. Calculate the required

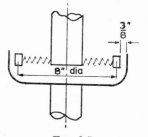

Fɪɢ. 6.5

value of the revolving weight A. What is the force on the clutch rim at 1,000 rev/min?

(0·67 lb; 53·2 lb)

8. An earth satellite is to be put into orbit at a height of 1,000 miles above the earth's surface. Determine the velocity it must have in order to do this. Make the following assumptions: (a) the orbit is circular; (b) the gravitational attraction varies inversely as the square of the distance from the centre of the earth; (c) g is 32·18 ft/sec² at the earth's surface; (d) the radius of the earth is 3,960 miles.

(15,780 m.p.h.)

6.5. Vehicle Rounding a Curve

Fig. 6.6 shows a two-wheeled vehicle (e.g. a cycle) rounding a curve of radius r at constant speed v. The cycle has weight W; A and B are the points of contact of the front and rear wheels, respectively, with the ground; O is the centre of rotation. For simplicity assume the rolling resistance to motion negligible. Hence there is no friction or other resisting force at A or B tangent to the path. Radial forces are necessary in order that the vehicle shall move in a curved path and not a straight line, and these are provided by radially-inward friction forces F_1 and F_2 at A and B, respectively.

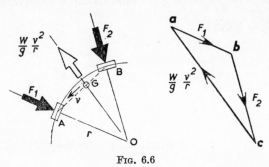

FIG. 6.6

Owing to rotation, every particle of weight dW of which the vehicle is composed has an inertia force $\dfrac{dW}{g}\dfrac{v^2}{r}$ acting upon it radially outward. The net radial effect of all these forces is equivalent to a force acting at the centre of mass (i.e. the centre of gravity G). The forces F_1, F_2 and the inertia force are in equilibrium and are represented in the force diagram, Fig. 6.6, by **ab**, **bc** and **ca**, respectively.

In practice the angle $\angle$AOB is often small and the forces F_1, F_2 approximately in the same straight line. The total friction force $F = F_1 + F_2$ is then, for an unbanked flat track, equal and opposite to the inertia force, or

$$F = \frac{Wv^2}{gr}$$

The friction force is here an active force in that it causes the vehicle to deviate from a straight line. A vehicle on a perfectly smooth sheet of ice, for example, could not move except in a straight line. When the limiting friction force is insufficient to provide the centripetal acceleration (radially inward) the vehicle tends to move in a straight line. It then appears to be skidding "outwards."

Example. A car of weight 2 tons rounds an unbanked curve of 200 ft radius at 45 m.p.h. Calculate the side thrust on the tyres.

Solution

The radial forces acting on the car are: (*a*) the outward inertia force, $\dfrac{Wv^2}{gr}$; (*b*) the inward force F exerted by the road on the tyres, i.e. the side thrust Fig. 6.7. These two forces are in balance, therefore

$$F = \frac{Wv^2}{gr}$$

$$= \frac{2 \times 2{,}240}{32 \cdot 2} \times \frac{66^2}{200} \quad \text{since 45 m.p.h.} = 66 \text{ ft/sec}$$

$$= \textbf{3{,}030 lb}$$

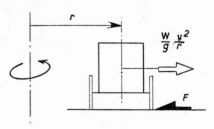

FIG. 6.7

Example. Calculate the maximum speed at which a motor cycle and rider can traverse an unbanked curve of 100 ft radius. The limiting coefficient of sliding friction between tyres and road is 0·6.

Solution

Let W = weight of vehicle.

Friction force causing cycle to traverse curve
$$= \mu W$$
$$= 0 \cdot 6\ W, \text{ radially inwards}$$

Inertia force due to rounding curve
$$= \frac{Wv^2}{gr}$$
$$= \frac{Wv^2}{32 \cdot 2 \times 100}, \text{ radially outwards}$$

For balance of forces—

$$\text{inertia force} = \text{friction force}$$

$$\frac{Wv^2}{32 \cdot 2 \times 100} = 0 \cdot 6\ W$$

hence
$$v = \textbf{44 ft/sec or 30 m.p.h.}$$

Example. A four-wheeled vehicle of weight 4 tons traverses an unbanked curve of 300 ft radius at 30 m.p.h. The wheel track width is 6 ft and the centre of gravity of the vehicle is 2·5 ft above the road. Calculate the normal reactions at each wheel.

Solution

The forces acting on the vehicle are: (*a*) the normal reactions P and Q at the inner and outer pairs of wheels; (*b*) the weight W acting through the centre of gravity; (*c*) the inertia force acting radially outward at the centre of gravity.

$$\text{Inertia force} = \frac{Wv^2}{gr} = \frac{4 \times 2{,}240 \times 44^2}{32{\cdot}2 \times 300} = 1{,}795 \text{ lb}$$

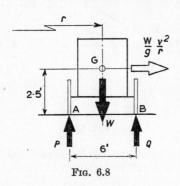

Fig. 6.8

Taking moments about inner wheel track A—

$$Q \times 6 = 1{,}795 \times 2{\cdot}5 + 4 \times 2{,}240 \times 3$$

thus

$$Q = 5{,}228 \text{ lb}$$

therefore

$$\text{force on } each \text{ outer wheel} = \frac{5{,}228}{2}$$
$$= \mathbf{2{,}614 \text{ lb}}$$

Since net vertical force must be zero

$$P + Q = W$$
$$P + 5{,}228 = 4 \times 2{,}240$$
$$P = 3{,}732 \text{ lb}$$

therefore

$$\text{force on } each \text{ inner wheel} = \frac{3{,}732}{2}$$
$$= \mathbf{1{,}866 \text{ lb}}$$

Example. A racing car travels at 120 m.p.h. on a track banked at 30° to the horizontal. The limiting coefficient of friction between tyres and track is 0·7. Calculate the minimum radius of curvature of the track if the car is not to slide "outwards."

Solution

The *total* reaction R of the track on the car acts at an angle ϕ to the normal, where $\tan \phi = \mu = 0\cdot7$, *see* paragraph 3.2. This reaction is in balance with the inertia force and the weight of the car. These

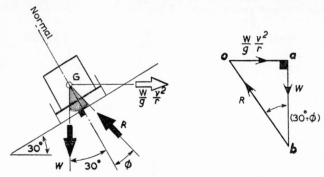

Fig. 6.9

three forces act at a point and can be represented by the triangle of forces, **oab**, Fig. 6.9. From the triangle of forces

$$\tan (30° + \phi) = \frac{Wv^2}{gr} \div W = \frac{v^2}{gr}$$

But $\tan \phi = 0\cdot7$, thus $\phi = 35°$;

and $\qquad\qquad\qquad v = 120 \text{ m.p.h.} = 176 \text{ ft/sec}$

hence $\qquad\quad \tan (30° + 35°) = \dfrac{176^2}{32\cdot2 \times r}$

therefore $\qquad\quad r = \dfrac{962}{\tan 65°} = \dfrac{962}{2\cdot145} = \textbf{449 ft}$

6.6. Superelevation of Tracks

The superelevation of a railway track is the amount by which the outer rail is raised above the level of the inner rail. The wheels of a train are flanged, the flanges being on the inside of the rails. As the train rounds a curved track the centripetal force required to provide the circular motion is provided by the inward thrust of the outer rail. To reduce the magnitude of this lateral load a second rail may sometimes be provided on the inside curve so that the inner wheel flange is contained between two rails. This second rail then takes some of the side thrust. More generally, the side thrust may be eliminated completely at a particular speed by suitable banking of the track. The speed chosen is usually the average speed at which a train may be expected to take the curve; at any speed higher than the one suitable for that angle of banking there will be a side thrust on the outer rail; at lower speeds there will be a side thrust on the inner rail.

The banking of a car race track serves a similar purpose to the superelevation of a rail track, i.e. to eliminate side thrust on the tyres. To serve its purpose for cars of different speed the gradient of the banking is increased towards the outside of the curve.

Example. Calculate the superelevation of the outside rail of a curved track if a train is to traverse the curve without side thrust on the rails at 30 m.p.h. The radius of the curve is 600 ft and the track gauge is 56·5 in.

What is the lateral force on the track due to a 60-ton vehicle at 60 m.p.h. with this angle of banking?

Solution

If the superelevation is h and the track width a, the angle of banking θ is given by—

$$\sin \theta = \frac{h}{a}$$

The forces acting on the vehicle are: the weight W, the total reaction R and the inertia force Wv^2/gr. Since there is no side

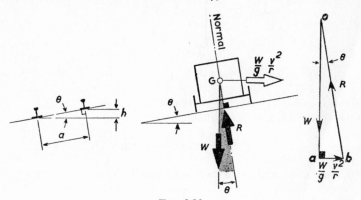

Fig. 6.10

thrust the reaction R exerted by the track on the vehicle must be normal to the track incline. From the triangle of forces (Fig. 6.10)—

$$\tan \theta = \frac{\mathbf{ab}}{\mathbf{oa}} \quad \text{where} \quad \mathbf{oa} = W$$

$$\mathbf{ab} = \frac{Wv^2}{gr} = \frac{W}{32 \cdot 2} \times \frac{44^2}{600} = 0 \cdot 1W$$

Hence $\quad \tan \theta = \dfrac{W \times 0 \cdot 1}{W} = 0 \cdot 1$

But since $\tan \theta$ is small, $\tan \theta = \sin \theta$, approximately

therefore $\quad \tan \theta = \dfrac{h}{56 \cdot 5}$

thus $\quad h = 56 \cdot 5 \tan \theta = 56 \cdot 5 \times 0 \cdot 1 = \mathbf{5 \cdot 65 \ in.}$

At 60 m.p.h. the total reaction R is no longer normal to the plane, since its component parallel to the incline must provide the side thrust of the track to balance the component parallel to the incline

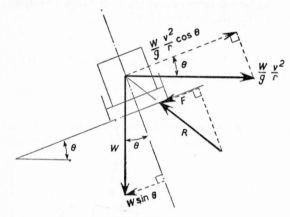

Fig. 6.11

of the increased inertia force. Therefore, resolving parallel to the track (Fig. 6.11) the side thrust F is given by—

$$F = \frac{Wv^2}{gr} \cos \theta - W \sin \theta$$

but, since θ is small, $\cos \theta \simeq 1$, $\sin \theta \simeq 0 \cdot 1$. Hence

$$F = \frac{60}{32 \cdot 2} \times \frac{88^2}{600} \times 1 - 60 \times 0 \cdot 1$$

$$= \mathbf{18 \ tons}$$

If θ is not assumed to be small the more accurate answer, $F = 17 \cdot 95$ tons, is obtained. Evidently the approximation is sufficient for all practical purposes.

6.7. Passenger Comfort—the Pendulum Car

Anyone who has been thrown outwards while in a vehicle travelling round a curve at speed will be familiar with the reality of the radial inertia force. Of course, what is experienced by a passenger is the tendency to move in a straight line while the vehicle turns. Experiments carried out by the French national railways showed that an uncompensated radial acceleration (v^2/r) in excess of about $0\cdot1g$ ($3\cdot2$ ft/sec²) is definitely unpleasant. This acceleration would be attained at about 60 m.p.h. on a 2,500 ft radius curve. One solution already exists—superelevation of the track. In addition to reducing

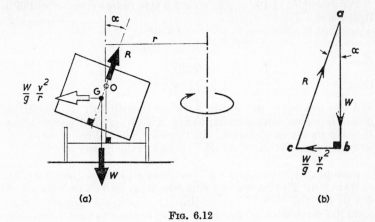

(a) (b)

Fɪɢ. 6.12

the side thrust on the rails superelevation tends to ensure that the resultant force due to weight and inertia force is normal to the seat. Then if the superelevation is sufficient there is no side force tending to slide the passenger across the seat. However, if a train moves slowly or stops on a curve the inside rail is subject to considerable thrust, and in practice the amount of superelevation is usually limited to about 6 in.

A second solution to the problem is to allow the body of the carriage to swing like a pendulum about a longitudinal axis O, placed above its centre of gravity G, Fig. 6.12 (a). The forces acting on the swinging carriage are: its weight W, the inertia force Wv^2/gr radially outward, and the reaction R at the pivot. The three forces are in equilibrium, hence all three forces pass through G. The line of action of R is therefore from G to O. The resultant force is always normal to the carriage floor; a similar argument applies also to any passenger seated in the swinging carriage (*see* Plate III).

The triangle of forces **abc** is shown in Fig. 6.12 (b). If there is no superelevation of the track the angle between the vertical and the reaction R is the angle α through which the carriage swings about O. From the triangle of forces—

$$\tan \alpha = \frac{\text{bc}}{\text{ab}}$$

$$= \frac{Wv^2}{gr} \div W$$

$$= \frac{v^2}{gr}$$

For example, at 100 m.p.h. on a 2,500 ft radius curve, $v = 146\cdot6$ ft/sec, and

$$\tan \alpha = \frac{146\cdot6^2}{32\cdot2 \times 2,500}$$

$$= 0\cdot267$$

thus $\qquad \alpha = 14° \; 57'$

and the pendulum car swings outwards nearly 15°. It should be noted, however, that allowing the carriage to pivot does not affect the side thrust on the track. In this case, since there is no super-elevation the side thrust would be equal to the inertia force.

Example. A "pendulum car" traverses a curve of 2,500 ft radius at 90 m.p.h. The track has a superelevation of 5 in. on a gauge of 4 ft $8\frac{1}{2}$ in. Calculate the angle through which the carriage swings from the vertical and the angle of swing relative to the underframe.

If the total weight of the carriage and frame is 60 tons find the side thrust on the track.

Solution

The triangle of forces is as shown, Fig. 6.13. The angle α between the vertical and the line of action GO of the reaction R at the pivot is given by

$$\tan \alpha = \frac{v^2}{gr}$$

$$= \frac{(90 \times \frac{88}{60})^2}{32\cdot2 \times 2,500}$$

$$= 0\cdot2165$$

therefore $\qquad \alpha = 12° \; 13'$

The angle of swing of the carriage is $\angle$ GON, where N is the foot of the perpendicular from O on to the floor of the carriage. Thus

$$\text{angle of swing} = \angle \text{GON}$$
$$= \alpha - \theta$$

where θ is the angle of elevation of the track. But

$$\tan \theta = \frac{5}{56 \cdot 5} = 0 \cdot 0886$$

hence $$\theta = 5° \, 4'$$

Therefore the carriage swings through an angle of $12° \, 13' - 5° \, 4'$

$$= 7° \, 9'$$

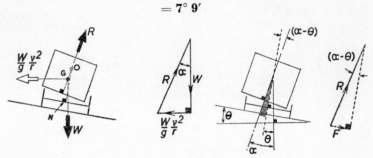

FIG. 6.13

The resultant force R of the track on the carriage is found by equating vertical forces, thus

$$R \cos \alpha = W$$

where W is the *total* weight of the vehicle. Thus

$$R = \frac{W}{\cos \alpha}$$

$$= \frac{60}{0 \cdot 9774}$$

$$= 61 \cdot 4 \text{ tons}$$

The component of this force parallel to the track is—

$$F = R \sin (\alpha - \theta)$$
$$= 61 \cdot 4 \times \sin 7° \, 9'$$
$$= 61 \cdot 4 \times 0 \cdot 1245$$
$$= \mathbf{7 \cdot 65 \text{ tons}}$$

The side thrust on the track is equal and opposite to this force F.

PROBLEMS

1. Calculate the minimum limiting coefficient of friction between tyres and road in order that a car shall negotiate an unbanked curve of 400 ft radius at 60 m.p.h.

$$(0 \cdot 6)$$

2. Calculate the minimum radius of unbanked track which a motor cycle may traverse without skidding outwards at 80 m.p.h., if the coefficient of sliding friction is 0·6.

(715 ft)

3. A vehicle travels at 45 m.p.h. round a track banked at 20° to the horizontal. The coefficient of sliding friction between tyres and road is 0·5. Calculate the radius at which skidding would occur.

(128 ft)

4. A race track is to be banked so that at 75 m.p.h. a car can traverse a 600-ft radius curve without side thrust on the tyres. Calculate the angle of banking required.

(32°)

5. A car travels round a curve of 200 ft radius which is banked at 10° to the horizontal, the slope being *away* from the inside of the curve. If the coefficient of friction between tyres and road is 0·7 calculate the maximum speed at which the curve can be traversed without skidding.

(38 m.p.h.)

6. A vehicle traverses a banked track of radius 300 ft and angle of banking 60°. If its speed is 40 ft/sec, calculate the minimum coefficient of friction between tyres and track if the vehicle is not to slip *down* the track.

(1·21)

7. A road curve of 250 ft radius is banked so that the resultant reaction for any vehicle is normal to the road surface at 45 m.p.h. Calculate the angle of banking and the value of the coefficient of friction if skidding outwards commences for a car travelling at 75 m.p.h.

(28° 27′; 0·53)

8. A car weighs 1 ton and has a track width of 5 ft. The centre of gravity is 2 ft above road level. The car travels round a curve of 200 ft radius at 45 m.p.h. If the track is banked at 30° find the total normal reaction on the outer wheels.

(0·64 ton)

9. A railway carriage built on the pendulum-car principle has a maximum angle of tilt of 20°. What is the maximum allowable speed on a 2,000-ft radius unbanked curve and what is the corresponding side thrust on the track if the carriage weighs 50 tons?

(104·3 m.p.h.; 18·2 tons)

7

Stability and Overturning

7.1. Stability of Equilibrium

CONSIDER the equilibrium of a uniform sphere or cylinder lying on the inside of a curved surface, Fig. 7.1. Evidently it will remain at rest in the lowest position as shown. Now consider what happens when it is displaced slightly to one side. When displaced the centre of gravity must rise and when then released the cylinder will tend to return to its equilibrium position at the bottom of the curved surface. If the sphere lies on the outside of a curved surface the

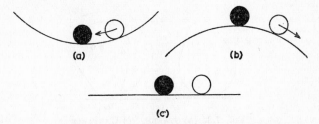

(a)

(b)

(c)

FIG. 7.1. (a) STABLE EQUILIBRIUM. (b) UNSTABLE EQUILIBRIUM. (c) NEUTRAL EQUILIBRIUM

only equilibrium position is at the top, Fig. 7.1 (b); any slight displacement results in the body moving further away from the top. When the sphere lies on a flat horizontal surface all positions are equilibrium positions, Fig. 7.1 (c).

Thus a body acted upon by a system of forces may be in equilibrium and yet the *position* of the body under these forces may depend critically upon what happens if it should move slightly away from the equilibrium position. When the body is displaced slightly the forces acting may tend to return it to the original position or they may tend to displace it still further.

If when displaced the body returns to its equilibrium position it is said to be in *stable equilibrium*; if when displaced slightly the

displacement increases it is said to be *unstable*; if the effect of the
force system is indifferent to the displacement then every slightly
displaced position is an equilibrium position and the body is then
said to be in *neutral equilibrium*. The different kinds of equilibrium
are illustrated in the following cases.

CASE 1

A cylinder, to which a weight W is attached vertically below the
central axis C, is in stable equilibrium, Fig. 7.2 (*a*). If the weight

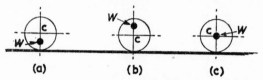

FIG. 7.2. (*a*) STABLE. (*b*) UNSTABLE. (*c*) NEUTRAL

is attached above C the equilibrium is unstable (Fig. 7.2 (*b*)). If the
weight is at the centre of the cylinder it is in neutral equilibrium,
Fig. 7.2 (*c*).

In general, if a body is placed on a flat surface and its centroid
G is below the point C about which it tends to rotate then it is in
stable equilibrium (Fig. 7.3 (*a*)). On the other hand if the centroid

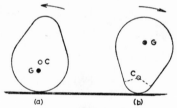

FIG. 7.3. (*a*) STABLE. (*b*) UNSTABLE

is above C the body is unstable (Fig. 7.3 (*b*)). For example, an egg
placed on either end is unstable, while if it is placed on its side it is
stable when rocked from end to end and in neutral equilibrium
when rotated about its longer axis. If a body does not rest on a
horizontal plane but is pivoted at any point C, then it is in stable
equilibrium when the centroid G is vertically below C and is unstable
when G is vertically above C. When G and C coincide it is in neutral
equilibrium.

A study of the above examples indicates an important principle
of stability. When a body is displaced from a position of stable
equilibrium the centre of gravity rises; displaced from an unstable
position the centre of gravity falls. Also the degree of stability of a
body in a position of equilibrium depends on the distance of the
centre of gravity from the pivot or centre of rotation. Thus the

degree of stability of a body may be improved by increasing this distance, i.e. by making the position of the centre of gravity as low as possible. Not all stability problems depend upon the position of the centre of gravity.

CASE 2

Two links OA, AB are pinned at A, the end O is pinned to a fixed bearing, and the end B is constrained to move in a straight line, Fig. 7.4 (a). If, when OAB lies in a straight line the end B is loaded

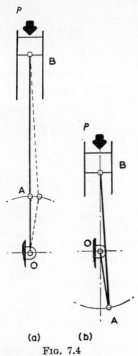

(a)   (b)

FIG. 7.4

by a force P acting along the same straight line then the two links are in a position of equilibrium. P being balanced by the reaction of the bearing at O. If, however, any small displacement of A occurs then the link OA rotates as a crank about O and the two links form an engine mechanism. The initial position was therefore unstable.

Now consider what happens when the crank pin A is on the other side of the bearing O. For clarity, Fig. 7.4 (b) shows A in a slightly displaced position. Evidently A will return to the equilibrium position owing to the piston force P. Thus this equilibrium position is a stable one.

CASE 3

Let a body A be attached to one end of a horizontal spring and slide in smooth guides as shown, Fig. 7.5. When A is displaced along the spring axis it will tend to return to its original position, provided the spring is not "overstretched." If the body A, the spring and its guides are now rotated together about the fixed axis O–O, then A will rotate at a definite radius, which is determined by the spring stiffness, the speed of rotation and the mass of A.

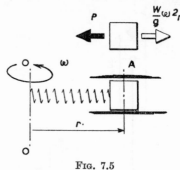

FIG. 7.5

When displaced radially from this equilibrium radius the body will usually tend to return to that radius. However, there is a speed of rotation at which the body will not return to its original position but will fly radially outwards. At this speed the radius tends to become indefinitely large and A is then unstable. Such problems of dynamic instability are of great importance in rotating and other machinery in motion. A particular example is that of a spring controlled governor for an engine.

Example. A body of weight W is whirled round in a horizontal plane at angular speed ω about a fixed point O at the end of a spring of stiffness S. The unstretched length of the spring is l. When $W = 50$ lb and $S = 100$ lb/ft find the speed at which the system becomes unstable.

Solution

The radial forces acting on the body A, Fig. 7.5, are the spring force P and the inertia force $(W/g)\omega^2 r$ due to the rotation. Hence for equilibrium

$$P = \frac{W}{g}\,\omega^2 r$$

If the spring extension is x ft, then the spring force

$$P = S \times x$$

But the extension x is final length minus original length, i.e.

$$x = r - l$$

therefore

$$P = S(r - l)$$

$$S(r - l) = \frac{W}{g}\,\omega^2 r$$

and, solving for r

$$r = \frac{Sl}{S - (W/g)\omega^2}$$

Now r tends to infinity as the denominator tends to zero, i.e. the condition for instability is

$$S - \frac{W}{g}\,\omega^2 = 0$$

i.e.

$$\omega^2 = \frac{Sg}{W}$$

$$= \frac{100 \times 32 \cdot 2}{50}$$

therefore

$$\omega = 8 \cdot 025 \text{ rad/sec}$$

$$= \frac{8 \cdot 025 \times 60}{2\pi}$$

$$= \mathbf{76 \cdot 5 \text{ rev/min}}$$

Such a speed is called a *critical speed*. A machine running at a critical speed may suffer considerable damage and an effort must be made to avoid such speeds by correct design. The value of ω given by the above method coincides with the equivalent angular velocity for the simple vibration of the same spring supported mass, *see* Chapter 9.

7.2. Overturning

A box with a flat base which is subject to a horizontal push or pull may either slide or tip over. We wish to know what force will just overturn the box if it does not slide and the force is maintained constant. Consider the rectangular box, Fig. 7.6 (a), of weight W and base a, resting on a rough horizontal floor. The line of action of the overturning force P is at a constant height b above the floor. The forces acting on the box are P, the weight W and the total reaction R of the ground. If P is not too large these three forces are in equilibrium. Hence they pass through one point—the point of intersection C of P and W. In general the reaction R acts at some point X within the base AB and the box is in stable equilibrium.

As the tipping force P is increased the point X at which the reaction R cuts AB moves to the right until eventually it coincides with B. At the corresponding value of P the end A can lift so as

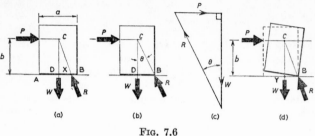

Fig. 7.6

to allow the box to pivot about B. For this critical value of the tipping load R acts along BC, which makes an angle θ with the vertical given by (Fig. 7.6 (b))—

$$\tan \theta = \frac{\text{BD}}{\text{DC}}$$

$$= \frac{\frac{1}{2}a}{b}$$

Also, from the triangle of forces (Fig. 7.6 (c))—

$$\tan \theta = \frac{P}{W}$$

hence

$$\frac{P}{W} = \frac{a}{2b}$$

The box is still in equilibrium, but we now show that it is unstable. Let the box rotate clockwise about B through a small angle. Let Y be the intersection of the line of action of the weight with the horizontal. Then, taking moments about B (Fig. 7.6 (d))—

$$P \times \text{CY} = W \times \text{YB}$$

thus

$$P = W \times \frac{\text{YB}}{\text{CY}}$$

$$= W \times \frac{\text{YB}}{b}$$

Before rotation the base is horizontal and $\text{YB} = \frac{1}{2}a$, so that $P = W \times \frac{1}{2}a/b$ as before. After rotation YB is less than $\frac{1}{2}a$, so that the value of P required to maintain equilibrium would be less than its initial value. Thus the box will remain in equilibrium after rotation only if the overturning force P is reduced. If P is held constant the box is no longer in equilibrium and will overturn. In other words, the restoring moment $W \times$ YB, due to the weight, decreases with rotation about B, whereas the tipping moment is constant. Once tipping has started the box will continue to rotate about B until it topples and it cannot return to its base unless P is reduced. In addition, once the centre of gravity is vertically above B the box can topple without any overturning force. The box is therefore in unstable equilibrium under the force $P = Wa/2b$, i.e. after any arbitrarily small clockwise rotation the box will not return to its equilibrium position.

The box may also topple over while in uniform or in accelerated motion, i.e. when sliding as shown in the first worked example.

7.3. Overturning of Vehicles

The tendency of a vehicle to slide "outwards" when rounding a curve was dealt with in Chapter 6. It was shown that there was a limiting speed at which sliding just occurs. In addition there is also a limiting speed at which the vehicle will overturn. To maintain a vehicle in a circular path requires a centripetal force at the centre of mass, but this force can only be supplied by friction at the road surface or the side thrust of a rail track. This lateral force is equivalent to the same force at the centre of mass together with a couple tending to rotate the vehicle about the centre of mass (Fig. 7.7). The two forces forming this couple are the lateral force at the

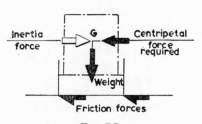

Fɪɢ. 7.7

track surface and the inertia force at the centre of mass. Alternatively, the inertia force acting radially outwards may be thought of as tending to tip the vehicle about its offside wheels. As in the case of the box the weight provides the balancing couple tending to maintain stable equilibrium and prevent tipping.

Example. The box shown weighs 100 lb and is dragged along the ground with an acceleration f by the horizontal force P. The centre of gravity of the box is 3 ft above the ground and the base is 4 ft wide. The force acts 4 ft above the ground. Calculate the maximum acceleration before tipping can occur. The coefficient of sliding friction is 0·2.

Solution

When the box is about to tip the reaction at A is zero. The forces acting are P, weight $W = 100$ lb, friction force F at B, and the inertia force Wf/g at the centre of mass G (Fig. 7.8).

Friction force $F = \mu W = 0\cdot2 \times 100 = 20$ lb

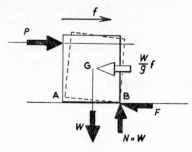

Fig. 7.8

For balance of horizontal forces

$$P = \frac{Wf}{g} + F = \frac{100 \times f}{32\cdot2} + 20$$

$$= 3\cdot11 f + 20 \text{ lb} \qquad . \qquad . \qquad . \qquad (7.1)$$

Taking moments about B—

$$P \times 4 = \frac{Wf}{g} \times 3 + W \times 2$$

$$4 P = 9\cdot33 f + 200$$

Substituting for P from equation (7.1) gives

$$4 (3\cdot11 f + 20) = 9\cdot33 f + 200$$

hence $f = \mathbf{38\cdot5 \text{ ft/sec}^2}$

Example. A car traverses an unbanked curve of 100 ft radius at a speed of v ft/sec. The wheel base is 5 ft and the centre of gravity is 3 ft above the road. Calculate the maximum value of v before the car overturns.

Solution

When the car is about to overturn the inner wheels lift and the reaction at these wheels is therefore zero. The total reaction R of the road on the car must therefore pass through wheel track B

(Fig. 7.9). The forces acting on the car are: the weight W, the inertia force Wv^2/gr radially outwards at the centre of gravity G, and the total reaction R. These three forces must pass through one

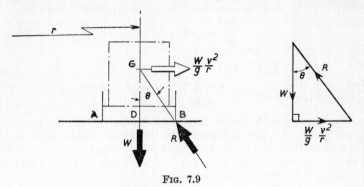

FIG. 7.9

point, i.e. the point G. The triangle of forces is shown in Fig. 7.9. The angle θ which R makes with the vertical is given by—

$$\tan \theta = \frac{Wv^2}{gr} \div W$$

$$= \frac{v^2}{gr}$$

$$= \frac{v^2}{32\cdot2 \times 100}$$

but from the geometry of the car

$$\tan \theta = \frac{DB}{GD}$$

$$= \frac{2\cdot5}{3}$$

hence
$$\tan \theta = \frac{v^2}{32\cdot2 \times 100} = \frac{2\cdot5}{3}$$

$$v = \textbf{51\cdot7 ft/sec} \quad \text{or} \quad \textbf{35\cdot2 m.p.h.}$$

Note that this speed is independent of the weight of the car.

Example. A vehicle has a track width of 54 in. and its centre of gravity is 26 in. above the road surface in the centre plane. If the limiting coefficient of friction between tyres and road is 0·6 determine whether the vehicle will first overturn or sideslip when rounding a curve of 400 ft radius at speed on a level track. State the maximum permissible speed on the curve.

Solution

Let v be speed of vehicle in feet per second and $r =$ radius of curve (400 ft). For sideslip to occur the inertia force must be just equal to or greater than the limiting inward friction force, i.e.

$$\frac{Wv^2}{gr} = \mu W$$

or

$$\frac{Wv^2}{32 \cdot 2 \times 400} = 0 \cdot 6\ W$$

i.e.

$$v = \sqrt{(0 \cdot 6 \times 32 \cdot 2 \times 400)}$$
$$= 88 \text{ ft/sec or } 60 \text{ m.p.h.}$$

For overturning to occur the ground reaction at the inner wheels must be zero, i.e. the tilting moment due to the inertia force must be greater than the stabilizing moment due to the dead weight. Taking moments about the outer wheel track B (Fig. 7.9) and assuming the car just about to overturn—

$$\frac{Wv^2}{gr} \times \frac{26}{12} = W \times \frac{27}{12}$$

i.e.

$$\frac{Wv^2 \times 26}{32 \cdot 2 \times 400 \times 12} = W \times \frac{27}{12}$$

i.e.

$$v = \sqrt{(32 \cdot 2 \times 400 \times \tfrac{27}{26})}$$
$$= 116 \text{ ft/sec \quad or \quad 79 m.p.h.}$$

Sideslip takes place first at the lower speed of **60 m.p.h.** and this, therefore, is the maximum speed permissible on the curve.

Example. Calculate the maximum speed at which a car may traverse a banked track of 100 ft radius without overturning if the centre of gravity of the car is 3 ft above ground level and the track width of the wheels is 5 ft. The track is banked at 30° to the horizontal.

Solution

When overturning starts the inner wheels at A (Fig. 7.10) just lift and the car starts to rotate about the outer wheels at B. Hence

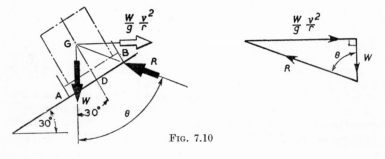

FIG. 7.10

the total reaction R of the track on the car must pass through B. The condition for (unstable) equilibrium is that R, the weight W and the inertia force Wv^2/gr shall all pass through one point. Since both the weight and the inertia force act through the centre of gravity G then the reaction R must act along BG at an angle θ to the vertical. From the geometry of the car

$$\theta = 30° + \angle DGB$$

and, since $\quad \tan \angle DGB = \dfrac{DB}{GD} = \dfrac{2\cdot 5}{3} = 0\cdot 833$

then $\qquad\qquad \angle DGB = 39° \, 48'$

hence $\qquad\qquad\quad \theta = 30° + 39° \, 48'$

$$= 69° \, 48'$$

From the triangle of forces—

$$\tan \theta = \frac{Wv^2}{gr} \div W$$

or $\qquad \tan 69° \, 48' = \dfrac{v^2}{32\cdot 2 \times 100}$

thus $\qquad\qquad v^2 = 32\cdot 2 \times 100 \times \tan 69° \, 48'$

$$= 32\cdot 2 \times 100 \times 2\cdot 718$$

and $\qquad\qquad\quad v = 93\cdot 5 \text{ ft/sec} \quad \text{or} \quad 63\cdot 7 \text{ m.p.h.}$

The same car on an unbanked track would overturn at 35·2 m.p.h. (*see* example on p. 109).

Alternative Solution

First resolve the weight and the inertia force into components parallel and perpendicular to the track. Thus the weight has a

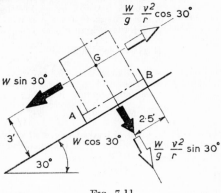

FIG. 7.11

component $W \sin 30°$ acting down the incline and a component $W \cos 30°$ normal to the incline (Fig. 7.11). Similarly the inertia force has a component $\dfrac{Wv^2}{gr}\cos 30°$ acting up the bank and a component $\dfrac{Wv^2}{gr}\sin 30°$ acting normal to the track. These components are shown in Fig. 7.11. At the point of overturning there is no ground reaction at the inside wheel A. Taking moments about B we have, since the reaction at B has no moment about B—

$$\frac{Wv^2}{gr} \times \cos 30° \times 3 - W \sin 30° \times 3$$

$$= \frac{Wv^2}{gr} \times \sin 30° \times 2·5 + W \cos 30° \times 2·5$$

$$\frac{v^2}{32·2 \times 100} \times 0·866 \times 3 - 0·5 \times 3$$

$$= \frac{v^2}{32·2 \times 100} \times 0·5 \times 2·5 + 0·866 \times 2·5$$

$0·000808\,v^2 - 0·000389\,v^2 = 3·665$

therefore $\qquad\qquad v = \mathbf{93·5\ ft/sec}$, as before.

PROBLEMS

1. A rectangular box is pulled along a rough horizontal path with uniform velocity. Its weight is 100 lb and the pull is horizontal, at a height of 4 ft above the ground. The coefficient of friction is 0·2. Show that the box will not tip if its base is 2 ft wide.

2. A casting with a flat base weighs 1,000 lb. Its centre of gravity is 2 ft above the ground and it is subject to a horizontal pull 3 ft above the ground. Its base in contact with the ground, is 2 ft wide in the direction of the motion. The coefficient of friction is 0·2. Calculate (a) the maximum acceleration allowed without overturning, (b) the magnitude of the pull at which the casting overturns.

(12·88 ft/sec²; 600 lb)

3. Calculate the maximum speed at which a car can traverse an unbanked curve of 80 ft radius if its wheels are 6 ft apart and its centre of gravity is 4 ft above the road. Assume that slipping does not occur.

(30 m.p.h.)

4. Calculate the smallest radius unbanked curve which a racing car can traverse at 100 m.p.h. without overturning if its wheels are 5 ft apart and its centre of gravity is 2 ft above the road.

(535 ft)

5. A sports car is to be built capable of rounding a 200-ft curve at 60 m.p.h. and its wheels are to be 5 ft apart. Calculate the maximum allowable height of its centre of gravity above ground level.

(2·08 ft)

6. Calculate the maximum speed at which a car can traverse a 100 ft radius track banked at 20° to the horizontal. Its centre of gravity is 3 ft above the ground and its wheels are 4 ft 6 in. apart.

(47·8 m.p.h.)

7. A double-deck bus whose wheels are 8 ft apart and whose centre of gravity is 5 ft above the ground is to round a road banked at 10° to the horizontal at 30 m.p.h. Calculate the minimum radius of the curve if over-turning is not to occur.

(53 ft)

8. A control mechanism is to be actuated by a weight of 10 lb rotating at the end of a spring at 300 rev/min. Calculate the minimum stiffness of spring required if the control is to be just stable at this speed.

(25·5 lb/in.)

9. A body of weight 4 lb is whirled round at the end of a spring of stiffness 10 lb/in. extension at a speed of 60 rev/min. Calculate the radius of the path of the body if the unstretched length of the spring is 6 in. At what speed would the radius tend to be infinitely great?

(6·26 in.; 297 rev/min)

10. A four-wheeled vehicle turns a corner of radius 35 ft on a level track. Its centre of gravity is 3 ft above road level and its wheels are 5 ft apart. Calculate (a) the fastest speed at which it may traverse the bend without the inner wheels leaving the ground; (b) the fastest speed at which it may travel round on two outer wheels without tipping more than 30°.

(30·65 ft/sec; 14 ft/sec)

11. Determine the speed at which overturning will occur for a vehicle whose wheels are 5 ft apart and whose centre of gravity is 3 ft above the ground, when travelling round a banked track of 200 ft radius: the banking is 10° away from the inside of the curve. Calculate the angle of banking which would tip the vehicle when at rest.

(87 ft/sec; 39° 48′)

12. A car weighing 2,500 lb is travelling along a curved unbanked road of radius 200 ft. Its wheel track is 4·5 ft and its centre of gravity is 3 ft above the ground, and mid-way between front and rear axles. The coefficient of friction is 0·5. Find (a) the vertical ground reaction at each wheel when the car is travelling at 50 ft/sec; (b) the maximum speed without overturning; (c) the skidding speed.

(302 lb, 949 lb; 69·5 ft/sec; 56·76 ft/sec)

13. A car is rounding a curve of radius 60 ft which is banked at 20°. The track width is 4 ft and the centre of gravity is 3 ft above the ground. At what speed can the car round the bend without overturning?

(35 m.p.h.)

8

Balancing

8.1. Static Balance—Two Bodies in a Plane

CONSIDER a light arm pivoted freely at the fulcrum O (Fig. 8.1) and carrying weights W_1, W_2 at distances r_1, r_2 from O, respectively.

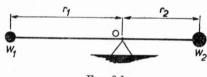

FIG. 8.1

In general the arm will rotate about O and the system is said to be out of balance. For equilibrium there must be balance of moments about O, i.e.

$$W_1 \times r_1 = W_2 \times r_2$$

When in balance the arm may be set in any position and it will remain at rest in that position. The weights are said to be in *static balance* and the centre of gravity of the system is located at O.

8.2. Dynamic Balance—Two Masses in a Plane

Now consider two light arms fixed to a shaft at bearing O and rotating with angular velocity ω, Fig. 8.2 (*a*). The arms are in the same plane and carry masses M_1, M_2 at radii r_1, r_2 respectively. Owing to the rotation each mass exerts an inertia force radially outward on the bearing O.

The force due to M_1 is $M_1\omega^2 r_1$ (**oa** in the force diagram, Fig. 8.2 (*b*)).

The force due to M_2 is $M_2\omega^2 r_2$ (**ab** in the force diagram).

The resultant out of balance force on the bearing is given by **ob** in the force diagram.

When the dynamic load on the bearing is zero the rotating system is said to be in *dynamic balance*. The condition for no load at O is that the two inertia forces shall: (*a*) act along the same straight line but with opposite sense; (*b*) be equal in magnitude.

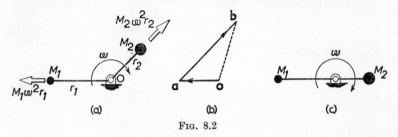

FIG. 8.2

The relative positions of the masses are as in Fig. 8.2 (*c*); the condition for equal inertia forces is—

$$M_1\omega^2 r_1 = M_2\omega^2 r_2$$

or, writing the masses in terms of their weights W_1 and W_2, respectively

$$\frac{W_1}{g}\omega^2 r_1 = \frac{W_2}{g}\omega^2 r_2$$

Thus, since ω^2 is the same for both masses and g a common factor

$$W_1 r_1 = W_2 r_2$$

This is also the condition for static balance. Hence, if two bodies in the same plane are in static balance when pivoted about a given axis they will be in dynamic balance at any speed when rotating about the same axis.

8.3. Method of Balancing Rotors

It was shown above that for a two mass system to be in static balance the Wr product for each mass had to be the same. This is

FIG. 8.3

also the condition for the masses to be balanced when rotating, and suggests a method for ensuring balance for rotating rotors such as turbine disks or car-wheel assemblies.

Fig. 8.3 shows a turbine rotor idealized in the form of a disk, mounted on a shaft placed on a pair of parallel knife-edges. The rotor may be allowed to rotate freely on the knife-edges and, if not uniform, the heavier section will rotate to the lowest point. This point is marked with chalk and a small balance weight attached at a point diametrically opposite. The rotor is turned through 90° and again allowed to rotate freely and again the heavier section will rotate to the bottom. The balance weight is then increased or decreased accordingly and the process repeated until the rotor remains at rest in any position. It is then in static balance and remains balanced when rotating at speed.

In practice it is usually possible to balance a rotor to an accuracy of 2 in.-oz, i.e. the amount of residual unbalance is equivalent to a weight of 1 oz at 2 in. radius. For a rotor weighing 20,000 lb this is equivalent to a displacement x of the centre of gravity from the axis of rotation given by

$$20,000 \times x = \tfrac{1}{16} \times 2$$

i.e. $$x = 0.000006 \text{ in.}$$

The corresponding out-of-balance centrifugal force when running at 3,600 rev/min is

$$\frac{W}{g}\,\omega^2 r = \frac{20,000}{32 \cdot 2} \times \left[\frac{2\pi\,3,600}{60}\right]^2 \times \frac{0 \cdot 000006}{12}$$
$$= 44 \cdot 1 \text{ lb}$$

It is usual to limit the out-of-balance force to be not greater than 1 per cent of the rotor weight.

8.4. Static Balance—Several Weights in One Plane

We now consider the static balance of several weights in the same plane, of magnitudes $W_1, W_2, \ldots$, at radii $r_1, r_2, \ldots$ from a common pivot O (Fig. 8.4). If the system is to be in static balance the shaft

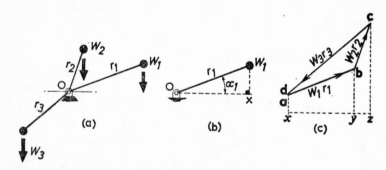

Fig. 8.4

at O must remain at rest in all positions, i.e. there must be no resultant moment about O. When the centre of gravity of the system is at the centre of the shaft the resultant vertical force due to the dead weight of all the attached bodies passes through O and the shaft is then in static balance.

The static moment of weight W_1 about O

$$= W_1 \times \text{OX} \quad (\text{Fig. 8.4 }(b))$$
$$= W_1 \times r_1 \cos \alpha_1$$

Similarly for W_2 and W_3. For static balance the sum of all such moments must be zero. Now construct a polygon in the following way—

     Draw **ab**, magnitude W_1r_1, parallel to radius r_1 (Fig. 8.4. (c)).
     Draw **bc**, magnitude W_2r_2, parallel to radius r_2.
     Draw **cd**, magnitude W_3r_3, parallel to radius r_3.

If the polygon closes, **d** coincides with **a**. Hence from Fig. 8.4 (c), if x, y, z are the feet of the perpendiculars from **a**, **b**, **c**, respectively, on to a horizontal line

$$\mathbf{xy} + \mathbf{yz} + \mathbf{zx} = 0 \text{ for a closed polygon, as shown}$$

But
$$\mathbf{xy} = W_1r_1 \cos \alpha_1$$
$$= \text{moment of } W_1 \text{ about O}$$

Similarly for W_2, W_3. Hence

$$\mathbf{xy} + \mathbf{yz} + \mathbf{zx} = \text{sum of moments of all the weights about O}$$
$$= 0 \text{ for static balance}$$

But this is also the condition for the polygon to close. Hence the condition for static balance is that the vector polygon formed by the Wr values must close. This result is unchanged for all angular positions of the shaft; thus if the polygon closes for one position it closes for all positions.

8.5. Dynamic Balance of Several Masses in One Plane

     Suppose the shaft and attached masses shown in Fig. 8.5 (a) to be rotating with angular velocity ω. Owing to the rotation there

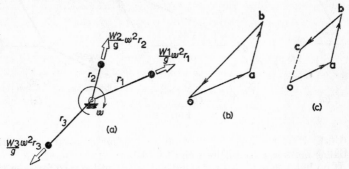

F𝐼G. 8.5

will be inertia forces of magnitude $(W_1/g)\omega^2 r_1$, $(W_2/g)\omega^2 r_2$, . . .,
acting radially outward at each mass. These forces can be repre-
sented by a force polygon which must close if there is no resultant
unbalanced force, as shown in Fig. 8.5 (*b*). Since the quantity ω^2/g
is a common factor for each inertia force it is convenient to replace
the force polygon by a Wr polygon. But this is the polygon obtained
when investigating the static balance of the same system, Fig. 8.4.

Thus the conditions for static and dynamic balance are identical,
i.e. that the Wr polygon must close.

If the inertia forces are not in balance the Wr polygon will not
close, Fig. 8.5 (*c*). The closing line **co** taken in the sense **c** to **o**
represents the Wr value required to produce balance. The line **oc**
taken in the sense **o** to **c** represents the resultant unbalanced Wr
effect. To obtain the actual magnitude of the unbalanced forces
multiply by ω^2/g. Thus the resultant unbalanced force on the shaft is—

$$\mathbf{oc} \times \frac{\omega^2}{g}, \text{ in direction } \mathbf{o} \text{ to } \mathbf{c}$$

required *balancing* force (equilibrant) is—

$$\mathbf{co} \times \frac{\omega^2}{g}, \text{ in direction } \mathbf{c} \text{ to } \mathbf{o}$$

An unbalanced inertia force produces a load on the shaft bearing
which, in a machine, results in increased wear and leads to early
failure of the bearing metal.

Example. A shaft carries two rotating masses of weights 3 lb and
1 lb, attached at radii 2 ft and 4 ft, respectively, from the axis of
rotation. The angular positions of the masses are shown in Fig.

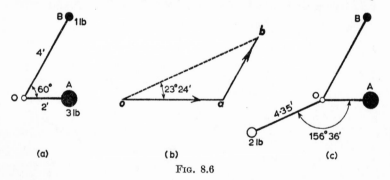

(a)   (b)   (c)

Fig. 8.6

8.6 (*a*). Find the angular position and radius of rotation r of the
balance mass required if its weight is 2 lb.

If no balance mass is used what is the out-of-balance force on the
shaft bearing at 120 rev/min?

Solution

The Wr values are 6 lb-ft for A and 4 lb-ft for B and these are represented by **oa** and **ab**, respectively, in the "force" polygon, Fig. 8.6 (*b*). The resultant out-of-balance Wr value is given by **ob** in direction **o** to **b**. From a scale drawing—

$$\mathbf{ob} = 8\cdot71 \text{ lb-ft}$$

The equilibrant is equal and opposite to the out-of-balance force, and since the Wr value for the balance weight is—

$$2 \times r \text{ lb-ft}$$

therefore, for balance

$$2 \times r = 8\cdot71$$

and $r = 4\cdot35 \text{ ft}$

thus the radius of rotation of the balance weight is **4·35 ft.**

The balance weight must be positioned so that its inertia force is acting in direction **b** to **o**, i.e. at an angle of 156° 36' to the radius of mass A, as shown in Fig. 8.6 (*c*). If no balance weight is used

$$\text{out-of-balance force} = \mathbf{ob} \times \frac{\omega^2}{g}$$

$$= 8\cdot71 \times \left[\frac{2\pi \times 120}{60}\right]^2 \times \frac{1}{32\cdot2}$$

$$= \mathbf{42\cdot7 \text{ lb}}$$

Example. Four masses A, B, C and D are rigidly attached to a shaft which rotates at 480 rev/min. The masses are all in the same plane and the weights and radii of rotation, together with their relative angular positions, are: A, 1 lb, 4 ft, 0°; B, 2 lb, 2 ft, 30°; C, 3 lb, 1 ft, 120°; D, 4 lb, ½ ft, 165°. Find the resultant out-of-balance force on the shaft and hence determine the magnitude and position of the balance weight required at 2 ft radius.

Solution

Fig. 8.7 (*a*) shows the relative angular positions of the masses.

$$\text{For mass A, } Wr = 1 \times 4 = 4 \text{ lb-ft}$$
$$\text{B, } Wr = 2 \times 2 = 4 \text{ lb-ft}$$
$$\text{C, } Wr = 3 \times 1 = 3 \text{ lb-ft}$$
$$\text{D, } Wr = 4 \times \tfrac{1}{2} = 2 \text{ lb-ft}$$

The Wr polygon is shown in Fig. 8.7 (*b*), each Wr value being taken *in order* and following the direction of the corresponding radius, outwards from the shaft. The closing line **od** taken in direction **o** to **d** is the resultant out-of-balance Wr value. From a scale drawing—

$$\mathbf{od} = 6{\cdot}51 \text{ lb-ft}$$

∴ out-of-balance force on shaft $= \mathbf{od} \times \dfrac{\omega^2}{g}$

$$= 6{\cdot}51 \times \left[\frac{2\pi \times 480}{60}\right]^2 \times \frac{1}{32{\cdot}2}$$

$$= \mathbf{510 \ lb}$$

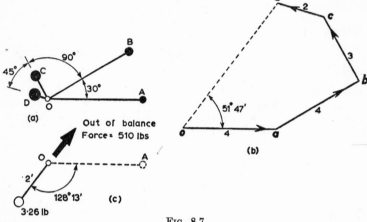

Fig. 8.7

od makes an angle of 51° 47′ with **oa**. The equilibrant is equal and opposite to the resultant force, i.e. in direction **d** to **o**. The Wr value for the balance weight is $W \times 2$ lb-ft. Therefore for balance

$$W \times 2 = 6{\cdot}51$$

i.e. $\qquad\qquad\qquad\qquad W = \mathbf{3{\cdot}26 \ lb}$

The balance weight must be positioned so that its inertia force acts in the direction **d** to **o**. Its position relative to A is shown in Fig. 8.7 (c).

PROBLEMS

1. Two weights revolve together in the same plane at an angular distance 45° apart. The first is a 3 lb weight at a radius of 9 in., the second 5 lb at 7 in. radius. Calculate the out-of-balance force at 120 rev/min and the position of a 10 lb balance weight required to reduce this force to zero.

(23·45 lb; balance weight at 5·74 in. radius and 160° 33′ to 5 lb weight)

2. A casting is bolted to the face plate of a lathe. It is equivalent to 2 lb at 2 in. from the axis of rotation, another 1 lb at 3 in. radius and 4 lb at 1 in. radius. The angular positions are, respectively, 0°, 30°, 75°. Find the balance weight required at 6 in. radius to eliminate the out-of-balance force. State the angular position of the balance weight.

(1·56 lb; 215° from 2 lb weight)

3. A turbine casing is placed on a rotating table mounted on a vertical axis. The casing is symmetrical except for a projecting lug weighing 30 lb at a radius of 4 ft and a cast pad weighing 50 lb at 3 ft radius. The lug and the pad are positioned at right angles to one another. The casing is bolted down symmetrically with respect to the axis of rotation. Find the magnitude and position of the balance weight required at a radius of 5 ft.

(38·4 lb at 141° 40′ to pad)

4. Two equal holes are drilled in a uniform circular disk at a radius of 16 in. from the axis. The weight of material removed is 6 oz. Calculate the resultant out-of-balance force if the holes are spaced at 90° to each other and the speed of rotation is 1,000 rev/min.

Where should a weight be placed at a radius of 10 in. in order to balance the disk, and what should be its magnitude?

(120·5 lb; 0·423 lb at 45° to a drilled hole)

5. Three masses are bolted to a face plate as follows: 10 lb at 5 in. radius, 20 lb at 3 in. radius, and 15 lb at 4 in. radius. The masses must be arranged so that the face plate is in balance. Find the angular position of the masses relative to the 10-lb mass.

(Each at 114° 36′ to 10 lb-wt.)

6. Four masses, A, B, C and D, rotate together in a plane about a common axis O. The weights and radii of rotation are as follows: A, 2 lb, 2 ft; B, 3 lb, 3 ft; C, 4 lb, 4 ft; D, 5 lb, 5 ft. The angles between the masses are: $\angle$AOB = 30°, $\angle$BOC = 60°, $\angle$COD = 120°. Find the resultant out-of-balance force at 720 rev/min and the radius of rotation and angular position of a 10-lb weight required for balance.

(2,240 lb; 1·27 ft, 39° 7′ to OA)

7. A cast-steel rotor is 1·5 in. thick and has four holes drilled at radii 2, 4, 5 and 6 in., respectively. The holes are 1 in. diameter and located as shown in Fig. 8.8. Find the magnitude of the total unbalanced force on the spindle

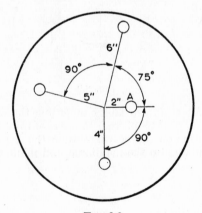

Fɪɢ. 8.8

bearings at 720 rev/min. Where should a hole of $\frac{1}{2}$ in. diameter be drilled for balance? Steel weighs 0·282 lb/in.³.

(16·6 lb; at 13·5 in. radius, 112° 32′ clockwise to hole A)

8.6. Dynamic Forces at Bearings

If a shaft carries rotating masses *not in the same plane* it may be in static balance and therefore balanced as regards inertia forces, but it may yet be subject to an unbalanced couple. Whether the masses are in the same plane or not the inertia forces act radially outwards and may therefore balance; but since the lines of action of the inertia forces act in different planes each force produces a different moment about any given plane of the shaft. Thus an unbalanced moment may arise.

For a shaft to be in complete dynamic balance there must be no unbalanced force or couple.

An unbalanced couple cannot, of course, exist in practice, but must be resisted by reactions at the bearings. As the shaft rotates so does the direction of the unbalanced couple and the bearings are therefore subject to rotating radial forces. Also, since the dead weight reactions are constant and upwards it means that the bearing reactions are constantly changing in direction and magnitude as the shaft rotates. This condition if allowed to persist sets up undesirable vibrations. The following examples will be used to show the existence of unbalanced couples and to bring out the main points in the methods of calculating the bearing reactions.

Example. A shaft is supported in bearings at A and B, 6 ft apart, Fig. 8.9. A rotor of total weight 64·4 lb is mounted at a point 2 ft

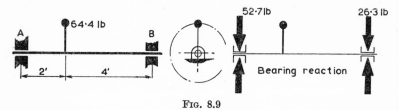

Fig. 8.9

from bearing A. Owing to faulty mounting the centre of gravity of the rotor is offset 0·12 in. from the axis of rotation O. Calculate the dynamic loads on the bearings when the shaft rotates at 600 rev/min. Calculate also the maximum and minimum loads on the bearings.

Solution

$$\text{Inertia force} = \frac{W}{g}\,\omega^2 r$$

$$= \frac{64\cdot4}{32\cdot2} \times \left(\frac{2\pi\,600}{60}\right)^2 \times \frac{0\cdot12}{12}$$

$$= 79\,\text{lb}$$

Taking moments about bearing B—

$$R_A \times 6 = 79 \times 4$$
$$R_A = 52{\cdot}7 \text{ lb}$$

Taking moments about bearing A—

$$R_B \times 6 = 79 \times 2$$
$$R_B = 26{\cdot}3 \text{ lb}$$

(or $R_A + R_B = 79$, i.e. $R_B = 79 - 52{\cdot}7 = 26{\cdot}3$ lb).

Therefore the dynamic loads on the bearings are **52·7 lb** at A and **26·3 lb** at B. Both reactions oppose the unbalanced inertia forces as shown.

When at rest, taking moments about B—

$$R_A{}' \times 6 = 64{\cdot}4 \times 4$$
$$R_A{}' = 42{\cdot}93 \text{ lb}$$

and $\qquad\qquad R_A{}' + R_B{}' = 64{\cdot}4 \text{ lb}$

thus $\qquad\qquad\quad R_B{}' = 21{\cdot}47 \text{ lb}$

The dead weight reactions are therefore **42·93 lb** at A and **21·47 lb** at B, both vertically upwards.

As the shaft rotates the dynamic load on each bearing rotates. The maximum and minimum bearing reactions therefore occur when the lines of action of the dynamic and dead weight reactions coincide.

Maximum bearing reaction at A $= 42{\cdot}93 + 52{\cdot}7$
$$= 95{\cdot}63 \text{ lb (upwards).}$$

Minimum bearing reaction at A $= 42{\cdot}93 - 52{\cdot}7$
$$= -9{\cdot}77 \text{ lb (downwards).}$$

Maximum bearing reaction at B $= 21{\cdot}47 + 26{\cdot}3$
$$= 47{\cdot}8 \text{ lb (upwards).}$$

Minimum bearing reaction at B $= 21{\cdot}47 - 26{\cdot}3$
$$= -4{\cdot}83 \text{ lb (downwards).}$$

Example. The shaft shown in Fig. 8.10 (*a*) carries two masses at C and D in the same axial plane but diametrically opposite to one another. Calculate the dynamic loads on the bearings when the shaft rotates at 144 rev/min. Each mass is 3 lb-wt. at 2 ft radius.

Solution

Fig. 8.10 (*b*) shows the end view when the masses are in the vertical plane; the shaft is evidently in static balance since the Wr values are equal and opposite. When rotating, therefore, the inertia forces are in balance. Nevertheless the two rotating masses exert a pure couple anticlockwise due to the two equal inertia forces acting at distance CD apart.

$$\text{Moment of couple} = \frac{W}{g}\,\omega^2 r \times CD$$

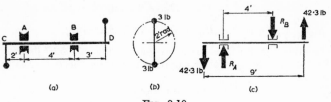

FIG. 8.10

This couple is in equilibrium with reactions R_A and R_B at bearings A and B, respectively, acting as shown in Fig. 8.10 (c) to produce a clockwise couple. For each rotating mass

$$\text{inertia force} = \frac{W}{g}\,\omega^2 r$$

$$= \frac{3}{32\cdot2} \times \left[\frac{2\pi\,144}{60}\right]^2 \times 2$$

$$= 42\cdot3\ \text{lb}$$

To calculate the reactions take moments about each bearing in turn. Moments about A—

$$R_B \times 4 = 42\cdot3 \times 7 + 42\cdot3 \times 2$$
$$= 380$$
$$R_B = \textbf{95 lb}$$

Moments about B—

$$R_A \times 4 = 42\cdot3 \times 6 + 42\cdot3 \times 3$$
$$= 380$$
$$R_A = \textbf{95 lb}$$

The two reactions are equal since they together form a pure couple exerted by the bearings, in opposition to that exerted by the inertia forces of the rotating masses. The reactions in this case could have been found by simply equating the two couples, i.e.

$$R \times 4 = \text{inertia force} \times CD$$
$$= 42\cdot3 \times 9$$
$$R = \textbf{95 lb}$$

However, when the two masses have unequal inertia forces, i.e. when the shaft is not in static balance, the bearing reactions are generally not equal. The reactions must then be found by taking moments about each bearing in turn.

8.7. Balancing of Three Masses in Different Planes of Rotation

The balancing of several masses in different planes of rotation cannot be dealt with completely at this stage but for the particular case of *three* masses it will be shown in the following example that for complete balance the masses must be in the same axial plane, that is, in the same plane when viewed from the end of the shaft.

Example. A shaft carries a mass of 30 lb at a radius of 2 ft. Find the balance masses required for complete dynamic balance if they are to be placed in planes 2 ft and 4 ft to either side of the 30 lb mass at radii of 2 ft and 4 ft, respectively, from the shaft axis.

Solution

Fig. 8.11 shows the arrangement, A and C denoting the balance planes. For complete dynamic balance there must be no out-of-

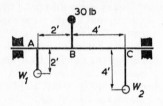 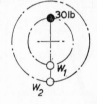

FIG. 8.11

balance force or couple. However, dynamic balance can be investigated by considering couples about two planes and confirmed by checking for static or force balance. Taking moments about A using Wr values, since ω^2/g is a common factor—

$$W_2 \times 4 \times AC = 30 \times 2 \times AB$$

i.e. $W_2 \times 4 \times 6 = 30 \times 2 \times 2$

therefore $W_2 = \textbf{5 lb}$ for balance of couples about plane A

This only satisfies the condition that the couples are balanced numerically. For couples to balance they must act *in the same plane*. Therefore, W_2 and the 30 lb mass must lie in the same plane and they must be diametrically opposite.

Similarly by taking moments about C—

$$W_1 \times 2 \times 6 = 30 \times 2 \times 4$$
$$W_1 = \textbf{20 lb}$$

and again the couples will balance only if W_1 lies in the same plane as the 30 lb mass and diametrically opposite to it. Thus for no unbalanced couple on the shaft W_1, W_2 and the 30 lb mass all lie in the same axial plane when viewed from the end of the shaft, as shown in Fig. 8.11.

Finally, for static balance there must be no out-of-balance force (or Wr value), i.e.

$$W_1 r_1 + W_2 r_2 = 30 \times 2$$

or $$20 \times 2 + 5 \times 4 = 60$$

and it can be seen that the condition for static balance is satisfied.

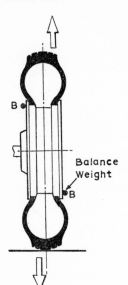

Note—In this problem the simplest way of balancing the 30 lb mass is by means of a similar mass diametrically opposite to it at the same radius. However, there are many cases in practice where such a method is not possible.

8.8. Car Wheel Balancing

Present-day motor cars require accurately balanced wheels. If a wheel assembly is out of balance, forces come into play which may affect steering and tyre wear and cause rough running. Even when a wheel and tyre is in static balance it may be dynamically out of balance owing to a heavy spot on one side of the wheel. This dynamic unbalance is apparent in wobble of the wheel when rotated at speed.

A car wheel may be statically balanced as a rotor, except that when the balance weight has been determined it is usual to split it into two parts, placing one part on each side of the wheel. Dynamic balance is achieved by running the wheel at speed in a suitable machine to check the wobble. Balance weights to correct for dynamic unbalance must be placed on opposite sides of the wheel, 180° apart, in order to provide the necessary couple, Fig. 8.12.

Fig. 8.12

Balance
Weight

B

B

PROBLEMS

1. A casting of mass 50 lb is bolted to the faceplate of a lathe rotating at 120 rev/min. If the centre of gravity of the casting is offset 1 in. from the axis of rotation and 3 in. in front of the spindle bearing, calculate the out-of-balance couple carried by the bearing.

(5·1 lb-ft)

2. A mass of 50 lb revolves at a radius of 2 ft. It is mounted on a shaft which runs in two bearings distant 2 ft and 3 ft, respectively, on either side

of its plane of rotation. Calculate the dynamic force on each bearing at a speed of 144 rev/min.

(282 lb; 423 lb)

3. A shaft rotates in bearings 6 ft apart. A mass of 30 lb rotates with the shaft at a radius of 6 in. in a plane 2 ft from the left-hand bearing. A second mass of 24 lb at a radius of 9 in. is in the central plane of the shaft. Both masses are in the same axial plane when viewed from the end of the shaft and on the same side of the shaft. Calculate the dynamic force on each bearing at 300 rev/min.

(429 lb; 582 lb)

4. A mass of 200 lb revolves with a shaft at a radius of 9 in. Find the magnitude of the balance weights required at 24 in. radius in planes 12 in. and 36 in. from the plane of rotation of the 200 lb mass: (a) when the planes of rotation of the balance weights are on opposite sides of the 200 lb mass; (b) when they are both on the same side.

(18·75 lb, 56·25 lb; 112·5 lb, 37·5 lb)

5. A shaft ABCDE runs at 360 rev/min in bearings at A and E. It carries a mass of 20 lb at C, distant 5 ft from A and rotating at 3 ft radius. If the bearings are 9 ft apart calculate the load on each due to rotation.
If balance masses at 2 ft radius are to be placed at B and D on either side of C where BC = 3 ft and CD = 2 ft, find the magnitude of these masses if there is to be no load on the bearings.

(1,470, 1,180; 18, 12 lb)

6. A single cylinder reciprocating engine has a crank radius of 1 ft. The crankshaft rotates at 480 rev/min in bearings at 6 in. and 12 in. to left and right, respectively, of the crank pin. The crank pin may be considered to carry a rotating mass of 200 lb. Calculate the load on each bearing.
Rotating with the crankshaft are two flywheels, one distant 12 in. to the left of the crank pin, the other distant 24 in. to the right. If 100 lb balance weights are to be placed in each flywheel calculate their respective radii of rotation for no dynamic load on the bearings.

(10,460 lb, 5,230 lb; 1·33 ft, 0·67 ft)

7. A shaft, running in bearings X and Y, has two concentrated masses of 4 and 6 lb rigidly fixed to it as shown in Fig. 8.13. The masses and the axis

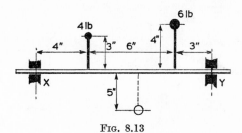

Fig. 8.13

of the shaft are all in the same plane. Find the reactions at the bearings at 480 rev/min.
In order that there shall be no load on the bearings due to rotation a mass is fixed to the shaft at a radius of 5 in. as shown dotted in the figure. Find the magnitude of this mass and the distance of its plane from bearing X.

(X, 90·8 lb; Y, 145 lb; 7·2 lb at 8 in. from X)

9

Periodic Motion

9.1. Periodic Motion

WHEN a body moves to and fro so that every part of its motion recurs regularly it is said to have *periodic motion*. For example, in

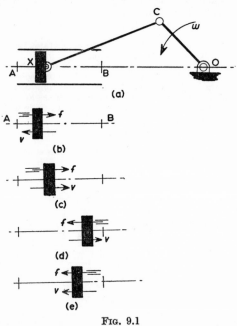

FIG. 9.1

the engine mechanism of Fig. 9.1 (*a*) when crank OC rotates uniformly the piston X moves back and forth between the two limiting points A and B, the motion being repeated at regular intervals of time. It is important to note that neither the velocity nor the acceleration of the piston is uniform and the methods and formulae for uniformly accelerated motion do not apply.

Now consider the motion of piston X more carefully. As X moves towards A its velocity v is from right to left, Fig. 9.1 (*b*). At A it comes instantaneously to rest and reverses direction. Before reaching A it must be slowing down or retarding, i.e. the acceleration f of X is from left to right, in the opposite sense to the velocity. After reversing direction X accelerates from rest, both v and f are from left to right, Fig. 9.1 (*c*). At B the piston comes again instantaneously to rest, hence near B it is retarded and the acceleration f is from right to left, Fig. 9.1 (*d*). After reversal of the motion at B both v and f are from right to left, Fig. 9.1 (*e*). As X reaches A for the second time the whole sequence repeats itself.

The periodic reciprocating motion of the engine piston is complex but is approximately the same as an important but simpler periodic motion termed *simple harmonic motion*. This latter type of motion will now be dealt with in detail.

9.2. Simple Harmonic Motion

We define simple harmonic motion (s.h.m.) as a periodic motion in which—

1. The acceleration is always directed towards a fixed point in its path.

2. The acceleration is proportional to its distance from the fixed point.

The motion is similar to the periodic motion of the engine piston except that the acceleration has been exactly described in a particular way. In order to fix ideas we study a particular case.

9.3. Simple Harmonic Motion Derived from a Circular Motion

Fig. 9.2 shows a "Scotch yoke" mechanism. A pin P in a circular disk rotates at a uniform angular velocity ω about a fixed point O.

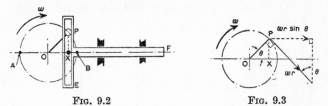

FIG. 9.2   FIG. 9.3

The pin engages in a slot in the vertical link E attached to bar F; the latter is constrained to move in a straight line. As the pin rotates bar F reciprocates back and forth with a periodic motion. This motion corresponds exactly with that of an imaginary point X which is the projection of P on the horizontal line OB. The motion of X is identical with the horizontal component of the motion of P. The velocity of P is tangent at P to the circle of rotation and its magnitude is ωr where $r = OP$. The velocity of X is the horizontal component of the velocity of P (Fig. 9.3), i.e.

$$v_X = \omega r \sin \theta \qquad . \qquad . \qquad . \qquad (9.1)$$

The centripetal acceleration of P is $\omega^2 \times OP$, or $\omega^2 r$, and is directed radially inwards from P to O, Fig. 9.4. The acceleration of X is the horizontal component of the acceleration of P, i.e.

$$\begin{aligned} f_X &= \omega^2 r \cos \theta \\ &= \omega^2 \times OX \\ &= \omega^2 x \qquad . \qquad . \qquad . \qquad (9.2) \end{aligned}$$

The acceleration of X is therefore proportional to its distance x from the fixed point O. From Fig. 9.4 it can be seen that the

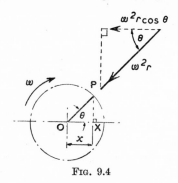

Fig. 9.4

acceleration of X is always directed towards O. The motion of X (and of bar F) is therefore simple harmonic.

Note particularly the following special cases—

1. The velocity of X is zero at A and B, Fig. 9.5. At these points the velocity of P is vertical and therefore has no component along AB.

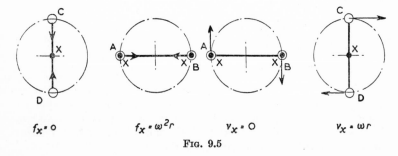

$f_X = 0$ $f_X = \omega^2 r$ $v_X = 0$ $v_X = \omega r$

Fig. 9.5

2. When P is at C or D, X coincides with O, the mid-point of its path and its velocity is that of P, i.e. its velocity reaches its maximum value ωr.

3. When P is at C or D its acceleration is vertical and therefore has no horizontal component, i.e. $f_X = 0$, when $\theta = 90°$ or $270°$.

4. When P is at A or B the acceleration of X is the centripetal acceleration of P, i.e.

$$f_X = \omega^2 r$$

and this is the maximum acceleration of X.

These results are shown pictorially in Fig. 9.5. Two important facts should be particularly noted—

1. When the acceleration of X is zero the velocity is a maximum.
2. When the velocity of X is zero the acceleration is a maximum.

This latter statement should not be surprising since s.h.m. requires that the acceleration is proportional to the distance from O, and therefore reaches its maximum value at its greatest distance from O. Fig. 9.6 shows the variation in the velocity and acceleration

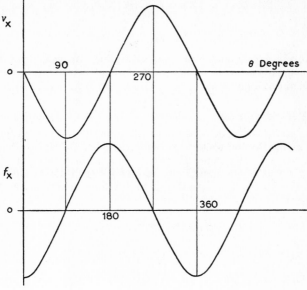

Fig. 9.6

of X for one complete revolution of P. Positive values of v_X mean that the velocity is from left to right, negative that v_X is from right to left. A similar convention applies to f_X.

9.4. Velocity and Acceleration at Any Point in Terms of Displacement

The velocity of a point moving with s.h.m. is given by

$$v_X = \omega r \sin \theta$$

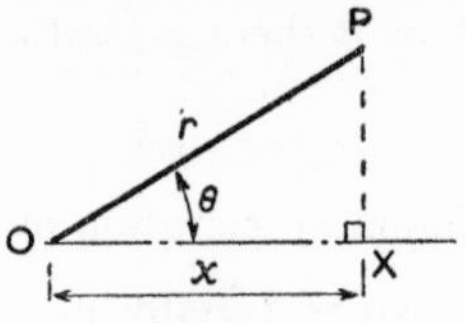

FIG. 9.7

This may be written in terms of the displacement x of the point X from the fixed point O. Thus from Fig. 9.7—

$$\sin \theta = \frac{PX}{OP}$$

thus

$$v_X = \omega r \frac{PX}{OP}$$

$$= \frac{\omega r \sqrt{(r^2 - x^2)}}{r}$$

$$= \omega \sqrt{(r^2 - x^2)} \qquad . \qquad . \qquad . \quad (9.3)$$

This gives a convenient method of finding the velocity from the displacement x. The acceleration at displacement x is given by equation (9.2), i.e.

$$f_X = \omega^2 x$$

9.5. Periodic Time

The *periodic time* or *period* T of s.h.m. is the time taken for point X to complete one to-and-fro oscillation, i.e. to pass through any point twice in the same direction. This is also the time for the rotating arm OP to sweep out an angle 2π rad at ω rad/sec. The line OP is said to generate the s.h.m. and ω is sometimes called the *circular frequency*. Thus

$$\text{period, } T = \frac{2\pi}{\omega} \text{ sec}$$

Also, since $f_X = \omega^2 x$

$$\omega = \sqrt{\left(\frac{f_X}{x}\right)}$$

hence

$$T = 2\pi \sqrt{\left(\frac{x}{f_X}\right)}$$

therefore

$$T = 2\pi \sqrt{\left(\frac{displacement}{acceleration}\right)} \qquad (9.4)$$

9.6. Frequency

The *frequency* (*n*) of oscillation is the number of complete cycles, back and forth, made in unit time. The frequency *n* is therefore the reciprocal of the period *T*. Thus

$$n = \frac{1}{T}$$

$$= \frac{\omega}{2\pi} \text{ cycles per second}$$

therefore
$$n = \frac{1}{2\pi} \sqrt{\left(\frac{acceleration}{displacement}\right)} \qquad (9.5)$$

9.7. Amplitude

The distance *r* through which the point X moves on either side of the fixed point O is called the *amplitude* of the motion. The total distance 2*r* is called the *stroke* or *travel*.

Note—The above results were obtained for the motion of a point X reciprocating to-and-fro due to the rotation of a point P. These results, however, apply to any body performing s.h.m.

Example. A body moving with s.h.m. has a velocity of 12 ft/sec when 18 in. from the mid-position and an acceleration of 4 ft/sec² when 12 in. from the mid-position. Calculate the periodic time and the amplitude.

Solution

To calculate *T* we must first find *ω*.

$$f = \omega^2 x$$

therefore
$$\omega = \sqrt{\left(\frac{f}{x}\right)}$$

$$= \sqrt{\left(\frac{4}{1}\right)}$$

since $f = 4$ ft/sec² when $x = 1$ ft.

i.e. $\omega = 2$ rad/sec

therefore $T = \dfrac{2\pi}{\omega} = \dfrac{2\pi}{2} = \mathbf{3 \cdot 142}$ **sec**

To calculate the amplitude *r*, refer to Fig. 9.7. When $x = 1 \cdot 5$ ft

$$v = 12 \text{ ft/sec}$$

and $v = \omega \sqrt{(r^2 - x^2)}$

thus $12 = 2\sqrt{(r^2 - 1 \cdot 5^2)}$

hence $r = \mathbf{6 \cdot 2}$ **ft**

Example. A body performs s.h.m. in a straight line. Its velocity is 40 ft/sec when the displacement is 2 in., and 10 ft/sec when the displacement is 4 in., the displacement being measured from the mid-position. Calculate the frequency and amplitude of the motion. What is the acceleration when the displacement is 3 in. ?

Solution

First determine the amplitude r. From

$$v = \omega\sqrt{(r^2 - x^2)}$$

when $x = 2$ in., $v = 40$ ft/sec, and

$$40 = \omega\sqrt{\left\{r^2 - \left(\frac{2}{12}\right)^2\right\}} \qquad . \qquad . \qquad . \quad (9.6)$$

when $x = 4$ in., $v = 10$ ft/sec, and

$$10 = \omega\sqrt{\left\{r^2 - \left(\frac{4}{12}\right)^2\right\}} \qquad . \qquad . \qquad . \quad (9.7)$$

Divide equation (9.6) by equation (9.7)—

$$\frac{40}{10} = \frac{\sqrt{\{r^2 - (2/12)^2\}}}{\sqrt{\{r^2 - (4/12)^2\}}}$$

Squaring both sides

$$16 = \frac{r^2 - 1/36}{r^2 - 1/9}$$

hence $\qquad\qquad\qquad r = \textbf{0·342 ft}$

To find ω, from equation (9.6)—

$$40 = \omega\sqrt{\left\{0·342^2 - \frac{1}{36}\right\}}$$

hence $\qquad\qquad\qquad \omega = \textbf{134 rad/sec}$

thus $\qquad\qquad$ frequency $n = \dfrac{\omega}{2\pi}$

$$= \frac{134}{2\pi}$$

$$= \textbf{21·3 c/s}$$

To find the acceleration when $x = 3$ in. From

$$f = \omega^2 x$$

$$f = 134^2 \times \frac{3}{12}$$

$$= \textbf{4,490 ft/sec}^2$$

Example. A piston is driven by a crank and connecting rod as shown in Fig. 9.8. The crank is 3 in. long and the rod 18 in. Assuming the acceleration of the piston to be simple harmonic find its velocity and acceleration in the position shown when the crank

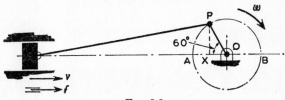

Fɪɢ. 9.8

speed is 360 rev/min clockwise. What is the maximum acceleration of the piston and where does it occur?

Solution

It can be seen that the motion of the piston is approximately the same as that of point X, the projection of crank-pin P on the line of stroke. The greater the length of the rod compared with that of the crank the more closely does the motion of the piston agree with that of X and therefore of s.h.m.

$$\text{amplitude } r = 3 \text{ in.}$$

$$\omega = \frac{2\pi \times 360}{60} = 37 \cdot 7 \text{ rad/sec}$$

For the position shown

$$x = \text{OX} = 3 \times \cos 60° = 1 \cdot 5 \text{ in.}$$

velocity of piston, $v = \omega \sqrt{(r^2 - x^2)}$

$$= 37 \cdot 7 \sqrt{(3^2 - 1 \cdot 5^2)}$$

$$= \textbf{98 in./sec (inwards towards O)}$$

Acceleration of piston, $f = \omega^2 x$

$$= 37 \cdot 7^2 \times 1 \cdot 5$$

$$= \textbf{2,130 in./sec}^2 \textbf{ (inwards}$$
$$\textbf{towards O)}$$

Maximum acceleration of piston $= \omega^2 r$

$$= 37 \cdot 7^2 \times 3$$

$$= \textbf{4,260 in./sec}^2$$

The maximum acceleration occurs when X coincides with A or B, i.e. when the piston is at the top or bottom dead centre position. To be exact there is a difference in the accelerations at A and B.

PROBLEMS

1. Find the periodic time of a point which has simple harmonic motion, given that it has an acceleration of 36 ft/sec² when 3 in. from the mid-position. If the amplitude of the motion is 4 in., find the velocity when 3 in. from the mid-position.

(0·524 sec; 2·65 ft/sec)

2. A body has s.h.m., its velocity being 10 ft/sec at 6 in. displacement, and 8 ft/sec at 9 in. displacement, from the mid-position. Find the periodic time and the amplitude.

(0·585 sec; 12·67 in.)

3. A body moves with s.h.m. and completes twenty oscillations per second. Its speed at a distance of 1 in. from the centre of oscillation is one-half the maximum speed. Find the amplitude and the maximum acceleration of the body.

(1·155 in.; 1,515 ft/sec²)

4. A body oscillates along a straight line with s.h.m. The amplitude is 12 in. and when the body is at point A, 6 in. from the centre of oscillation, it is moving with a speed of 10 ft/sec. Calculate the shortest time taken from A to reach a point 10·4 in. from the centre of oscillation.

(0·0454 sec)

5. A valve, initially and finally at rest, moves through a distance of 0·4 in. in 0·006 sec. Find (a) the maximum velocity; (b) the maximum acceleration. The motion of the valve is to be assumed simple harmonic.

(8·73 ft/sec; 4,570 ft/sec²)

6. In a simple crank and connecting rod mechanism the crank is 2 in. long and the connecting rod is 14 in. long. When the crank is 30° from the top dead centre position find the velocity and acceleration of the piston at 600 rev/min. Assume the motion of the piston to be simple harmonic. What is the maximum velocity and acceleration of the piston?

(62·8 in./sec; 6,820 in./sec²; 125·6 in./sec; 7,894 in./sec²)

9.8. Dynamics of Simple Harmonic Motion

A simple harmonic motion, or close approximation to it, occurs in many important mechanical problems, e.g. a mass oscillating at the end of a spring, the simple pendulum, the motion of a piston on a connecting rod which is long compared to its crank. In every case it is necessary to *show* that the motion is simple harmonic or to find the degree of approximation involved. In order to do this the procedure is—

1. Write down an "equation of motion," i.e. balance the inertia and applied forces.
2. Check if the acceleration of the body is proportional to its displacement from a fixed point or mid-point of its motion.·
3. Check if the acceleration is *always* directed towards the fixed point.

Having checked the conditions for s.h.m. we may conclude that the motion is simple harmonic or, alternatively, note the approximation involved in the equation of motion in order to consider the motion as simple harmonic. For example, the motion of a Scotch yoke is exactly s.h.m. whereas that of an engine piston is only very approximately s.h.m. unless the connecting rod is at least six times the crank length.

9.9. The Mass and Spring

(*a*) HORIZONTAL MOTION

Consider a body A of weight W, mass W/g, attached to a light spring of stiffness S, which is anchored at B, Fig. 9.9. The body is

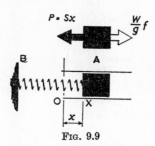

FIG. 9.9

constrained to move in horizontal guides, assumed frictionless, and in the rest position it is at point O.

Imagine the body to be pulled to the right a distance a and then released. The pull P in the spring will initially cause the body to move from rest towards the left. When it is a distance x from O the pull P of the spring is from right to left and, since x is also the extension of the spring at this instant—

$$P = Sx$$

This pull is "balanced" by the inertia force $(W/g)f$, where f is the acceleration of the body. This inertia force must be from left to right and therefore f is from right to left as expected. For equilibrium

$$P = \frac{W}{g}f$$

or

$$Sx = \frac{W}{g}f$$

thus

$$f = \frac{Sg}{W} \times x$$

$$= (\text{constant}) \times x$$

The acceleration of the body is therefore proportional to the distance x from the fixed point O and directed from right to left, i.e. towards O.

When the spring is compressed and the body is to the left of O, then both the spring force and the inertia force are reversed in direction so that acceleration f is still directed towards O. Thus the acceleration is *always* directed towards O. Hence the motion of the body is simple harmonic.

Now compare the expressions—

$$f = \omega^2 x \text{ for s.h.m.}$$

and

$$f = \frac{Sg}{W} x \text{ for body A}$$

Evidently

$$\omega^2 = \frac{Sg}{W}$$

or

$$\omega = \sqrt{\left(\frac{Sg}{W}\right)}$$

By comparison with the Scotch yoke mechanism ω is sometimes called the *equivalent angular velocity*.

The frequency of oscillation is

$$n = \frac{\omega}{2\pi}$$

i.e.

$$n = \frac{1}{2\pi} \sqrt{\left(\frac{Sg}{W}\right)}$$

and the period is

$$T = \frac{2\pi}{\omega}$$

i.e.

$$T = 2\pi \sqrt{\left(\frac{W}{Sg}\right)}$$

(*b*) VERTICAL MOTION

Let the body A be supported vertically by the spring, Fig. 9.10.

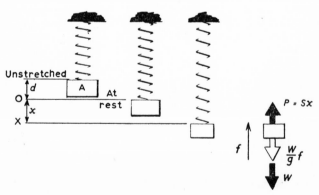

FIG. 9.10

At rest, the force in the spring is W. Hence the deflexion at rest or *static* deflexion d, is given by—

$$W = S \times d$$

or

$$d = \frac{W}{S}$$

Let the body be pulled a distance a below the static position O and then released. We should expect the body to move upwards from this position with an acceleration towards O due to the upward pull of the spring. At X, a distance x from O, the total extension of the spring is $d + x$. Hence the spring force is

$$P = S(d + x)$$

This force is balanced by the weight W together with the inertia force $(W/g)f$, both acting downwards. Hence

$$P = W + \frac{W}{g}f$$

or

$$S(d + x) = W + \frac{W}{g}f$$

but $S \times d = W$, and thus

$$W + Sx = W + \frac{W}{g}f$$

or

$$Sx = \frac{W}{g}f$$

i.e.

$$f = \frac{Sg}{W}x$$

$$= \text{constant} \times x$$

The acceleration f is therefore proportional to the distance x from the position of equilibrium O (a fixed point) and always directed towards O. The motion of the body A is therefore simple harmonic.

The period is the same as for horizontal motion, i.e.

$$T = 2\pi \sqrt{\left(\frac{W}{Sg}\right)}$$

but in this case

$$\frac{W}{S} = d$$

the static deflexion, so that the period may be written—

$$T = 2\pi \sqrt{\left(\frac{d}{g}\right)}$$

The amplitude of the motion is the maximum value of the displacement x, i.e. the initial displacement a given to the mass. The body therefore oscillates an equal distance a above and below the static rest position O.

Note—The results are the same whether the mass is oscillating vertically or horizontally. The only difference in the two cases is in the position about which the oscillation takes place. In vertical motion the body oscillates about the static deflected position whereas in horizontal motion it oscillates about the unstretched position of the spring. *In the vertical motion the dead weight is a constant force acting in a constant direction (downwards) and such a force has no effect on an oscillation.*

Example. A load is suspended from a vertically mounted spring. At rest it deflects the spring $\frac{1}{2}$ in. Calculate the number of complete oscillations per second.

If the load weighs 6 lb what is the maximum force in the spring when it is displaced a further 1 in. below the rest position and then released?

Solution

$$\text{Period } T = 2\pi \Big/ \sqrt{\left(\frac{W}{Sg}\right)} = 2\pi \Big/ \sqrt{\left(\frac{d}{g}\right)}$$

where d, the static deflexion, equals $\frac{1}{2}$ in. Thus

$$T = 2\pi \Big/ \sqrt{\left(\frac{1/2}{32 \cdot 2 \times 12}\right)}$$

$$= 0 \cdot 226 \text{ sec}$$

But

$$\text{frequency } n = \frac{1}{T} = \frac{1}{0 \cdot 226} = 4 \cdot 42 \text{ c/s}$$

If the load is pulled down 1 in. the amplitude of oscillation, $r = 1$ in.

$$\text{maximum acceleration, } f_{\max} = \omega^2 r$$

where

$$\omega = 2\pi n$$

$$= 2\pi \times 4 \cdot 42$$

$$= 27 \cdot 8 \text{ rad/sec}$$

therefore

$$f_{\max} = 27 \cdot 8^2 \times \tfrac{1}{12}$$

$$= 64 \cdot 3 \text{ ft/sec}^2$$

$$\text{Maximum inertia force} = \frac{W}{g} f_{max}$$

$$= \frac{6 \times 64 \cdot 3}{32 \cdot 2}$$

$$= 12 \text{ lb}$$

The maximum force in the spring occurs when the mass is at its lowest position. Then the spring force must balance *both* the weight and the inertia force. Hence maximum spring force = 6 + 12 = **18 lb.**

Example. An instrument of weight 20 lb is attached to a spring mounted horizontally. The periodic time was observed to be 1·3 sec. Find the stiffness of the spring.

The assembly is now placed in a vehicle with the axis of the spring horizontal and parallel to the longitudinal axis of the vehicle, Fig. 9.11. Find the resulting extension of the spring when the

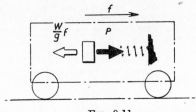

Fɪɢ. 9.11

vehicle accelerates smoothly at 12 ft/sec² and the instrument does not vibrate. Neglect friction.

Solution

$$T = 2\pi \sqrt{\left(\frac{W}{Sg}\right)}$$

thus

$$1·3 = 2\pi \sqrt{\left(\frac{20}{S \times 32·2}\right)}$$

$$S = \frac{(2\pi)^2 \times 20}{1·3^2 \times 32·2}$$

$$= \textbf{14·5 lb/ft}$$

The accelerating vehicle will in turn accelerate the spring-mounted mass through the force in the spring. The forces on the instrument are the spring force P, and the inertia force $(W/g)f$. For balance

$$P = \frac{W}{g}f$$

$$= \frac{20}{32·2} \times 12$$

$$= \textbf{7·45 lb}$$

but $P = Sx$, where x is the extension of the spring due to the acceleration of the vehicle. Therefore

$$x = \frac{P}{S}$$

$$= \frac{7 \cdot 45}{14 \cdot 5}$$

$$= 0 \cdot 514 \text{ ft}$$

PROBLEMS

1. A helical spring, of stiffness 100 lb/in., supports a body weighing 50 lb. The body is given a free vibration of amplitude $\frac{1}{2}$ in. Determine (a) the period of the motion, (b) the maximum acceleration, (c) the maximum velocity.

(0·226 sec; 32·2 ft/sec²; 1·16 ft/sec)

2. A weight of 5 lb is hung vertically from a spring of stiffness 30 lb/in. Calculate the maximum amplitude of vibration if the weight is not to jump from the hook.

(0·167 in.)

3. A mass of weight 10 lb is hung from the end of a thin wire. It is found that the static stretch in the wire is 0·102 in. Calculate the period of free vibration when a mass of 14 lb-wt. is on the wire.

(0·0865 sec)

4. The load required to hold a spring-loaded valve open at its full opening of $\frac{1}{8}$ in. is 20 lb. The load between valve and seat is 10 lb when fully closed. If the weight of the moving part of the valve is 2 lb and the spring axis is horizontal calculate the time taken for the valve to close if suddenly released. Assume the motion of the valve to be simple harmonic.

(0·025 sec)

5. An instrument is spring mounted to the body of a rocket, the spring axis lying along the rocket axis. The natural frequency of the instrument upon its mount is 40 c/s. If the rocket is accelerated smoothly to an accelera- tion ten times that of gravity in such a way that the instrument is not set into vibration find the static deflexion of the instrument on its mounting during the acceleration.

(0·0673 in.)

6. A body weighing 70 lb performs s.h.m. in a straight path, the greatest distance from its mid-position being 30 in. Calculate the force acting on the body, (a) at the beginning of its travel, (b) mid-way between the end of its path and mid-position, if it makes eighty strokes per minute.

(95·3 lb; 47·65 lb)

7. A spring-loaded slide valve weighing 8 lb opens and closes with s.h.m. It has a lift of $\frac{1}{2}$ in., equal to twice the amplitude of the s.h.m. If the total time to open and close the valve is 0·1 sec, find (a) the stiffness of the spring, (b) the maximum accelerating force exerted by the spring.

(980 lb/ft.; 20·45 lb)

8. A mass of 4 lb is hung vertically on the end of a spring. When set in vibration it makes ninety-six oscillations per minute. Find the stiffness of the spring.

If the maximum total extension of the spring during the vibration is 6 in., what is the amplitude of the vibration?

(1·045 lb/in.; 2·17 in.)

9. A weight of 12 lb is suspended from a vertically mounted spring. The static extension is ¼ in. A further load of 24 lb is hung from the spring, pulled ½ in. below the equilibrium position and released. Find (a) the period of the resulting oscillation, (b) the maximum spring tension.

(0·276 sec; 60 lb)

10. Ⓐ Scotch-yoke mechanism reciprocates with s.h.m. The period is 0·1 sec, the amplitude 12 in. and the mass of the reciprocating parts 60 lb. When the mechanism is 6 in. from the mid-position calculate (a) the velocity, (b) the acceleration, (c) the accelerating force, (d) the horse power delivered to, or returned from, the mechanism at this point. Neglect friction.

(54·3 ft/sec; 1,970 ft/sec²; 3,670 lb; 363 h.p.)

9.10. Simple Pendulum

A simple pendulum is formed by a concentrated mass of weight W at the end of a light cord of length l suspended at Q, Fig. 9.12.

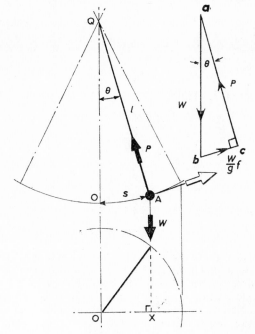

Fig. 9.12. Simple Pendulum

When displaced with the cord taut from the rest position O, the mass moves in an arc about Q. When released from a displaced position A it tends to return to the rest position, i.e. the mass always accelerates towards O from any displaced position along the arc AO. The forces acting on the mass at A are—

1. The weight W, vertically downwards.
2. The tension P in the cord at A, acting from A to Q.
3. The inertia force $(W/g)f$ required for balance. This force acts tangentially to the arc at A, i.e. perpendicular to QA.

These three forces are represented in the triangle of forces, **abc**. Thus

$$\sin \theta = \frac{\mathbf{bc}}{\mathbf{ab}}$$

$$= \frac{(W/g)f}{W}$$

$$= \frac{f}{g}$$

For *small* angular displacements of the cord, we may assume—

$$\sin \theta = \theta \text{ rad}$$

$$= \frac{s}{l}$$

where $s = $ arc OA. Thus

$$\theta = \frac{f}{g}$$

i.e.
$$f = g\theta$$

$$= g \times \frac{s}{l}$$

$$= \frac{g}{l} \times s$$

$$= \text{constant} \times s$$

Thus the acceleration f is directed along the tangent to the arc at A, towards O, and is proportional to the distance s from O, measured along the arc. The motion of the pendulum is therefore *approximately* simple harmonic. It is approximate since we have had to limit θ to small values. However, it turns out to be a very good approximation even when $\theta = 10°$. Other approximations are involved in assuming that the size of the mass is small compared with the length of the cord and that the cord is weightless.

Compare now

$$f = \frac{g}{l} s$$

where f is an acceleration tangent to an arc and s a distance measured along an arc, with

$$f = \omega^2 x$$

where f is directed along a straight line and x is a distance along the straight line. Then

$$\omega^2 = \frac{g}{l}$$

and the period

$$T = \frac{2\pi}{\omega}$$

i.e.

$$T = 2\pi \sqrt{\left(\frac{l}{g}\right)}$$

Note that the period is the time for one complete swing, to and fro. It is proportional to the square root of the length of the pendulum and independent of the weight of the suspended mass. It does, however, depend on the value of g, the acceleration due to gravity.

Example. A simple pendulum was observed to perform forty oscillations in 100 sec, of amplitude 4°. Find (*a*) the length of the pendulum, (*b*) the maximum linear acceleration of the pendulum bob, (*c*) the maximum velocity of the bob, (*d*) the maximum angular velocity of the pendulum.

Solution

(*a*) Periodic time, $T = \dfrac{100}{40} = 2 \cdot 5$ sec.

therefore

$$2 \cdot 5 = 2\pi \sqrt{\left(\frac{l}{32 \cdot 2}\right)}$$

i.e.

$$l = \mathbf{5 \cdot 1 \ ft}$$

(*b*) Since $T = \dfrac{2\pi}{\omega}$; $\quad \omega = \dfrac{2\pi}{T} = \dfrac{2\pi}{2 \cdot 5} = 2 \cdot 51$ rad/sec.

Maximum acceleration of the bob occurs at either extreme position when the displacement is a maximum (Fig. 9.13), i.e.

$$f_{max} = \omega^2 r$$

where

$$r = \text{arc OA} = \text{OQ} \times \angle\text{OQA}$$

$$= 5 \cdot 1 \times 4 \times \frac{\pi}{180}$$

$$= 0 \cdot 356 \ \text{ft}$$

therefore

$$f_{max} = 2 \cdot 51^2 \times 0 \cdot 356$$

$$= \mathbf{2 \cdot 23 \ ft/sec^2}$$

(c) Maximum linear velocity of the bob occurs when the bob passes the mid-position O, i.e.

$$v_{max} = \omega r$$
$$= 2 \cdot 51 \times 0 \cdot 356$$
$$= \mathbf{0 \cdot 893 \ ft/sec}$$

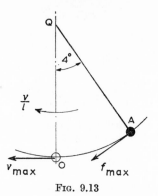

FIG. 9.13

(d) The angular velocity of the pendulum is the linear velocity of the bob divided by the length of the pendulum. Therefore the maximum angular velocity occurs when the bob has its maximum linear velocity.

$$\text{Maximum angular velocity} = \frac{v_{max}}{l}$$
$$= \frac{0 \cdot 893}{5 \cdot 1}$$
$$= \mathbf{0 \cdot 175 \ rad/sec}$$

Example. A simple pendulum is formed by a bob of weight 4 lb at the end of a cord 2 ft long. How many complete oscillations will it make per minute?

The same pendulum is suspended inside a train accelerating smoothly along the level at 10 ft/sec². If the pendulum is not set oscillating find the angle the cord makes with the vertical.

Solution

$$\text{Periodic time, } T = 2\pi \sqrt{\left(\frac{l}{g}\right)}$$
$$= 2\pi \sqrt{\left(\frac{2}{32 \cdot 2}\right)}$$
$$= 1 \cdot 565 \text{ sec}$$

The number of complete oscillations per minute (frequency) equals—

$$n = \frac{60}{1\cdot565}$$

$$= 38\cdot3$$

When suspended in a smoothly accelerating train the cord makes an angle θ with the vertical, Fig. 9.14. The forces acting on the bob

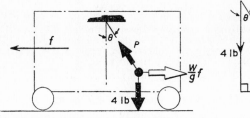

FIG. 9.14

are: the tension P in the cord, the weight of 4 lb, and the inertia force

$$\frac{W}{g}f = \frac{4}{32\cdot2} \times 10 = 1\cdot242 \text{ lb}$$

The inertia force acts in a direction opposite to that of the acceleration of the train. From the triangle of forces—

$$\tan \theta = \frac{1\cdot242}{4}$$

$$= 0\cdot31$$

therefore $\qquad \theta = 17° \ 14'$

The tension P is given by

$$P^2 = 4^2 + 1\cdot242^2$$

$$= 17\cdot55$$

hence $\qquad P = 4\cdot2 \text{ lb}$

PROBLEMS

1. A simple pendulum has a period of 4 sec. Find its length. If the amplitude is 1 ft find the velocity and acceleration of the bob at 4 in. displacement from the position of equilibrium. What is the maximum velocity and acceleration of the bob?

(13·03 ft; 1·48 ft/sec, 0·822 ft/sec²; 1·57 ft/sec, 2·466 ft/sec²)

2. Calculate the value of g if a simple pendulum of length 102 in. makes 100 complete oscillations in 325 sec.

(31·82 ft/sec²)

3. A mass of weight 4 lb suspended from a spring of stiffness 0·25 lb/in. is set in oscillation. What length of simple pendulum will have the same frequency of oscillation?

(16 in.)

4. A 5-lb weight hangs from a string of length 3 ft. Calculate the stiffness of spring required to give the same period as the pendulum when carrying the same mass.

The simple pendulum is hung inside a vehicle accelerating smoothly at 8 ft/sec². Calculate the horizontal displacement of the bob if the bob is not set swinging.

(1·67 lb/ft; 0·723 ft)

5. A small steel ball runs freely in a groove of radius R in a vertical plane. Show that for small displacements from the equilibrium position the motion of the ball is approximately simple harmonic, of period $T = 2\pi \, (R/g)$.

Calculate the radius R to give a period of 1 sec.

(9·78 in.)

9.11. Periodic Motion of a Conical Pendulum

Fig. 9.15 shows a mass of weight W suspended by a light arm or cord of length l. If the mass is rotated about a vertical axis at

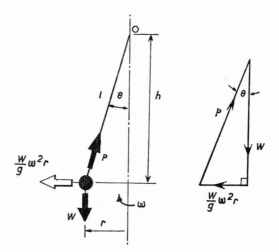

FIG. 9.15. CONICAL PENDULUM

uniform angular velocity ω rad/sec and at the same time the cord is slightly displaced so as to make a *small* angle θ rad with the vertical, the result is that the mass tends to rotate in a circular path in a horizontal plane. The forces acting on the mass when the radius of rotation is r, are: its weight W, the tension P in the cord and the inertia force $(W/g)f$. The inertia force acts radially outwards due to the centripetal acceleration $f = \omega^2 r$ which is directed inwards.

From the triangle of forces—

$$\tan \theta = \frac{(W/g)\omega^2 r}{W} = \frac{\omega^2 r}{g}$$

Since θ is small

$$\tan \theta \simeq \theta$$

thus

$$\theta = \frac{\omega^2 r}{g}$$

$$= \frac{\omega^2 l \theta}{g} \quad \text{since } r = l\theta$$

therefore

$$\omega = \sqrt{\left(\frac{g}{l}\right)}$$

This is the *minimum* value of ω at which a small displacement can occur and yet allow the mass to remain in equilibrium. If ω is less than this critical value the cord will remain vertical, if greater than the critical value the bob will start to rise, the cord then sweeping out a conical path.

For a simple pendulum,

$$\omega = \sqrt{\left(\frac{g}{l}\right)}$$

Thus ω for the simple pendulum corresponds exactly with the critical angular velocity of the conical pendulum.

When ω is large, the angle θ is no longer small and the approximation for $\tan \theta$ no longer holds. From the triangle of forces, therefore

$$\tan \theta = \frac{\omega^2 r}{g}$$

but

$$\tan \theta = \frac{r}{h}$$

hence

$$\frac{r}{h} = \frac{\omega^2 r}{g}$$

or

$$h = \frac{g}{\omega^2}$$

The distance h of the plane of rotation of the mass from the point of suspension O is known as the "height" of the pendulum. It is independent of both weight W and length l.

The conical pendulum performs a periodic motion, and its period is

$$T = \frac{2\pi}{\omega}$$

but
$$\omega^2 = \frac{g}{h}$$

hence
$$T = 2\pi \sqrt{\left(\frac{h}{g}\right)}$$

The tension P in the arm OA is given by

$$P \cos \theta = W$$

therefore
$$P \times \frac{h}{l} = W$$

and
$$P = W \frac{l}{h}$$

The conical pendulum forms the basis of the simple engine governor, a rise or fall in the height of the rotating mass being employed through suitable linkage to operate a fuel valve.

Example. A bob on the end of a light arm forms a simple pendulum of period 0·2 sec. The arm is allowed to hang vertically and the bob is then rotated about this vertical axis. At what speed would it start to rise?

When rotating as a conical pendulum at 400 rev/min, what would be the tension in the arm if the bob weighs ¼ lb?

Solution

For the simple pendulum

$$\omega = \frac{2\pi}{T} = \frac{2\pi}{0\cdot2}$$

$$= \textbf{31·42 rad/sec, or 300 rev/min}$$

This is also the speed at which the bob would start to rise in the equivalent conical pendulum. From

$$T = 2\pi \sqrt{\left(\frac{l}{g}\right)}$$

$$l = \frac{gT^2}{4\pi^2} = \frac{32\cdot2 \times 0\cdot2^2}{4\pi^2} = 0\cdot0326 \text{ ft}$$

At 400 rev/min

$$\omega = \frac{2\pi \times 400}{60} = 41\cdot9 \text{ rad/sec}$$

$$\text{height } h = \frac{g}{\omega^2} = \frac{32\cdot2}{41\cdot9^2} = 0\cdot0184 \text{ ft}$$

Thus tension in cord

$$P = \frac{W}{\cos \theta}$$

$$= \frac{Wl}{h}$$

$$= \frac{1/4 \times 0\cdot0326}{0\cdot0184}$$

$$= \mathbf{0\cdot445\ lb}$$

PROBLEMS

1. A mass hangs from a cord 12 in. long. If the body is rotated about the vertical axis at what speed would it just start to rise?
When the mass rises 3 in. above the lowest position what is the period of the conical pendulum?

(54·1 rev/min; 0·96 sec)

2. A conical pendulum rotates at 100 rev/min. The cord is 6 in. long and the weight of the bob 3 lb. Find (a) the amount by which the bob rises above its lowest position, (b) the period, (c) the tension in the cord.

(2·48 in.; 0·6 sec; 5·12 lb)

3. A simple governor is formed by a pair of balanced rotating masses, each weighing 5 lb. The link joining each mass to the rotating shaft is 12 in. from the shaft axis to the centre of gravity of the mass. Find (a) the change in height when the speed rises from 60 to 70 rev/min; (b) the force in the link at 60 rev/min.

(2·6 in.; 6·13 lb)

4. The arm of a simple conical pendulum is 18 in. long and the rotating mass weighs 2 lb. Find the "height" of the pendulum and the tension in the arm at 120 rev/min. What decrease in speed is necessary to increase the height by 20 per cent? The weight of the arm may be assumed negligible.

(2·45 in., 14·7 lb, 10·8 rev/min)

Dynamics of Rotation

10.1. Angular Acceleration

IF the line OA, Fig. 10.1, rotates about a fixed point O, so that its angular velocity increases from ω_0 in position OA to ω in position

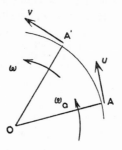

FIG. 10.1

OA′ in time t then the *average angular acceleration* α of the line is defined as

$$\alpha = \frac{\text{change in angular velocity}}{\text{time taken}}$$

$$= \frac{\omega - \omega_0}{t}. \qquad . \qquad . \qquad . \qquad . \qquad (10.1)$$

The units of α are rad/sec² if ω is in radians per second and t in seconds.

If the angular velocity increases by equal amounts in equal times the acceleration is *uniform*. For uniform acceleration α, we have, by rearranging equation (10.1)—

$$\omega = \omega_0 + \alpha t \qquad . \qquad . \qquad . \qquad . \qquad (10.2)$$

Now if u and v are the linear velocities of point A when the angular velocities of line OA are ω_0 and ω, respectively, and f is the linear acceleration of point A, then

$$u = \omega_0 r$$
$$v = \omega r$$

where OA $= r$, and

$$v = u + ft$$

thus

$$\omega r = \omega_0 r + ft$$

or

$$\omega = \omega_0 + \frac{f}{r}t$$

Comparing this equation with equation (10.2) it is clear that

$$\frac{f}{r} = \alpha$$

or

$$f = \alpha r \quad . \qquad . \qquad . \qquad . \qquad . \quad (10.3)$$

10.2. Angular Velocity–Time Graph

The relation between angular velocity and time for uniform or constant angular acceleration is given by

$$\omega = \omega_0 + \alpha t$$

and this is represented graphically in the velocity–time graph, Fig. 10.2. For uniform angular velocity the graph is a horizontal line CB, and OC $= \omega_0$.

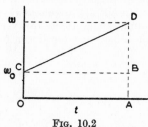

FIG. 10.2

For uniformly accelerated motion the graph is a straight line CD, and AD $= \omega$, OA $= t$. Hence

$$\alpha = \frac{\omega - \omega_0}{t} = \frac{\text{AD} - \text{OC}}{\text{OA}} = \frac{\text{BD}}{\text{CB}}$$

Thus the angular acceleration α is given by the gradient BD/CB of the graph.

When the acceleration is uniform the *average* angular velocity is simply the mean of the initial and final velocities, or

$$\text{average angular velocity} = \frac{\omega + \omega_0}{2} \quad . \qquad . \quad (10.4)$$

But

$$\text{average velocity} = \frac{\text{angle turned through}}{\text{time taken}} = \frac{\theta}{t}$$

hence

$$\frac{\theta}{t} = \frac{\omega + \omega_0}{2}$$

or

$$\theta = \tfrac{1}{2}(\omega + \omega_0) \times t \qquad . \qquad . \qquad . \ (10.5)$$

But $\omega = \omega_0 + \alpha t$, so

$$\theta = \tfrac{1}{2}[(\omega_0 + \alpha t) + \omega_0] \times t$$

thus

$$\theta = \omega_0 t + \tfrac{1}{2}\alpha t^2 \qquad . \qquad . \qquad . \ (10.6)$$

This gives the angle turned through in time t. Again from equation (10.5)

$$\theta = \tfrac{1}{2}(\omega + \omega_0)t$$

but

$$t = \frac{\omega - \omega_0}{\alpha}$$

therefore

$$\theta = \tfrac{1}{2}(\omega + \omega_0) \times \frac{(\omega - \omega_0)}{\alpha}$$

$$= \frac{\omega^2 - \omega_0{}^2}{2\alpha}$$

and rearranging

$$\omega^2 = \omega_0{}^2 + 2\alpha\theta \qquad . \qquad . \qquad . \qquad . \ (10.7)$$

This is a useful equation in that it does not involve the time t.

The equations for uniformly accelerated angular motion are summarized below and, since they are very similar to those for linear motion, the equations for linear motion are given for comparison.

$$v = u + ft \qquad\qquad \omega = \omega_0 + \alpha t$$

$$s = \frac{u + v}{2}\,t \qquad\qquad \theta = \frac{\omega_0 + \omega}{2}\,t$$

$$s = ut + \tfrac{1}{2}ft^2 \qquad\qquad \theta = \omega_0 t + \tfrac{1}{2}\alpha t^2$$

$$v^2 = u^2 + 2fs \qquad\qquad \omega^2 = \omega_0{}^2 + 2\alpha\theta$$

10.3. Use of ω–t Graph

Many problems are conveniently solved by making use of the fact that the area under the ω–t graph is equal to the angle turned through. Fig. 10.3 shows the graph CD for uniformly accelerated motion—

$$\text{area under } \omega\text{–}t \text{ graph} = \text{area OADC}$$

$$= \text{area OABC} + \text{area CBD}$$

$$= \text{OC} \times \text{OA} + \tfrac{1}{2} \times \text{CB} \times \text{BD}$$

$$= \omega_0 t + \tfrac{1}{2} \times t \times (\omega - \omega_0)$$
$$= \omega_0 t + \tfrac{1}{2} t \times \alpha t, \text{ since } \omega - \omega_0 = \alpha t$$
$$= \omega_0 t + \tfrac{1}{2} \alpha t^2$$
$$= \theta, \text{ from equation (10.6)}$$
$$= \text{angle turned through in time } t$$

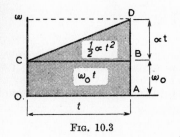

FIG. 10.3

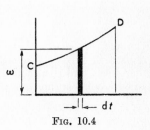

FIG. 10.4

In the general case when the motion is not uniformly accelerated suppose CD, Fig. 10.4, represents the ω–t graph. Since

$$\frac{d\theta}{dt} = \omega$$

then
$$d\theta = \omega \, dt$$

and
$$\theta = \int \omega \, dt$$
$$= \text{area under } \omega\text{–}t \text{ graph}$$

Example. The speed of a shaft increases from 300 to 360 rev/min while turning through eighteen complete revolutions. Calculate (a) the angular acceleration; (b) the time taken for this change.

Solution

(a)
$$\omega_0 = 300 \times \frac{2\pi}{60} = 31\cdot 42 \text{ rad/sec}$$

$$\omega = 360 \times \frac{2\pi}{60} = 37\cdot 67 \text{ rad/sec}$$

$$\theta = 18 \times 2\pi = 113 \text{ rad}$$

Using
$$\omega^2 = \omega_0{}^2 + 2\alpha\theta$$

angular acceleration, $\alpha = \dfrac{\omega^2 - \omega_0{}^2}{2\theta}$

$$= \frac{37\cdot 67^2 - 31\cdot 42^2}{2 \times 113}$$

$$= \mathbf{1\cdot 91 \text{ rad/sec}^2}$$

(b) $$\omega = \omega_0 + \alpha t$$

thus $$t = \frac{\omega - \omega_0}{\alpha}$$

$$= \frac{37 \cdot 67 - 31 \cdot 42}{1 \cdot 91}$$

$$= \mathbf{3 \cdot 27} \text{ sec}$$

Example. A shaft is accelerated uniformly from 8 rev/sec to 14 rev/sec in 2 sec. It continues accelerating at this rate for a further 4 sec, and then continues to rotate at the maximum speed attained. What is the time taken to complete the first 200 revolutions?

Solution

The speed–time graph is shown in Fig. 10.5. ABC represents the uniform acceleration for 6 sec; CD represents the motion at constant

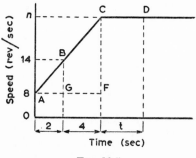

Fig. 10.5

(maximum) speed for time t sec. It is convenient in this case to measure the vertical ordinate in revolutions per second, then the area under the graph gives directly the number of revolutions turned through.

Since ABC is a straight line the maximum speed n rev/sec at C is given by proportion from similar triangles—

$$\frac{CF}{BG} = \frac{AF}{AG}$$

or $$\frac{n - 8}{14 - 8} = \frac{6}{2}$$

thus $$n = 26 \text{ rev/sec}$$

The angle turned through during the first 6 sec

$$= \text{average speed} \times \text{time taken}$$

$$= \frac{8 + 26}{2} \times 6$$

$$= 102 \text{ rev}$$

Therefore revolutions to be turned through at uniform speed = $200 - 102 = 98$. Thus time to turn through 98 rev at maximum speed

$$= \frac{\text{no. of revolutions}}{\text{speed}}$$

$$= \frac{98}{26}$$

$$= 3 \cdot 77 \text{ sec}$$

Total time taken to turn through 200 rev

$$= 6 + 3 \cdot 77$$

$$= \mathbf{9 \cdot 77 \text{ sec}}$$

PROBLEMS

1. The speed of an electric motor rises from 1,430 to 1,490 rev/min in $\frac{1}{2}$ sec. Find the average angular acceleration and the number of revolutions turned through in this time.

$$(12 \cdot 57 \text{ rad/sec}^2; \ 12 \cdot 2 \text{ rev})$$

2. A flywheel 4 ft in diameter is uniformly accelerated from rest and revolves completely sixty times in reaching a speed of 120 rev/min. Find (*a*) the time taken, (*b*) the angular acceleration, (*c*) the linear acceleration of a point on the rim.

$$(1 \text{ min}; \ 0 \cdot 2095 \text{ rad/sec}^2; \ 0 \cdot 419 \text{ ft/sec}^2)$$

3. After the power to drive a shaft is shut off it is seen to describe 120 rev in the first 30 sec, and finally comes to rest in a further 30 sec. If the retardation is uniform calculate the initial angular velocity in revolutions per minute (rev/min) and the retardation in radians per second per second (rad/sec²).

$$(320 \text{ rev/min}; \ 0 \cdot 558 \text{ rad/sec}^2)$$

4. A swing bridge has to be turned through a right angle in 140 sec. The first 60 sec is a period of uniform angular acceleration; the subsequent 40 sec is a period of uniform angular velocity and the third period of 40 sec a uniform angular retardation. Find the maximum angular velocity, the acceleration and the retardation.

$$(0 \cdot 0175 \text{ rad/sec}; \ 0 \cdot 00029 \text{ rad/sec}^2; \ 0 \cdot 000437 \text{ rad/sec}^2)$$

10.4. Dynamics of a Rotating Particle

In the same way as a change of linear motion requires a force, we shall find that a change of angular motion requires a driving torque.

Let a concentrated mass of weight W be attached to the end A of a light arm OA of length r, pivoted at O, Fig. 10.6. OA will rotate freely without the application of a force, provided there is no friction at the pivot. In order to start the rotation, or accelerate the mass, a force P is required at A perpendicular to OA. If a torque is applied to the arm then this force P is provided by the connexion of the arm to the mass. If α is the angular acceleration at the

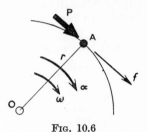

Fig. 10.6

instant considered and f is the linear acceleration of the mass tangent to the circle of motion, then the force required at A is

$$P = \frac{W}{g} f$$

$$= \frac{W}{g} \alpha r \quad \text{since} \quad f = \alpha r$$

The moment of force P about O is the torque T required, i.e.

$$T = P \times r$$

$$= \frac{W}{g} \alpha r \times r$$

$$= \frac{W}{g} r^2 \alpha \qquad . \qquad . \qquad . \qquad . \qquad (10.8)$$

The term $(W/g)r^2$ is a most important quantity and is known as the *second moment* of the mass about O, or its *moment of inertia*, denoted by I. The radius r (for a concentrated mass) is called the *radius of gyration* of the mass about O, denoted by k. Thus, for example, if $W = 1$ lb, $r = 2$ ft and $\alpha = 3$ rad/sec^2, then

$$\text{torque} = \frac{W}{g} r^2 \alpha$$

$$= \frac{1}{32 \cdot 2} \times 2^2 \times 3$$

$$= 0 \cdot 373 \text{ lb-ft}$$

Note—Equation (10.8) is directly applicable to a thin ring of mean radius r rotating about its axis, since every particle of the ring may be considered as concentrated at the same distance r from the axis of rotation.

PROBLEMS

1. A mass of 8 oz is mounted on the end of a light arm 9 in. long. The arm is accelerated uniformly from rest to 3,000 rev/min in 20 sec. Find the torque required.

(1·645 lb-in.)

2. A light arm, 30 in. long, pivoted at its centre carries a 20 lb mass at *each* end. If a couple of 3 lb-ft is applied to the arm calculate the angular acceleration produced.

(1·546 rad/sec²)

3. A flywheel is made up of a thin ring 1 in. thick and 6 in. wide, with a mean diameter of 5 ft. Calculate the time taken to come to rest from 600 rev/min due to a friction couple of 6 lb-ft. The steel weighs 0·28 lb/in.³ and the effects of the spokes may be neglected.

(643 sec)

10.5. Dynamics of a Rotating Body

Consider a body of total mass M accelerated about a fixed axis O, Fig. 10.7. It is required to find the torque to give the body an

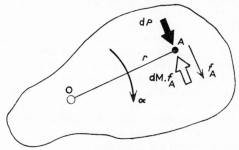

Fig. 10.7

angular acceleration α about O. It is necessary to find the torque required to accelerate each particle such as A of mass dM and add these elementary torques to determine the total torque. The force required at A is

$$dP = dM\,f_A, \text{ normal to OA}$$

where f_A is the linear acceleration of A, tangent to its circular path of motion.

The torque required for the acceleration of A is

$$dT = dP \times r$$
$$= dM\,f_A \times r$$

where r is the radius of rotation of A about O. The total torque T is found by summation of all the elementary torques dT for the whole body. Therefore

$$T = \int dT$$

$$= \int dM\, f_A r$$

But f_A differs for every particle, since it depends on radius r, hence we write

$$f_A = \alpha r$$

thus

$$T = \int dM\, \alpha r \times r$$

and since angular acceleration α is the same for every line such as OA, it is therefore a constant at the instant considered; then

$$T = \alpha \cdot \int dM\, r^2$$

or

$$T = I\alpha$$

where

$$I = \int dM\, r^2$$

I is the *second moment* or *moment of inertia* of the whole mass of the body about the axis of rotation O. I is the summation of the quantities (mass) times (radius)^2 for all the particles of the body and depends on the shape and size of the body. Its value depends on the distribution of the mass as well as on the total mass.

It is useful to imagine all the mass of a body concentrated at a particular radius k from the axis O such that the moment of inertia of the concentrated mass is the same as that of the actual body. Thus the *radius of gyration* k is defined by

$$Mk^2 = I$$

or

$$\frac{W}{g}\, k^2 = I$$

10.6. Inertia Couple

Comparing the formulae

$$P = Mf$$

and

$$T = I\alpha$$

it is seen that moment of inertia I plays the same part in a change of angular motion as mass M does in change of linear motion. By analogy with the idea of inertia force we may regard the torque T

as being balanced by an *inertia couple Iα*, whose sense is *opposite* to that of the angular acceleration α, Fig. 10.8. The problem is then in effect reduced to a static one.

The reality of the effect of an inertia couple will be appreciated by anyone who has tried to accelerate a bicycle wheel rapidly by hand. Although the weight may be carried wholly by the bearings an effort is required to set the wheel spinning. An inertia couple is, of course, *reactive*.

10.7. Accelerated Shaft

Consider a shaft (Fig. 10.9) carrying a rotor having a moment of inertia I about the shaft axis. If the bearing friction is equivalent

FIG. 10.8   FIG. 10.9   FIG. 10.10

to a couple T_f then, in order to accelerate the shaft and rotor, the driving torque T must balance both the inertia couple $Iα$ and the friction couple T_f. Thus

$$T = Iα + T_f$$

10.8. Shaft being Brought to Rest

If the shaft is being brought to rest by a braking torque T the friction couple T_f assists the braking action so that T and T_f together must balance the inertia couple $Iα$; α is now a retardation, its sense being opposite to that of the motion (Fig. 10.10). Thus

$$T + T_f = Iα$$

If there is no braking torque, the friction couple alone brings the shaft to rest, then

$$T_f = Iα$$

Note, in both cases, that

(*a*) the friction couple T_f opposes the motion, and
(*b*) the inertia couple $Iα$ opposes the *change* of motion.

10.9. Units of *I*

The units of moment of inertia need cause no difficulty if it is remembered that: (*a*) I is the product of mass times (distance)^2;

(b) we usually calculate torque in pound-feet (lb-ft). Consider the formula

$$I = \frac{W}{g} k^2$$

where

$$\frac{W}{g} = \text{mass, in slugs};$$

k^2 is in square feet (ft²);

thus

$$I = \frac{W}{g} \text{(slugs)} \times k^2 \text{(ft}^2\text{)}$$

Hence I may be expressed as *slugs* $\times$ *ft²*.

The torque $T = I\alpha$

$$= I \text{ (slugs-ft}^2\text{)} \times \alpha \text{ (rad/sec}^2\text{)}$$

$$= \text{slugs} \times \text{ft}^2/\text{sec}^2$$

since the radian has no units. But slugs may be written

$$\frac{W}{g} \frac{\text{(lb)}}{\text{(ft/sec}^2)}, \text{ or lb-sec}^2/\text{ft}$$

therefore

$$T = \frac{\text{lb-sec}^2}{\text{ft}} \times \frac{\text{ft}^2}{\text{sec}^2}$$

$$= \text{lb-ft, as required.}$$

For example, if I is given as 1,000 lb-ft², i.e. W (lb-wt) $\times$ k^2 (ft²); we divide by g (32·2 ft/sec²), to express I as a moment of *inertia*, and hence obtain T in (lb-ft) units. If, however, the expression "1,000 lb-ft²" is interpreted to mean 1,000 (lb-mass) $\times$ ft², we divide by the *number* 32·2, since 1 lb-mass = 32·2 slugs.

Whether we interpret "lb" to mean weight or mass the numerical work is the same, i.e.

$$T = \frac{1,000}{32 \cdot 2} \times \alpha \text{ lb-ft}$$

(where α is in radians per second per second).

10.10. Values of *I* for Simple Rotors

The derivation of formulae for the mass moment of inertia is left as an exercise in mathematics. Formulae for the moment of inertia I for cylinders and disks about a longitudinal axis are given here without proof.

1. Solid Disk or Cylinder

For a uniform solid circular cylinder of diameter d, the moment of inertia about the axis O–O, Fig. 10.11 is

$$I = \frac{W}{g} \frac{d^2}{8}$$

where W is the weight of the cylinder. By comparison with the formula

$$I = \frac{W}{g}\, k^2$$

we see that the radius of gyration k for a solid cylinder is given by

$$k^2 = \frac{d^2}{8}$$
$$= \frac{(2r)^2}{8}$$

where r = radius of cylinder; i.e.

$$k = \frac{r}{\sqrt{2}} \text{ or } 0\cdot707\, r$$

Thus the radius of gyration of a uniform solid circular cylinder is about $0\cdot71$ times the radius of the cylinder.

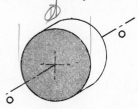 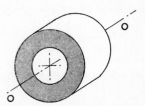

FIG. 10.11   FIG. 10.12

Hollow Circular Cylinder

A hollow circular cylinder is formed by removing from a solid cylinder a concentric cylinder of smaller radius, Fig. 10.12. If suffixes 1 and 2 denote outer and inner cylinders, respectively, then for a hollow cylinder the I about longitudinal axis O–O is given by subtraction, thus

$$I = I_1 - I_2$$
$$= \frac{W_1}{g}\frac{d_1{}^2}{8} - \frac{W_2}{g}\frac{d_2{}^2}{8}$$

where W_1 is the weight of the "solid" outer cylinder and W_2 that of the inner cylinder.

If w is the weight of material per unit volume and l the length of the cylinder, then

$$W_1 = w \times \frac{\pi d_1{}^2}{4} \times l$$

$$W_2 = w \times \frac{\pi d_2{}^2}{4} \times l$$

and if W is the weight of the actual hollow cylinder, then

$$W = W_1 - W_2$$
$$= w \times \frac{\pi(d_1{}^2 - d_2{}^2)}{4} \times l$$

Thus

$$I = \frac{w}{g} \left[\frac{\pi d_1^2}{4} l \times \frac{d_1^2}{8} \right] - \frac{w}{g} \left[\frac{\pi d_2^2}{4} l \times \frac{d_2^2}{8} \right]$$

$$= \frac{w}{g} \frac{\pi}{4} (d_1^4 - d_2^4) \frac{l}{8}$$

$$= \frac{1}{g} \left[\frac{w\pi(d_1^2 - d_2^2)}{4} l \right] \frac{(d_1^2 + d_2^2)}{8}$$

$$= \frac{W}{g} \frac{(d_1^2 + d_2^2)}{8}$$

This formula gives I in terms of the weight W of the actual hollow cylinder. The corresponding radius of gyration k is given by

$$k^2 = \frac{d_1^2 + d_2^2}{8}$$

Note particularly the *positive* sign in the formulae for I and k.

Example. A steel cylinder 2 ft outside diameter and 1 ft inside diameter is set in rotation about its axis. If the cylinder is 3 ft long and weighs 480 lb/ft³ calculate the torque required to give it an angular acceleration of 0·5 rad/sec².

Solution

Weight of cylinder, W = volume × density

$$= \frac{\pi}{4} (2^2 - 1^2) \times 3 \times 480$$

$$\doteqdot 3,390 \text{ lb}$$

$$I \doteqdot \frac{W}{g} \frac{(d_1^2 + d_2^2)}{8}$$

$$= \frac{3,390}{32\cdot2} \times \frac{(2^2 + 1^2)}{8}$$

$$= 65\cdot7 \text{ lb-ft-sec}^2 \text{ or slug-ft}^2$$

Torque required, $T = I\alpha$

$$= 65\cdot7 \times 0\cdot5$$

$$= \mathbf{32\cdot85 \text{ lb-ft}}$$

Example. A flywheel, together with its shaft, has a total weight of 600 lb, and its radius of gyration is 3 ft. If the effect of bearing friction is equivalent to a couple of 50 lb-ft, calculate the braking torque required to bring the flywheel to rest from a speed of 720 r.p.m. in 8 sec.

Solution

$$720 \text{ rev/min} = 720 \times \frac{2\pi}{60} = 75\cdot4 \text{ rad/sec}$$

thus   retardation $\alpha = \dfrac{\omega}{t}$

$$= \frac{75\cdot4}{8}$$

$$= 9\cdot42 \text{ rad/sec}^2$$

I of flywheel and shaft $= \dfrac{W}{g} k^2$

$$= \frac{600}{32\cdot2} \times 3^2$$

$$= 167\cdot5 \text{ lb-ft-sec}^2 \text{ or slug-ft}^2$$

Inertia couple $= I\alpha = 167\cdot5 \times 9\cdot42 = 1{,}580 \text{ lb-ft}$

The braking torque T together with the friction couple of 50 lb-ft are in equilibrium with the inertia couple, i.e. together they bring the shaft to rest.

$$T + 50 = 1{,}580$$

thus $T = \textbf{1,530 lb-ft}$

PROBLEMS

● A flywheel has a moment of inertia of 8 slug-ft². Calculate the angular acceleration of the wheel due to a torque of 6 lb-ft if the bearing friction is equivalent to a couple of 2 lb-ft. What would be the acceleration if the moment of inertia were 8 lb-ft²?

(0·5 rad/sec², 16·1 rad/sec²)

2. A light shaft carries a disk 15 in. diameter, 2 in. thick, of steel weighing 0·28 lb/in.³. Calculate its moment of inertia about an axis through the centre of the disk and perpendicular to the plane of the disk.

What torque would be required to accelerate the disk from 60 to 120 rev/min in 1 sec, neglecting friction?

If a friction torque of 1 lb-ft acts, what braking torque would be required to bring the disk to rest from 60 rev/min in 1 sec?

(0·602 slug-ft² or 19·35 lb-ft²; 3·78 lb-ft; 2·78 lb-ft)

3. The rotor of an electric motor weighs 400 lb and has a radius of gyration of 6 in. Calculate the torque required to accelerate it from rest to 1,500 rev/min in 6 sec. Friction resistance may be neglected.

(81·3 lb-ft)

Ⓠ A light shaft carries a turbine rotor which weighs 2 tons and has a radius of gyration of 2 ft. The rotor requires a uniform torque of 700 lb-ft to accelerate it from rest to 6,000 rev/min in 10 min. Find (*a*) the friction couple, (*b*) the time taken to come to rest when steam is shut off.

(118 lb-ft, 49 min 24 sec)

5. A drum rotor is a *thin* cylinder of 4 ft diameter, $\frac{3}{16}$ in. thick, and 2 ft long. The material is mild steel of specific weight 0·28 lb/in.³. Calculate the moment of inertia of the rotor about the polar axis.

Find the time taken for the rotor to reach a speed of 3,600 rev/min from rest if the driving torque is 40 lb-ft and the friction torque is 3·5 lb-ft.

(760 lb-ft²; 244 sec)

6. The flywheel of an engine consists essentially of a thin cast-iron ring of mean diameter 6 ft. The cross-section of the ring is 2 in. by 2 in. Calculate the moment of inertia of the flywheel (in slug-ft²) and find the change in speed of the flywheel if a constant torque of 80 lb-ft acts on it for 5 sec. Specific weight of cast iron = 0·26 lb/in.³.

(65·8 slug-ft², 58·2 rev/min)

7. A rotor weighs 2 tons and has a radius of gyration of 6 ft. Find the constant torque required to raise the speed from 100 to 280 rev/min in 60 sec if the friction torque is 60 lb-ft.

If the wheel is rotating freely at 280 rev/min and a brake is applied bringing it to rest in 120 rev find the brake torque assuming uniform retardation.

(1,630 lb-ft, 2,790 lb-ft)

8. A shaft carrying a rotor rotates at 180 rev/min. When the driving torque is removed the speed drops to 90 rev/min in 6 min due to the braking action of the bearing friction alone. If the rotor weighs 1,640 lb and has a radius of gyration of 18 in. find the average value of the friction couple at the bearings.

If the shaft is of 6 in. diameter and is supported in journal bearings what is the average value of the coefficient of friction at the bearing surface ?

(3 lb-ft, 0·0073)

9. The rotating table of a vertical boring machine weighs 1,535 lb and has a radius of gyration of 2·32 ft. Find the torque required to accelerate the table to 60 rev/min in three complete revolutions from rest.

(269 lb-ft)

10. The flywheel of an engine has a weight of 176 lb and a radius of gyration of 8·83 in. If the engine rotating parts have a moment of inertia of 100 lb-ft² find the torque necessary to accelerate the engine and flywheel from rest to 1,500 rev/min in 20 sec. Assume a constant friction torque of 4 lb-ft.

(51·5 lb-ft)

10.11. The Hoist

Hoist and pulley problems on connected bodies were dealt with in Chapter 4 but no account was taken there of the rotational inertia of the drum or pulley. We shall now study the effect of combining a hoist drum of moment of inertia I with a hanging load of weight W. Four cases will be considered, according as the load is rising or falling, being accelerated, or brought to rest. In every case two equations can be written down—

(*a*) the equation for the balance of couples at the hoist drum;
(*b*) the equation for the balance of forces at the load.

If the hoist drum radius is r a third equation connecting the angular acceleration α of the drum and the linear acceleration f of the load can be written down, i.e.

$$f = \alpha r$$

In every case we recall that the friction couple at the bearings or rope will oppose the rotation and the inertia couple will oppose the change of rotation.

CASE 1. LOAD RAISED, ACCELERATING UPWARDS, FIG. 10.13

Note—

1. Acceleration f is upwards, hence the inertia force is downwards.

2. Angular acceleration α is anticlockwise, hence the inertia couple is clockwise.

3. Rotation of the drum is anticlockwise hence the friction couple acts clockwise.

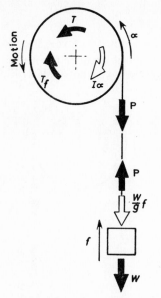 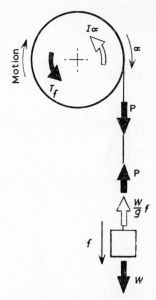

FIG. 10.13. ACCELERATED   FIG. 10.14. RUNAWAY HOIST;
HOIST; LOAD RAISED   LOAD ACCELERATING DOWNWARDS

For rotation of the hoist drum the driving torque T must balance the friction couple T_f, the inertia couple $I\alpha$, and the torque $P \times r$ due to the tension P in the rope at the drum. Thus

$$T = T_f + I\alpha + P \times r$$

For linear motion of the load, the tension P in the rope at the load must balance both the dead weight and the inertia force $(W/g)f$, thus

$$P = W + \frac{W}{g}f$$

CASE 2. LOAD FALLING AND ACCELERATING DOWNWARDS: (NO DRIVING TORQUE ACTING), FIG. 10.14

The load is allowed to fall freely, resisted only by friction and inertia forces and couples. For rotation of the hoist drum, the accelerating torque $P \times r$ due to rope tension must balance both the friction couple T_f, and the inertia couple $I\alpha$, thus

$$Pr = T_f + I\alpha$$

For linear motion of the load the accelerating force due to the weight must balance the upward tension P in the rope, and the inertia force $(W/g)f$, thus

$$W = P + \frac{W}{g}f$$

CASE 3. LOAD FALLING AND BEING BROUGHT TO REST, FIG. 10.15

We now consider the braking of the hoist drum as the load falls. The accelerations are therefore reversed as compared with the

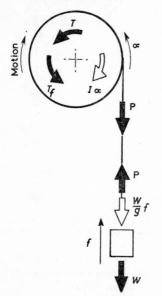

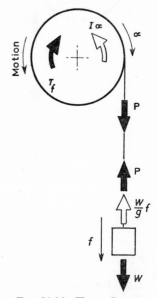

FIG. 10.15. BRAKED HOIST; LOAD FALLING

FIG. 10.16. HOIST COMING TO REST; LOAD RISING

previous case. For rotation of the drum the braking torque T is assisted by the friction couple to balance the accelerating torque $P \times r$ due to the rope tension, and the inertia couple $I\alpha$, thus

$$T + T_f = Pr + I\alpha$$

For the load, the retarding force is the rope tension P and this must balance both the weight and the inertia force, thus

$$P = W + \frac{W}{g} f$$

CASE 4. LOAD RISING: COMING TO REST UNDER FRICTION ONLY, FIG. 10.16

Since there is no braking torque applied the drum is retarded by the torque $P \times r$ due to the rope tension and the friction couple T_f. These two couples must balance the inertia couple of the drum, i.e.

$$P \times r + T_f = I\alpha$$

For the load the retarding force is the weight W and this must balance the tension P and the inertia force, i.e.

$$W = P + \frac{W}{g} f$$

Note—The student is not required to memorize the formulae for each of the four cases considered, indeed many other cases may be devised. He is required, however, to grasp firmly the following rules already mentioned, but repeated here for clarity, by which such problems may be solved—

1. The friction couple opposes the rotation.
2. The inertia couple opposes the change of rotation.
3. The inertia force opposes the change of linear motion.

It may be remarked also that in every case the direction of the rope tension P and the load weight W is unaltered, although their effect may be to accelerate or to retard the load.

Example. A hoist drum has a moment of inertia of 200 lb-ft² and is used to raise a lift weighing 1 ton with an upward acceleration of 5 ft/sec². The drum diameter is 3 ft. Determine (*a*) the torque required at the drum; (*b*) the horse-power required after accelerating for 3 sec from rest.

Solution

(*a*) The torque required at the hoist drum is made up of three parts—

1. Torque $I\alpha$, required to accelerate the drum.
2. Torque $W \times r$, required to hold the dead weight of the lift.
3. Torque $(W/g)f \times r$, required to accelerate the lift.

Thus

$$\text{total torque} = I\alpha + W \times r + \frac{W}{g}f \times r$$

$$= \frac{200}{32 \cdot 2} \times \frac{5}{1 \cdot 5} + 2{,}240 \times 1 \cdot 5 + \frac{2{,}240}{32 \cdot 2} \times 5 \times 1 \cdot 5$$

$$= 20 \cdot 7 + 3{,}360 + 522$$

$$= \mathbf{3{,}903 \ lb\text{-}ft}$$

$$\left(\text{Note that } \alpha = \frac{f}{r} = \frac{5}{1 \cdot 5} \text{ rad/sec}^2\right)$$

(b) After 3 sec, the lift speed

$$v = ft$$
$$= 5 \times 3$$
$$= 15 \text{ ft/sec}$$

and this is the speed of the drum circumference. Therefore angular velocity of the drum

$$\omega = \frac{v}{r} = \frac{15}{1 \cdot 5} = 10 \text{ rad/sec}$$

$$\text{Horse-power required} = \frac{\text{torque} \times \text{angular velocity}}{550}$$

$$= \frac{T\omega}{550}$$

$$= \frac{3{,}903 \times 10}{550}$$

$$= \mathbf{71}$$

This is the horse-power required at the instant after 3 sec.

Example. A wagon weighing 12 tons is lowered down an incline of 1 in 20 by means of a cable, parallel to the incline, wrapped round a drum at the top of the slope. The hoist drum weighs 1,000 lb, has a radius of gyration of 2·5 ft and effective diameter 6 ft. The weight of the cable may be neglected, but the friction couple at the drum bearings is 1,200 lb-ft, and the resistance to motion of the wagon is 300 lb. Find the braking torque on the hoist drum to bring the wagon to rest from 15 m.p.h. in 22 ft. The rotational inertia of the wagon wheels may be neglected.

Solution

$$15 \text{ m.p.h.} = 22 \text{ ft/sec}$$

$$\text{retardation, } f = \frac{v^2}{2s} = \frac{22^2}{2 \times 22} = 11 \text{ ft/sec}^2$$

Thus the angular retardation of the drum

$$\alpha = \frac{f}{r} = \frac{11}{3} \text{ rad/sec}^2$$

The pull P in the cable together with the tractive resistance of 300 lb balances the resolved part of the weight down the incline

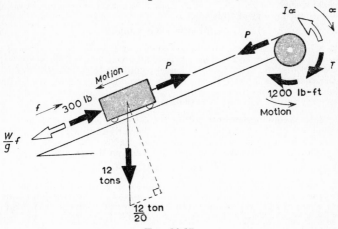

FIG. 10.17

($\frac{12}{20}$ tons) together with the inertia force due to the retardation of the wagon, $(W/g)f$, Fig. 10.17. Thus

$$P + 300 = \frac{12}{20} \times 2{,}240 + \frac{12 \times 2{,}240}{32 \cdot 2} \times 11$$

and $$P = 10{,}224 \text{ lb}$$

The braking torque T applied to the drum with the friction couple of 1,200 lb-ft together balance the torque $P \times r$ due to the pull P in the cable and the inertia couple $I\alpha$ due to the retardation of the drum, thus

$$T + 1{,}200 = P \times r + I\alpha$$
$$= 10{,}224 \times 3 + \left(\frac{1{,}000}{32 \cdot 2} \times 2 \cdot 5^2\right) \times \frac{11}{3}$$
$$= 31{,}384$$

therefore $$T = \mathbf{30{,}184 \text{ lb-ft}}$$

PROBLEMS

1. A load weighing 8 tons is to be raised with a uniform acceleration of 3 ft/sec² by means of a light cable passing over a hoist drum of 6 ft diameter. The drum weighs 1 ton and has a radius of gyration of 2·5 ft. Find the torque

required at the drum if friction is neglected. What is the horse-power exerted after 4 sec from rest?

(26·43 ton-ft; 430 h.p.)

2. A mine cage weighing 4 tons is to be raised with an acceleration of 5 ft/sec² using a hoist drum of 5 ft diameter. The drum weighs ¾ ton and has a radius of gyration of 2 ft. The effect of bearing friction is equivalent to a couple of 1 ton-ft at the hoist drum. What is the horse-power required when the load has reached a velocity of 20 ft/sec? What is the horse-power required at a *uniform* velocity of 20 ft/sec?

(415 h.p.; 358 h.p.)

3. A hoist drum has a weight of 800 lb and a radius of gyration of 2 ft. The drum diameter is 2 ft 6 in. A load of 1 ton hangs from a light cable wrapped round the drum and is allowed to fall freely. If the friction couple at the bearings is 2,000 lb-ft calculate the runaway speed of the load after falling for 2 sec from rest.

(9·62 ft/sec)

4. The maximum allowable pull in a hoist cable is 20 tons. Calculate the maximum load which can be brought to rest with a retardation of 16 ft/sec². The hoist drum has a moment of inertia of 20,000 lb-ft² and a diameter of 8 ft. What is the corresponding braking torque on the drum?

(13·35 tons; 81·12 ton-ft)

5. In an experiment, a flywheel is mounted on a shaft 2 in. diameter supported in bearings. Around the shaft is wrapped a light cord from which is hung a load of 4 lb. When allowed to fall and rotate the flywheel the load falls 6 ft from rest in 3 sec. The friction couple is 3 lb-in. Find the moment of inertia of the flywheel.

(0·14 lb-ft²)

Work and Energy

11.1. Work

WORK is done when a force is applied to a body and the body moves in the direction of the force. The amount of *work done* is measured by the product—

force × distance moved by point of application of force

Thus, if a uniform force P moves a body a distance s measured in the direction of the force, then

$$\text{work done by } P = P \times s$$

and the units of work are foot-pounds (ft-lb), or inch-tons (in.-tons), etc.

It may happen that the line of action of the force is at an angle to the direction of motion of the body. For example, let a uniform force of 20 lb act on a body at 30° to the horizontal as shown in Fig. 11.1, and let the body move a horizontal distance OA = 12 ft.

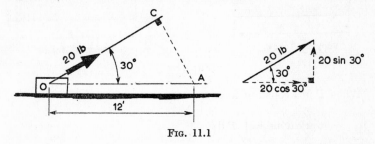

FIG. 11.1

The work done by the force is determined by the distance OC = 12 cos 30°, moved by the force *along its line of action*. Thus

$$\text{work done} = 20 \times OC$$
$$= 20 \times 12 \cos 30°$$
$$= 208 \text{ ft-lb}$$

Alternatively, the force may be resolved into components parallel and perpendicular to the direction of motion of the body, in this case, the horizontal direction OA.

Component of force parallel to OA $= 20 \cos 30°$

Component of force perpendicular to OA $= 20 \sin 30°$

The force of $20 \sin 30°$ perpendicular to OA does not move the body in this direction and therefore does no work. The force $20 \cos 30°$ moves the body through a distance of 12 ft, therefore

$$\text{work done} = 20 \cos 30° \times 12$$
$$= 208 \text{ ft-lb, as before}$$

11.2. Work Done by a Non-Uniform Force

If the force varies with distance the work done is found by taking the sum of the increments of work done in each small displacement ds. The work done by a force P in a small displacement ds is P ds. The work done in a displacement s is the sum

$$\int_0^s P \, ds$$

and this is represented by the area under a diagram of force P against displacement s, Fig. 11.2.

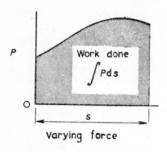
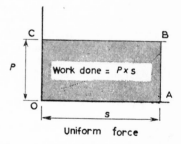

Fig. 11.2

When P is a constant force

$$\text{work done} = \int_0^s P \, ds$$
$$= P \int_0^s ds$$
$$= P \times s, \text{ as before}$$
$$= \text{area of rectangle OABC, Fig. 11.2.}$$

11.3. Kinetic Energy

Now consider the work done in accelerating a body of mass M from rest to a speed v over a distance s. The average acceleration required is given by

$$v^2 = 2fs$$

or

$$f = \frac{v^2}{2s}$$

The average force required to produce this acceleration is

$$P = Mf$$
$$= M \times \frac{v^2}{2s}$$

and the work done by this force P in moving a distance s is

$$P \times s = \frac{Mv^2}{2s} \times s$$
$$= \tfrac{1}{2} Mv^2$$

The expression $\tfrac{1}{2} Mv^2$ on the right-hand side of the equation is known as the *kinetic energy* or *energy of motion*, of the body at speed v. It is the energy possessed by the body by virtue of its mass and its speed.

Thus   **kinetic energy $= \tfrac{1}{2} Mv^2$**

Kinetic energy is a scalar quantity since it is not necessary to take the direction of the speed into account. Further, since P has been taken as the *average* force over the distance s, we note—

1. That the kinetic energy $\tfrac{1}{2} Mv^2$ is independent of the variation of the force during the acceleration to speed v.

2. That the work done on the body from rest is equal to the kinetic energy possessed by the body.

11.4. Work Done in Accelerating a Body Against Resistance

Since P is the average accelerating force the effect of friction, or other resisting forces, may be allowed for as follows: Let E be the total average tractive effort exerted. This effort must balance both the resisting force R and the inertia force (accelerating force), thus

$$E = R + P$$

and the work done over a distance s in accelerating from rest is

$$E \times s = (R + P) \times s$$
$$= Rs + Ps$$
$$= Rs + \tfrac{1}{2} Mv^2$$
$$= \text{work done against } R + \text{kinetic energy}$$

The total work done is therefore made up of two parts—

    1. The work done against the resistance, $R \times s$.
    2. The work done in providing the kinetic energy, $\frac{1}{2} Mv^2$.

11.5. Changes of Kinetic Energy

The work done in changing the speed of a body is equal to the change in its kinetic energy. This important result is proved as follows: Let the speed of a body be increased from u to v over a distance s, then the average acceleration f is given by

$$v^2 = u^2 + 2fs$$

or

$$f = \frac{v^2 - u^2}{2s}$$

The average accelerating force P is

$$P = Mf = M \times \frac{v^2 - u^2}{2s}$$

and the work done in distance s is (Fig. 11.3)—

$$P \times s = M \times \frac{v^2 - u^2}{2s} \times s$$

$$= M \times \frac{v^2 - u^2}{2}$$

$$= \tfrac{1}{2} Mv^2 - \tfrac{1}{2} Mu^2$$

$$= \text{final kinetic energy} - \text{initial kinetic energy.}$$

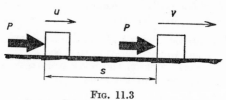

Fig. 11.3

The work done in accelerating the body is therefore equal to the *change* in the kinetic energy of the body.

11.6. Units of Kinetic Energy

In the ft-lb-sec system of units the unit of work is the ft-lb. In a consistent system of units kinetic energy should also be in ft-lb.

Now   kinetic energy $= \frac{1}{2} Mv^2$

and we may replace M by W/g slug, where W is the weight of the body in pounds (lb), then

$$\text{kinetic energy} = \frac{1}{2} \frac{W}{g} v^2$$

Substituting the units of W, v and g, the units of kinetic energy are

$$\frac{\text{lb}}{\text{ft/sec}^2} \times (\text{ft/sec})^2 = \text{ft-lb, as required}$$

Hence the kinetic energy is measured in foot-pounds (ft-lb) provided the mass is in slugs.

11.7. Potential Energy

The work done in lifting a load of weight W through a height h is Wh. This is known as the *potential energy* of the load referred to its original position and its units are those of work, i.e. ft-lb.

Thus   **potential energy = Wh**

Potential energy is a relative quantity since the original datum position may be chosen arbitrarily. Usually, therefore, it is the *changes* of potential energy with which we are concerned.

Evidently the work done against gravity in increasing the potential energy of a body may be recovered by allowing the body to fall back to its original position. Thus the potential energy is converted into kinetic energy by virtue of the work done on the body in falling under gravity.

Example. A drop hammer is allowed to fall from rest through a height of 20 ft on to a forging. Find the downward velocity of the hammer when it strikes the forging.

If the hammer weighs $\frac{1}{2}$ ton what is the work done by the forging and baseplate in bringing the hammer to rest in a distance of 2 in.?

Solution

In falling the loss of potential energy of the hammer is converted into a gain in kinetic energy

potential energy of hammer above forging $= W \times 20$ ft-lb

where W is the weight of the hammer in pounds. Thus

kinetic energy of hammer at forging $= \dfrac{1}{2}\dfrac{W}{g}v^2$

where v is the required downward velocity in feet per second. Equating

$$\frac{1}{2}\frac{W}{g}v^2 = W \times 20$$

hence $v = \sqrt{(2 \times 20 \times 32 \cdot 2)}$

$$= \textbf{35·9 ft/sec}$$

The work done on the hammer in bringing it to rest is made up of two parts—

1. The work done in "destroying" the kinetic energy of the hammer.

2. The work done against the weight W in resisting the downward motion of the hammer in the final 2 in.

Therefore

$$\text{total work done} = \frac{1}{2}\frac{W}{g}v^2 + W \times \frac{2}{12}$$

$$= W \times 20 + W \times \frac{2}{12}$$

$$= 1{,}120 \times 20 + 1{,}120 \times \frac{2}{12}$$

$$= \textbf{22{,}600 ft-lb}$$

This work represents energy lost in permanent deformation of the forging and reappears as heat. Some of the energy loss may also be accounted for in noise and vibration.

Example. A car of weight 2,500 lb descends a hill of 1 in 5 (sine). Calculate, using an energy method, the average braking force required to bring the car to rest from 45 m.p.h. in 50 yd. The frictional resistance to motion is 50 lb.

Solution

The total energy of the car when its speed is 45 m.p.h. is the sum of its kinetic and potential energies. This total energy is destroyed by the braking force and frictional resistance acting through a distance of 150 ft.

Vertical height corresponding to 150 ft on the slope is

$$\frac{150}{5} = 30 \text{ ft}$$

$$\text{Potential energy of car} = 2{,}500 \times 30 = 75{,}000 \text{ ft-lb}$$

$$\text{Kinetic energy of car} = \frac{1}{2}\frac{W}{g}v^2$$

$$= \frac{2{,}500 \times 66^2}{2 \times 32{\cdot}2}$$

$$= 169{,}000 \text{ ft-lb}$$

$$\text{total energy} = 75{,}000 + 169{,}000 = 244{,}000 \text{ ft-lb}$$

$$\text{work done by braking force} = P \times 150 \text{ ft-lb}$$

$$\text{work done by frictional resistance} = 50 \times 150 \text{ ft-lb}$$

Equating total work done to total energy destroyed—

$$P \times 150 + 50 \times 150 = 244,000$$

hence
$$P = \textbf{1,577 lb}$$

11.8. Strain Energy

The work done in compressing or stretching a spring is stored as *strain energy* in the spring provided that there is no permanent deformation (overstretching). The stiffness of a spring is the load per unit extension and is approximately constant within the working range of the spring; thus if S is the stiffness, the load P required to produce an extension x is given by

$$P = Sx$$

This gives a straight-line graph of P against x, Fig. 11.4.

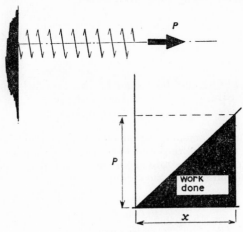

Fig. 11.4

Suppose a load gradually applied to a spring so that it varies from zero to a maximum value P and produces a maximum extension x. Then

$$\text{work done} = \text{average load} \times \text{extension}$$
$$= \tfrac{1}{2} P \times x$$
$$= \tfrac{1}{2} Sx \times x$$
$$= \tfrac{1}{2} Sx^2$$

Then, since strain energy

$$U = \text{work done}$$

thus
$$U = \tfrac{1}{2} Px = \tfrac{1}{2} Sx^2$$

Alternatively

$$U = \text{work done} = \text{area under graph (Fig. 11.4)}$$
$$= \tfrac{1}{2} Px$$
$$= \tfrac{1}{2} Sx^2$$

The units of strain energy are the same as those of work, i.e. ft-lb.

Example. A wagon weighing 12 tons travelling at 10 m.p.h. strikes a pair of parallel spring-loaded stops. If the stiffness of each spring is 40,000 lb/ft, calculate the maximum compression in bringing the wagon to rest.

Solution

$$v = 10 \text{ m.p.h.} = 14\cdot66 \text{ ft/sec}$$

$$\text{kinetic energy of wagon} = \frac{1}{2}\frac{W}{g}v^2$$

$$= \frac{1}{2} \times \frac{12 \times 2{,}240}{32\cdot2} \times (14\cdot66)^2$$

$$= 89{,}700 \text{ ft-lb}$$

This kinetic energy may be assumed to be absorbed equally by the two springs. Strain energy stored per spring is

$$\tfrac{1}{2} \times 89{,}700 = 44{,}850 \text{ ft-lb}$$

At maximum compression, the wagon is instantaneously at rest, the final kinetic energy is zero and the initial kinetic energy has been converted entirely into strain energy of the springs. Thus if x is the maximum compression of the springs,

$$\tfrac{1}{2} Sx^2 = 44{,}850$$
or
$$\tfrac{1}{2} \times 40{,}000 \, x^2 = 44{,}850$$

$$x = 1\cdot5 \text{ ft}$$

Example. A spring of stiffness 100 lb/in. is installed between plates so that it has an initial compression of 0·9 in. A body of weight 10 lb is dropped 6 in. from rest on to the compressed spring. Find the further compression of the spring neglecting loss of energy at impact.

Solution

$$\text{Let } x \text{ in.} = \text{further compression of the spring}$$
$$\text{initial spring force} = \text{stiffness} \times \text{initial compression}$$
$$= 100 \times 0\cdot9$$
$$= 90 \text{ lb}$$
$$\text{maximum spring force} = 90 + 100 \, x \text{ lb}$$

The load–compression graph is shown in Fig. 11.5. The loss of potential energy of the weight is equal to the work done on the spring which is given by the area under the load–compression graph.

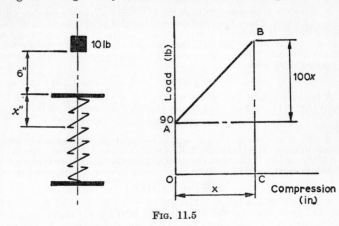

FIG. 11.5

Loss of potential energy $= 10(6 + x)$ in.-lb

work done on spring $=$ area OABC

$$= 90 \times x + \tfrac{1}{2} \times 100\, x \times x$$
$$= 90\, x + 50\, x^2 \text{ in.-lb}$$

Equating

$$10(6 + x) = 90\, x + 50\, x^2$$

hence $\quad x^2 + 1\cdot6\, x - 1\cdot2 = 0$

and $\qquad x = \dfrac{-1\cdot6 \pm \sqrt{(1\cdot6^2 + 4 \times 1\cdot2)}}{2}$

$$= \mathbf{0\cdot56 \text{ in.}} \text{ (neglecting negative answer)}$$

PROBLEMS

1. A hammer weighing 60 lb is held in a horizontal position and then released so that it swings in a vertical circle of radius 3 ft. What is the kinetic energy and the speed of the hammer at its lowest point?

If at the lowest point it strikes and breaks a metal specimen and moves on through an angle of 50° beyond the vertical before instantaneously coming to rest, how much energy has been absorbed by the specimen?

(180 ft-lb; 13·9 ft/sec; 115·7 ft-lb)

2. A car descends a hill of 1 in 6 (sine). Its weight is 2,000 lb and the frictional resistance to motion is 40 lb. Calculate, using an energy method, the average braking effort to bring the car to rest from 30 m.p.h. in 30 yd.

(961 lb)

3. A train is moving down an incline of 1 in 120 at a speed of 24 m.p.h. The wheels are locked by application of the brakes on all vehicles. If the

coefficient of sliding friction between wheels and track is 0·12 and the average wind resistance to motion is 18 lb/ton how far will the train move before coming to rest ?

(161 ft)

4. A locomotive weighing 80 tons hauls a train of twelve coaches up an incline of 1 in 80. The rolling resistance to motion is 12 lb/ton. Each coach weighs 20 tons. If the speed is increased from 15 to 30 m.p.h. in 600 yd and the time taken is 30 sec, find: (a) the change in kinetic energy of the train; (b) the total work done by the engine during this period; (c) the average horse-power developed.

(7,215 ft-tons; 17,500 ft-tons; 2,377 h.p.)

5. A bullet weighing ½ oz strikes a heavy steel plate at 2,000 ft/sec. It is brought to rest in 0·1 in. Calculate the average force exerted on the plate.

(23,300 lb)

6. A piston of a reciprocating engine moves with approximately simple harmonic motion. The crank speed is 1,440 rev/min and the crank arm is 6 in. long. If the weight of the piston is 10 lb find its maximum kinetic energy and the average force required to bring it to rest at inner and outer dead centres.

(882 ft-lb; 1,764 lb)

7. A wagon of weight 16 tons is brought to rest by two parallel spring-loaded stops. The springs are initially unloaded and each has a stiffness of 500 lb/in. If the initial speed of the wagon is 6 m.p.h. find the distance through which the springs are compressed to bring the truck to rest. What is then the maximum force in each spring ?

(2·68 ft; 16,080 lb)

8. A train of twenty loaded wagons, each of total weight 12 tons, is brought to rest by a pair of parallel buffer springs. The stiffness of each spring is 2,000 lb/ft and the initial resisting force in each spring before impact is 1,000 lb. If the train speed is 1 m.p.h. when it strikes the buffers calculate the maximum compression of the springs. *Hint*—the area under the load-compression graph is equal to the work done in compressing the spring.

(2·54 ft)

9. A spring requires a force of 20 lb, gradually applied, to compress it 1 in. Find the amount of compression when a 3-lb weight falls freely from rest on to the top of the spring through a height of 4 in. The spring is initially unloaded.

(1·26 in.)

10. A body of weight 2 lb falls 10 in. on to the top of a spring. The spring has an initial compression of 1 in. and is given a further compression of 1·2 in. by the falling weight. Find the stiffness of the spring.

(11·65 lb/in.)

11.9. Conservation of Energy

The *principle of conservation of energy* states that energy can be redistributed or changed in form but cannot be created or destroyed. The following examples will show how this occurs.

FALLING BODY   A falling body loses potential energy but gains a corresponding amount of kinetic energy.

MASS-SPRING   A mass vibrating at the end of a spring loses kinetic energy in stretching the spring but the spring then possesses potential or strain energy. When the motion is reversed and the spring is acting on the mass its strain energy is transferred to the mass as kinetic energy of motion.

"LOST" ENERGY WHEN FRICTION IS INVOLVED

A body moving along a rough surface loses kinetic energy corresponding to the work done against the friction forces. This work is generally "lost" for mechanical purposes but reappears as heat energy in the body and surface. Thus the total energy of the system, body and surface, is conserved. The work done in overstretching a spring so that it is permanently deformed is again lost for mechanical purposes and converted into heat.

COLLISION OF BODIES

When two perfectly elastic bodies collide, the work done in elastic deformation is recovered as they rebound. For example, when two steel balls bounce together there is compression of the steel on impact but as they move apart the steel recovers its shape and in doing so restores kinetic energy. *When perfectly elastic bodies collide the total kinetic energy before and after the collision is the same.* In a collision of inelastic bodies, as for example, when two balls of putty collide, all the kinetic energy may disappear to reappear as heat energy corresponding to the amount of work done in producing permanent deformation.

It is convenient to consider energy as a *capacity to do work*. A body which possesses potential, strain or kinetic energy is capable of doing work in moving some other body. Similarly work and the flow of heat may be considered as energy in transition.

So far we have considered mechanical energy and heat energy but there are other forms of energy. The operation of an engine requires the liberation of chemical energy by the burning of the fuel. Again, the electric motor requires a supply of electrical energy.

Consider the changes of energy in the operation of a petrol-engine driven car. The burning of a petrol–air mixture in the cylinder produces chemical energy which raises the temperature and pressure of the gases. The gases expand and do work in driving the piston and crankshaft. The mechanical system of the car produces the tractive effort at the road surface. The work done by the tractive effort provides—

1. The kinetic energy of motion.
2. The change in potential energy if driven up an incline.
3. The work done against the resistance to motion.

Finally it should be noted that the principle of conservation of energy is based upon observation and experiment and not upon mathematical proof.

11.10. Kinetic Energy of Rotation

Consider the work done in accelerating a shaft of moment of inertia I from rest to a speed ω while turning through an angle θ rad. The average angular acceleration α is given by

$$\omega^2 = \omega_0^2 + 2\alpha\theta$$

$$\alpha = \frac{\omega^2}{2\theta}$$

since $\omega_0 = 0$; hence the average torque required is

$$T = I\alpha$$

$$= I \times \frac{\omega^2}{2\theta}$$

The work done by the torque T in rotating the shaft through θ rad

$$= T\theta$$

$$= I\frac{\omega^2}{2\theta} \times \theta$$

$$= \tfrac{1}{2} I\omega^2$$

The term $\tfrac{1}{2} I\omega^2$ is known as the *kinetic energy of rotation*.

Similarly it may also be proved that the work done in accelerating a shaft from velocity ω_0 to velocity ω is equal to the *change* in kinetic energy of rotation, i.e.

$$T\theta = \tfrac{1}{2} I\omega^2 - \tfrac{1}{2} I\omega_0^2$$

When a friction couple is present, opposing motion, the total work required is

work done against friction + change in kinetic energy of rotation

As an aid to memorizing these formulae note the similarity between the expressions for kinetic energy of translation (linear motion) and kinetic energy of rotation—

kinetic energy of translation $= \tfrac{1}{2} Mv^2$

kinetic energy of rotation $= \tfrac{1}{2} I\omega^2$

So far we have considered only the kinetic energy of a shaft rotating about a *fixed* axis. When the axis of rotation is in motion the shaft possesses additional energy which we shall now consider.

11.11. Total Kinetic Energy of a Rolling Wheel

If a wheel rolls then the total kinetic energy is made up parts—

1. The kinetic energy of translation of the centre of mass.
2. The kinetic energy of rotation about the centre of mass.

This statement requires justification but the proof is lengthy and is omitted here. A proof may be found in *Textbook of Mechanics* by J. G. Jagger. Note that it is the motion of, and rotation about, the centre of mass which must be considered; however, in many practical cases the centre of mass coincides with the axis of rotation, as in a rolling wheel.

If v is the linear velocity of the wheel and I is the moment of inertia about its axis of rotation, then

$$\text{total kinetic energy} = \tfrac{1}{2} M v^2 + \tfrac{1}{2} I \omega^2$$

or, writing $\qquad M = \dfrac{W}{g}, \quad I = \dfrac{W}{g} k^2$

where W is the weight and k the radius of gyration of the wheel,

$$\text{total kinetic energy} = \frac{1}{2} \frac{W}{g} v^2 + \frac{1}{2} \frac{W}{g} k^2 \times \omega^2$$

and, since for rolling motion without slip $\omega = v/a$, where a is the wheel radius—

$$\text{kinetic energy of wheel} = \frac{1}{2} \frac{W}{g} v^2 + \frac{1}{2} \frac{W}{g} k^2 \frac{v^2}{a^2}$$

11.12. Function of a Flywheel

The flywheel serves to equalize the energy output of an engine during each cycle of operations and reduces the fluctuations of speed which would occur if it were not fitted. The cycle of operations in the engine cylinder is usually completed in one or two revolutions.

When the engine torque is greater than the resisting torque due to the load the engine speed increases; when the engine torque is less than the load torque the speed decreases. The flywheel acts as a reservoir of energy by virtue of its inertia. An excess of energy output is absorbed by the flywheel with only a small increase of speed; when the engine torque falls the absorbed energy is given up to the load.

For example, both the pressure on the piston of a reciprocating engine and the crank angle vary continuously during each revolution; the engine torque at the crankshaft therefore varies widely whereas the resistance due to the load may be constant. Similarly an electric motor delivering a constant torque may be used to drive a press or punch; the additional energy required momentarily during the punching operation is supplied by the flywheel.

The distinction between the functions of flywheel and governor should be noted: The flywheel determines the slight permissible variation of speed in one cycle of operations and acts as a store of energy. The governor controls the fuel supply to balance the average energy output with the load, while keeping the mean speed constant over a *period of time*.

Example. A shaft of moment of inertia 800 lb-ft² is initially running at 600 rev/min. It is brought to rest in eighteen complete revolutions by a braking torque; reversed, and accelerated in the opposite direction by a driving torque of 500 lb-ft. The friction couple is 120 lb-ft throughout. Find the braking torque required and the revolutions turned through in attaining full speed again.

Solution

$$600 \text{ rev/min} = \frac{2\pi}{60} \times 600 = 62 \cdot 83 \text{ rad/sec}$$

$$\text{initial kinetic energy} = \tfrac{1}{2} I\omega^2$$

$$= \frac{1}{2} \times \frac{800}{32 \cdot 2} \times 62 \cdot 83^2$$

$$= 49{,}000 \text{ ft-lb}$$

Work done by friction torque T_f in turning through angle θ rad is

$$T_f \times \theta = 120 \times (2\pi \times 18)$$
$$= 13{,}560 \text{ ft-lb}$$

Let T be the braking torque in pound-feet then—

$$\text{work done by braking torque} = T \times \theta$$
$$= T \times (2\pi \times 18)$$
$$= 113\ T \text{ ft-lb}$$

work done by brake + work done by friction couple = kinetic energy of rotation destroyed

$$113\ T + 13{,}560 = 49{,}000$$
thus $\qquad\qquad T = \textbf{314 lb-ft}$

If ϕ rad is the angle turned through by the shaft in accelerating from rest to full speed, then

$$\text{work done against friction} = 120\ \phi \text{ ft-lb}$$
$$\text{work done by accelerating torque} = 500\ \phi \text{ ft-lb}$$

work done by applied accelerating torque

$$= \text{work done against friction} + \text{increase of kinetic energy}$$

$$500\,\phi = 120\,\phi + 49{,}000$$
$$\phi = 129 \text{ rad}$$
$$= \mathbf{20\tfrac{1}{2} \text{ rev}}$$

Example. In an experiment to determine the moment of inertia of a flywheel and its shaft the wheel is allowed to roll on its shaft freely from rest down an incline formed by two parallel steel tracks (Fig. 11.6). The shaft rolls without slip. To allow for the work done

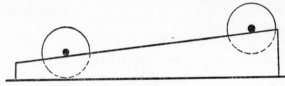

Fig. 11.6

against friction two tests are carried out, the slope of the incline being increased for the second test. The results of such an experiment were as follows: in the first test the flywheel fell through a height of 2 in. in rolling 5 ft down the incline in 50 sec; in the second test the flywheel fell 4 in. while rolling 5 ft in 30 sec. If the flywheel weighs 40 lb and the shaft diameter is 2 in. calculate the moment of inertia of the flywheel and shaft.

Solution

$$\text{Shaft radius } r = \tfrac{1}{12} \text{ ft}$$

$$\text{average speed in first test} = \tfrac{5}{50} = 0.1 \text{ ft/sec}$$

thus $\qquad\qquad$ maximum speed $v_1 = 2 \times 0.1 = 0.2$ ft/sec

and $\quad$ maximum angular velocity $\omega_1 = \dfrac{v_1}{r} = \dfrac{0.2}{1/12} = 2.4$ rad/sec

For the second test, maximum speed $v_2 = 0.333$ ft/sec and maximum angular velocity $\omega_2 = 4$ rad/sec. For each test—

loss of potential energy of wheel in rolling down incline

$$= \text{gain of kinetic energy} + \text{work done against friction}, R$$

Let I be the moment of inertia of the flywheel. Then

kinetic energy of flywheel = kinetic energy of rotation

$$+ \text{ kinetic energy of translation}$$

$$= \frac{1}{2}I\omega^2 + \frac{1}{2}\frac{40}{32\cdot2}v^2$$

For the first test—

$$\text{loss of potential energy} = 40 \times \frac{2}{12}$$

thus $\qquad 40 \times \frac{2}{12} = \frac{1}{2} I \times 2 \cdot 4^2 + \frac{1}{2} \times \frac{40}{32 \cdot 2} \times 0 \cdot 2^2 + R$

i.e. $\qquad 6 \cdot 64 = 2 \cdot 88 \, I + R$ . . . . . (11.1)

For the second test—

$$\text{loss of potential energy} = 40 \times \frac{4}{12}$$

therefore $\quad 40 \times \frac{4}{12} = \frac{1}{2} I \times 4^2 + \frac{1}{2} \times \frac{40}{32 \cdot 2} \times 0 \cdot 333^2 + R$

i.e. $\qquad 13 \cdot 3 = 8 \, I + R.$ . . . . . (11.2)

To eliminate R subtract equation (11.1) from equation (11.2)—

$$6 \cdot 66 = 5 \cdot 12 \, I$$

therefore $\qquad I = \mathbf{1 \cdot 3} \textbf{ slug-ft}^2$

Example. In an experiment to determine the radius of gyration of a flywheel the shaft is mounted in horizontal bearings and a light cord wrapped around the shaft, with the free end of the cord carrying a load of 4 lb (Fig. 11.7). When allowed to fall freely from

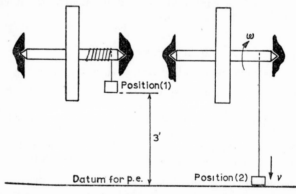

Fig. 11.7

rest the load falls 3 ft in 20 sec before striking the floor. The fly-wheel eventually comes to rest owing to bearing friction. The total number of shaft revolutions from start to finish is 30. If the shaft diameter is 1 in. and the flywheel weighs 24 lb calculate (*a*) the radius of gyration of the flywheel, (*b*) the friction torque at the bearings, assumed constant.

Solution

The motion of the flywheel is in two stages: (i) acceleration to a maximum angular velocity ω when the load reaches its maximum velocity v on striking the floor; (ii) deceleration to rest after the load strikes the floor due to the friction torque T_f at the bearings. Consider the first stage, Fig. 11.7—

> energy in position (1) = energy in position (2) + work done against friction between positions (1) and (2)

i.e.

> potential energy of load at (1) = kinetic energy of load at (2) + kinetic energy of flywheel at (2) + $T_f \times$ angle turned through by shaft

i.e.
$$4 \times 3 = \frac{1}{2} \frac{4}{32 \cdot 2} v^2 + \frac{1}{2} I \omega^2 + T_f \theta_1 \quad . \quad (11.3)$$

where $I =$ moment of inertia of flywheel and shaft;

$\theta_1 =$ angle turned through by shaft between positions (1) and (2).

thus
$$\theta_1 = \frac{\text{length of cord unwrapped}}{\text{shaft radius}}$$

$$= \frac{3}{1/24}$$

$$= 72 \text{ rad}$$

Now average velocity of falling load is
$$\tfrac{3}{20} = 0 \cdot 15 \text{ ft/sec}$$

therefore   (maximum) $v = 2 \times 0 \cdot 15 = 0 \cdot 3$ ft/sec

and
$$\omega = \frac{0 \cdot 3}{1/24} = 7 \cdot 2 \text{ rad/sec}$$

Equation (11.3) becomes

$$12 = \frac{1}{2} \frac{4}{32 \cdot 2} \times 0 \cdot 3^2 + \frac{1}{2} I \times 7 \cdot 2^2 + T_f \times 72$$

$$= 0 \cdot 0056 + 25 \cdot 9 I + 72 T_f. \quad . \quad . \quad . \quad (11.4)$$

Consider now the second stage. The kinetic energy of the flywheel, $\frac{1}{2} I \omega^2$, is destroyed by friction, thus

$$T_f \theta_2 = \tfrac{1}{2} I \omega^2$$

where $\theta_2 =$ angle turned through by the shaft in coming to rest after the load strikes the floor.

Total angle turned through by shaft = 30 rev = 188·5 rad

therefore $\theta_2 = 188·5 - 72 = 116·5$ rad

$$T_f \times 116·5 = \tfrac{1}{2} I \times 7·2^2$$

$$T_f = 0·223 \, I \text{ lb-ft}$$

Hence equation (11.4) becomes (neglecting the term 0·0056)—

$$12 = 25·9 \, I + 72 \times 0·223 \, I$$

$$I = 0·286 \text{ slug-ft}^2$$

$$\frac{W}{g} \, k^2 = 0·286$$

$$\frac{24}{32·2} \, k^2 = 0·286$$

$$k^2 = 0·384$$

$$k = \mathbf{0·62 \text{ ft}}$$

The radius of gyration of the flywheel and shaft = **0·62 ft**

$$T_f = 0·223 \, I$$
$$= 0·223 \times 0·286$$
$$= \mathbf{0·064 \text{ lb-ft}}$$

Example. A road roller has a *total* weight of 12 tons. The front roller has a weight of 2 tons, a radius of gyration of $1\tfrac{1}{2}$ ft and a diameter of 4 ft. The rear axle, together with its wheels, weighs $2\tfrac{1}{2}$ tons; it has a radius of gyration of 2 ft and a diameter of 5 ft. Calculate: (a) the kinetic energy of rotation of the wheels and axles at a speed of 8 m.p.h.; (b) the total kinetic energy of the road roller; (c) the braking force required to bring the roller to rest from 8 m.p.h. in 20 ft. on the level.

Solution

(a) The speed of the roller is 8 m.p.h., i.e. 11·74 ft/sec. The angular velocity of the front roller is

$$\omega = \frac{v}{a} = \frac{11·74}{2} = 5·87 \text{ rad/sec}$$

kinetic energy of front roller $= \dfrac{1}{2} \dfrac{W}{g} \, k^2 \omega^2$

$$= \frac{1}{2} \times \frac{2 \times 2,240}{32·2} \times 1·5^2 \times 5·87^2$$

$$= 5,400 \text{ ft-lb}$$

Angular velocity of rear wheels $= \dfrac{11 \cdot 74}{2 \cdot 5} = 4 \cdot 69$ rad/sec

$$\text{kinetic energy} = \frac{1}{2} \times \frac{2 \cdot 5 \times 2{,}240}{32 \cdot 2} \times 2^2 \times 4 \cdot 69^2$$

$$= 7{,}650 \text{ ft-lb}$$

Total kinetic energy of rotation of wheels $= 5{,}400 + 7{,}650$
$$= \mathbf{13{,}050 \text{ ft-lb}}$$

(b) Total kinetic energy of linear motion of road roller

$$= \frac{1}{2} \frac{W}{g} v^2$$

$$= \frac{1}{2} \times \frac{12 \times 2{,}240}{32 \cdot 2} \times 11 \cdot 74^2$$

$$= 57{,}600 \text{ ft-lb}$$

This includes the kinetic energy of translation of the wheels, since the *total* weight has been considered.

Total kinetic energy of road roller $=$ kinetic energy of translation
$$\qquad\qquad\qquad + \text{ kinetic energy of rotation}$$
$$= 57{,}600 + 13{,}050$$
$$= \mathbf{70{,}650 \text{ ft-lb}}$$

(c) Let E lb be the braking effort, then—

work done by braking effort $=$ change in kinetic energy

i.e. $\qquad\qquad\qquad E \times 20 = 70{,}650$

thus $\qquad\qquad\qquad E = \mathbf{3{,}530 \text{ lb}}$

Example. A car of chassis weight 3,000 lb is accelerated from rest to a speed of 30 m.p.h. in a distance of 400 ft up an incline of 1 in 12. The car has two axles each of which, together with the wheels, weighs 300 lb, has a radius of gyration of $1\frac{1}{4}$ ft and a tread diameter of 3 ft. The resistance to motion is 80 lb. Calculate the average tractive effort required.

Solution

Total weight of car $= 3{,}000 + 2 \times 300 = 3{,}600$ lb

increase in potential energy of car $=$ weight $\times$ change in height

$$= 3{,}600 \times \frac{400}{12}$$

$$= 120{,}000 \text{ ft-lb}$$

30 m.p.h. is equal to 44 ft/sec, hence

$$\text{kinetic energy of translation} = \frac{1}{2} \frac{W}{g} v^2$$

$$= \frac{1}{2} \times \frac{3,600}{32 \cdot 2} \times 44^2$$

$$= 108,250 \text{ ft-lb}$$

This includes the kinetic energy of translation of the wheels. Angular velocity of wheels is

$$\omega = \frac{v}{a} = \frac{44}{1 \cdot 5} = 29 \cdot 33 \text{ rad/sec}$$

Total weight of wheels equals 2×300 lb, hence

$$\text{kinetic energy of rotation} = \frac{1}{2} \frac{W}{g} k^2 \omega^2$$

$$= \frac{1}{2} \times \frac{600}{32 \cdot 2} \times 1 \cdot 25^2 \times 29 \cdot 33^2$$

$$= 12,500 \text{ ft-lb}$$

$$\text{Total kinetic energy of car at 30 m.p.h.} = 108,250 + 12,500$$
$$= 120,750 \text{ ft-lb}$$

This is also the change in kinetic energy in accelerating from rest. Work done against tractive resistance in travelling 400 ft is

$$80 \times 400 = 32,000 \text{ ft-lb}$$

Work done by tractive effort E = increase in potential energy + increase in kinetic energy + work done against resistance

thus

$$E \times 400 = 120,000 + 120,750 + 32,000$$

i.e.

$$E = \mathbf{682 \ lb}$$

PROBLEMS

1. A rotating shaft carries a load having a moment of inertia about the shaft axis of 1,200 lb-ft². Calculate, using an energy method, the torque required to accelerate the shaft from rest to a speed of 600 rev/min in 12 rev. The bearing friction is equivalent to a couple of 200 lb-ft.

(1,175 lb-ft)

2. A shaft rotating at 720 rev/min has a moment of inertia of 800 lb-ft². It is brought to rest by a brake block acting on the rim of a 3 ft diameter drum. Calculate the normal force on the brake block to bring the shaft to rest in 12 revolutions of the shaft if the coefficient of friction between block and drum is 0·45.

(1,390 lb)

3. A shaft having a moment of inertia of 12 slug-ft² is accelerated from 1,440 rev/min to 1,500 rev/min during two revolutions of the shaft. If the friction couple is 60 lb-ft calculate (a) the change in kinetic energy of rotation of the shaft, (b) the average torque required to accelerate the shaft.

(11,650 ft-lb, 985 lb-ft)

4. A flywheel having a weight of 50 lb is mounted on a 3 in. diameter shaft in horizontal bearings. Around the shaft is wrapped a light cord to which is attached a hanging load of weight 4 lb. If allowed to fall from rest and accelerate the flywheel the load is seen to fall 4 ft in 24 sec. Calculate by an energy method the radius of gyration of the flywheel. The effect of bearing friction may be neglected.

(3·4 ft)

5. A 6 in. diameter bar rolls freely down a slope of 1 in 50. What will be its speed after rolling 30 ft from rest down the incline? What is then its total kinetic energy? The bar weighs 60 lb.

(5·07 ft/sec; 36 ft-lb)

6. In an experiment to determine the moment of inertia of a flywheel, its shaft is mounted in horizontal bearings and a load of 20 lb is hung from a light cord attached to, and wrapped around, the shaft. It is found that when allowed to fall from rest the load travels downwards 3 ft in 15 sec. At the end of this period the falling load is arrested and ceases to accelerate the flywheel, which then turns through a further sixteen complete revolutions before coming to rest owing to bearing friction. The shaft diameter is 3 in. Find, by an energy method: (a) the moment of inertia of the flywheel; (b) the friction couple at the bearings.

(357 lb-ft²; 0·57 lb-ft)

7. A flywheel is mounted on a 2 in. diameter shaft. In order to determine its radius of gyration it is allowed to roll freely from rest down an incline formed by a pair of knife-edges on which the shaft may run. When one end of the track is raised 3 in. above the other the flywheel takes 30 sec to travel 5 ft from rest. When the raised end is 6 in. above the other end, it takes 20 sec to travel the same distance down the incline. If the work done against frictional resistance is the same in both tests find, by an energy method, the radius of gyration of the flywheel.

(0·895 ft)

8. A four-wheeled car has a total weight of 3,000 lb. Each axle, with its wheels, weighs 150 lb and has a radius of gyration of 1·3 ft. The wheel tread diameter is 3 ft. Calculate: (a) the total kinetic energy of the car (ft-lb) at 45 m.p.h.; (b) the average braking force required to stop it in 200 ft on a level road. The resistance to motion may be neglected.

(217,900 ft-lb; 1,090 lb)

9. A loaded truck has a total weight of 12 tons. Each of its axles weighs 1 ton, including the wheels, and the radius of gyration is 1·5 ft. The wheel tread diameter is 4 ft. The truck is accelerated from rest up an incline of 1 in 30 to a speed of 15 m.p.h. Find: (a) the final kinetic energy of the truck; (b) the distance travelled from rest up the incline due to an average tractive effort of 12,000 lb; the resistance to motion is 200 lb.

(220,800 ft-lb; 20·2 ft)

10. A wagon is shunted over the hump at a marshalling yard and has a speed of 3 ft/sec at the top of the hump when uncoupled from the train. It then runs 300 ft down an incline of 1 in 20. The total rolling resistance to motion is 300 lb and the wagon weighs 20 tons. The wagon has two axles,

each of which, with its wheels, weighs 2 tons. The radius of gyration is 2 ft and the wheel diameter is 4 ft 6 in. Find: (a) the speed at the end of the incline; (b) the energy which must be absorbed by a retarding brake at the rails in order to reduce the speed to 5 ft/sec at the end of the incline.

(27·15 ft/sec; 569,000 ft-lb)

11. A train of coal wagons weighs 60 tons fully loaded. It is hauled up an incline of 1 in 200 by a cable wrapped around a hoist drum at the top of the incline. The drum weighs 1 ton, has a radius of gyration of 4 ft and an effective diameter of 10 ft. The rolling resistance to motion of the wagons is 30 lb/ton. The bearing friction at the hoist drum may be neglected. Find: (a) the kinetic energy of the hoist drum when the wagons are hauled at 15 m.p.h. up the incline; (b) the total work done in accelerating the train from rest up the incline to a speed of 15 m.p.h. over a distance of 600 ft; (c) the average horse-power exerted if the hauling takes 2 min.

(10,800 ft-lb; 1,120 ft-tons; 38 h.p.)

12

Impulse and Momentum

12.1. Linear Momentum

CONSIDER a body of mass M acted upon by an average force P for a time t. The average acceleration f is given by—

$$f = \frac{v - u}{t}$$

where u and v are the initial and final velocities, respectively. Therefore

$$P = Mf$$
$$= M \times \frac{v - u}{t}$$

We now define the *impulse* of the force P to be the product—

average force × time

Thus

$$\text{impulse} = P \times t$$
$$= M \times \frac{v - u}{t} \times t$$
$$= M(v - u)$$

i.e.

$$Pt = Mv - Mu . \qquad . \qquad . \qquad . \quad (12.1)$$

The product

mass × velocity

is a measure of the "quantity of motion," called the *momentum* of the body. The first term Mv on the right-hand side of equation (12.1) is the final momentum of the body at the end of time t; the second term Mu is the initial momentum; the difference is the change of momentum. Thus the impulse Pt may be measured by the change in momentum it produces, i.e.

impulse = change of momentum

The following points should be noted—

1. The mass M is assumed unaltered in any way (i.e. no part falls away or is added to the body).

2. The symbols u and v refer to velocities, not speeds; hence direction must be taken into account and momentum treated as a *vector quantity*, having direction and sense corresponding to that of the velocity.

3. The force P is an average force (or may be uniform) and hence we may conclude that the change of momentum, or impulse $(Mv - Mu)$, does not depend on how the force P may vary during time t.

4. When no external impulse is applied the momentum remains unchanged.

The idea of momentum is useful in solving two particular types of problems—

(*a*) when the force P is not known or easily calculable, e.g. in an impact or sudden blow;

(*b*) Where the impulsive force P is so large that the body to which it is applied suffers permanent deformation, and is no longer elastic.

In the latter case the reader will appreciate that energy is "lost" (i.e. converted into heat, etc.) in producing this deformation, as in striking a ball of putty for example. Hence, since it is not usually possible to calculate the magnitude of this energy loss, the law of conservation of energy cannot be used directly. The law applies of course but we may have insufficient information to calculate all the quantities involved.

Finally, it should be noted that a change of momentum may be produced by a change of velocity (i.e. by a change of speed or a vector change of velocity) or by a change of mass. We shall consider only problems involving a change of velocity.

12.2. Units of Impulse and Momentum

Since

$$\text{momentum} = Mv$$

and

$$M = \frac{W}{g} \text{ slug, or lb-sec}^2/\text{ft}$$

then

$$\text{momentum} = \frac{W}{g} v$$

which has units—

$$= \frac{\text{lb-sec}^2}{\text{ft}} \times \frac{\text{ft}}{\text{sec}}$$

$$= \text{lb-sec}$$

Hence, if the mass is measured in slugs, momentum has the same units as impulse Pt, i.e. pounds $\times$ seconds (lb-sec).

12.3. Conservation of Linear Momentum

If there is no *external* impulse applied to a body, or a system of bodies, then the total linear momentum of the body or system remains constant in both magnitude and direction. This is known as the *principle of conservation of momentum*. This principle holds only—

1. If there is no external impulse, i.e. no external force.
2. If the total mass remains unaltered.

12.4. Application to Collision of Two Bodies

A body A, of mass M_1, moving with velocity u_1 collides with a second body B, of mass M_2, moving along the same straight line with velocity u_2, Fig. 12.1. During the collision there is an impulse Pt exerted by one body on the other. If the time t of the impact is very short, and hence the impulsive force very large, then the

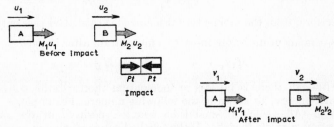

FIG. 12.1

change of momentum due to all other forces external to the two-body system (e.g. gravity, etc.) may be neglected. *Hence, the total momentum of the system remains constant during the impact and is therefore the same after the collision as before it.* This statement may be proved as follows.

Let v_1, v_2, be the velocities of A and B, respectively, after the impact. Then, the impulse on body B is measured by the change of momentum of the body, i.e.

$$\text{impulse on B} = \text{change of momentum of B}$$
$$= \text{momentum after impact}$$
$$\quad - \text{momentum before impact}$$

thus $\qquad Pt = M_2v_2 - M_2u_2$ . . . . (12.2)

(momentum has been taken positive from left to right).

For body A, the change of momentum is $(M_1v_1 - M_1u_1)$, but in this case the impulse Pt is from right to left, hence

$$- Pt = M_1v_1 - M_1u_1$$

or $\qquad Pt = - (M_1v_1 - M_1u_1)$ . . (12.3)

Now the impulses Pt are of equal magnitude, since each force P is the same magnitude and acts for the same time t, thus

$$Pt = -(M_1v_1 - M_1u_1) = (M_2v_2 - M_2u_2)$$

or, rearranging

$$M_1u_1 + M_2u_2 = M_1v_1 + M_2v_2 \qquad . \qquad . \ (12.4)$$

Therefore the total momentum of the system of two bodies taken together is unaltered, although each body separately suffers a change of momentum of equal magnitude but opposite sense.

The momentum principle gives us one equation to find two unknown quantities—the two final velocities. One other equation is required and to obtain it we must know: (a) either v_1 or v_2; or (b) that there is no rebound and the two bodies travel on coupled together with a common velocity v, i.e.

$$v_1 = v_2 = v$$

Therefore, from the momentum principle, for this latter case only—

momentum before impact = momentum after impact

i.e. $\qquad\qquad M_1u_1 + M_2u_2 = (M_1 + M_2)v$

Although there is no loss of momentum there is still a loss of kinetic energy, as shown in the following numerical example.

Note—All velocities should be counted positive in the same direction, e.g. left to right. If the two bodies are moving in opposite directions then one velocity will be negative.

Example. A body of weight 1 lb has a velocity of 4 ft/sec from left to right, and a body of weight 2 lb has a velocity of 3 ft/sec from right to left along the same straight line, Fig. 12.2. If the

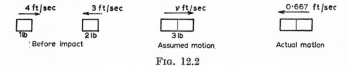

Fig. 12.2

bodies move off together after impact find their common velocity and the loss of kinetic energy due to impact.

Solution

Let v be the common velocity, then

momentum before impact = momentum after impact

$$1 \times 4 - 2 \times 3 = (1 + 2)v$$

hence $\qquad\qquad\qquad v = -\mathbf{0 \cdot 667} \ \text{ft/sec}$

The negative answer implies that the two bodies travel on together from right to left. Note—

1. In the momentum equation there is no need to convert pounds-wt to pounds-mass since the same quantities occur on both sides of the equation. Similarly velocities may be written in miles per hour.

2. We assumed in writing the equation that the velocity of 4 ft/sec from left to right was positive. The velocity of 3 ft/sec was therefore negative. Hence the total momentum before impact was, therefore, the difference of the momenta of the two bodies.

$$\text{Kinetic energy before impact} = \tfrac{1}{2} M_1 u_1{}^2 + \tfrac{1}{2} M_2 u_2{}^2$$

$$= \frac{1}{2} \times \frac{1}{32 \cdot 2} \times 4^2 + \frac{1}{2} \times \frac{2}{32 \cdot 2} \times 3^2$$

$$= 0 \cdot 528 \text{ ft-lb}$$

$$\text{Kinetic energy after impact} = \tfrac{1}{2} (M_1 + M_2) v^2$$

$$= \frac{1}{2} \times \frac{3}{32 \cdot 2} \times 0 \cdot 667^2$$

$$= 0 \cdot 021 \text{ ft-lb}$$

$$\text{loss of kinetic energy} = 0 \cdot 528 - 0 \cdot 021$$

$$= \mathbf{0 \cdot 507 \text{ ft-lb}}$$

Example. A wagon weighing 100 tons, moving at 4 m.p.h., collides with the back of a wagon, of weight 40 tons, moving in the same direction at 1 m.p.h. What is the velocity of the 100-ton wagon after the impact and the impulse between them if the 40-ton wagon moves off at 5 m.p.h. after the impact?

Solution

Equating momenta—

$$M_1 u_1 + M_2 u_2 = M_1 v_1 + M_2 v_2$$

$$100 \times 4 + 40 \times 1 = 100 \times v_1 + 40 \times 5$$

$$v_1 = \mathbf{2 \cdot 4 \text{ m.p.h.}}$$

The impulse on each wagon is equal to the change in its momentum. Therefore, for the 100-ton wagon—

$$\text{impulse} = M_1 u_1 - M_1 v_1$$

$$= \frac{100}{32 \cdot 2} (4 - 2 \cdot 4) \times \frac{88}{60}$$

$$= \mathbf{7 \cdot 3 \text{ ton-sec}}$$

or for the 40-ton wagon—

$$\text{impulse} = \frac{40}{32 \cdot 2} (1 - 5) \times \frac{88}{60} = \mathbf{- 7 \cdot 3 \text{ ton-sec}}$$

Note—In calculating the impulse it is necessary to convert tons-wt to ton-slugs and miles per hour to feet per second.

Example. A pile-driving hammer weighing $\frac{1}{2}$ ton falls 8 ft from rest on to a pile weighing 320 lb. There is no rebound and the pile is driven 6 in. into the ground. Calculate (*a*) the common velocity after impact, (*b*) the average resisting force of the ground in bringing the pile and driver to rest.

Solution

The velocity with which the hammer strikes the pile, after falling freely from rest, is found by equating the kinetic energy just before

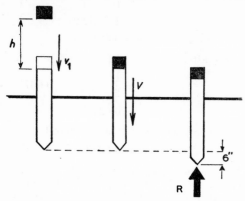

Fɪɢ. 12.3

impact to the initial potential energy of the hammer measured above the point of impact, Fig. 12.3.

Kinetic energy before impact = potential energy above pile

$$\frac{1}{2}\frac{W}{g}v_1{}^2 = Wh$$

thus

$$v_1 = \sqrt{(2gh)}$$

$$= \sqrt{(2 \times 32 \cdot 2 \times 8)}$$

$$= 22 \cdot 65 \text{ ft/sec}$$

During impact it is assumed that the impact force between pile and driver is very much greater than the resisting force offered by the ground and the effect of gravity. The latter forces may therefore be neglected *during* impact. There is therefore no appreciable external force acting on the pile and driver. Hence

momentum of pile and driver = momentum of driver before
    after impact   impact

Let v be the common velocity of pile and driver after impact, then

$$(1,120 + 320)v = 1,120 \times 22 \cdot 65$$

therefore $\qquad v = \mathbf{17 \cdot 62 \ ft/sec}$

Kinetic energy of system after impact $= \dfrac{1}{2} \dfrac{W}{g} v^2$

$$= \tfrac{1}{2}(1,120 + 320) \times \frac{(17 \cdot 62)^2}{32 \cdot 2}$$

$$= 6,940 \ \text{ft-lb}$$

loss of potential energy in descending a further 6 in.—

$$= (1,120 + 320) \times \tfrac{6}{12} = 720 \ \text{ft-lb}$$

therefore

work done by hammer and pile = kinetic energy lost +
$$\text{loss of potential energy}$$

$$= 6,940 + 720$$

$$= 7,660 \ \text{ft-lb}$$

But the work done against the resisting force R lb is $R \times \tfrac{6}{12}$ ft-lb.
Hence

$$R \times \tfrac{6}{12} = 7,660$$

$$R = \mathbf{15,300 \ lb}$$

PROBLEMS

1. Two similar vehicles, travelling at 30 m.p.h. in opposite directions, collide with one another. What would be their velocities after impact (a) in a perfectly elastic collision, (b) in a completely inelastic collision? Show that in case (b) both the impulse and the total kinetic energy loss are each one-half of that which occurs when a similar vehicle collides inelastically with a wall at 60 m.p.h.

(30 m.p.h.; zero)

2. A hammer weighing 4 tons, and moving at 20 ft/sec, strikes a body at rest. If the stationary body weighs 12 tons, and both hammer and body move on freely together after the impact, find the loss of kinetic energy due to the impact.

(18·6 ft-tons)

3. A wagon, of weight 20 tons, moving along a track at 12 m.p.h. collides with a second wagon, of weight 10 tons, moving at 7 m.p.h.; both wagons are moving in the same direction. Immediately after the collision the 10-ton wagon moves on at 11 m.p.h. Calculate the velocity of the 20-ton wagon after impact and the impulse between the wagons.

(10 m.p.h.; 1·82 ton-sec)

4. A rail wagon, of weight 20 tons, starts from rest down an incline of 1 in 24 in a marshalling yard. The resistance to rolling motion is 16 lb/ton. Half-way down the incline, which is 600 ft long, the wagon collides with a similar wagon at rest. Find (a) the velocity of the first wagon just before impact,

(b) the velocity of the two wagons immediately after impact if they travel on coupled together, (c) their common velocity at the end of the incline.

$$(25\cdot7 \text{ ft/sec}; \ 12\cdot85 \text{ ft/sec}; \ 28\cdot8 \text{ ft/sec})$$

5. A package weighing 60 lb slides 30 ft down a shute of gradient 1 in 6. At the bottom it collides with a stationary package of weight 100 lb. Both parcels then travel on together on a horizontal surface. If the coefficient of friction between each package and the shute is 0·05, on both the gradient and the level, find (a) the common velocity immediately after impact, (b) the distance travelled on the level before they both come to rest.

$$(5\cdot66 \text{ ft/sec}; \ 9\cdot95 \text{ ft})$$

6. A pile is driven into the ground by a hammer of weight 900 lb, dropped from a height of $12\frac{1}{4}$ ft. The pile weighs 100 lb and the average resistance of the ground to penetration is 10,000 lb. Find the common velocity of pile and hammer after impact and the distance through which the pile is driven into the ground.

$$(25\cdot2 \text{ ft/sec}; \ 13\cdot15 \text{ in.})$$

7. A steam hammer, of weight 8 tons, moves vertically downwards from rest through a distance of 6 ft on to a pile weighing 1 ton. The hammer falls under the influence of its own weight and a force due to steam pressure of 12 tons. What is the velocity of striking?

If the steam pressure is cut off at impact, and there is no rebound of the hammer, find the common velocity of hammer and pile immediately after impact. What is the average resistance to penetration if the pile is driven 18 in. at each blow?

$$(31\cdot05 \text{ ft/sec}; \ 27\cdot6 \text{ ft/sec}; \ 80 \text{ tons})$$

8. A weight is dropped from a height of 4 ft on to a stake and drives it into the ground. When the falling weight is three times as great as that of the pile to be driven it is found that it takes five impacts to drive the pile 10 in. Calculate the number of impacts required to drive the pile the same distance when the falling weight is five times as great as the pile, and the height through which it falls remains the same.

$$(\text{three}; \ 3\cdot8 \text{ in. per impact})$$

12.5. Thrust of a Jet

The thrust of a jet depends on the rate of change of momentum given to the jet fluid. Let v_1 be the jet fluid velocity relative to the engine at entry (Fig. 12.4) and v_2 the velocity of the jet relative to the engine at exit. Then

$$\text{initial momentum of } W \text{ lb of fluid} = \frac{W}{g} v_1$$

$$\text{final momentum} = \frac{W}{g} v_2$$

$$\text{change in momentum} = \frac{W}{g} v_2 - \frac{W}{g} v_1$$

$$= \frac{W}{g} (v_2 - v_1)$$

If W is the weight of fluid passing through the engine per second, the force exerted on the jet of fluid equals change of momentum per second, i.e.

$$\text{force} = \frac{W}{g}\,(v_2 - v_1)$$

Since the force exerted on the engine is equal and opposite to the force on the jet, this expression gives the total thrust exerted by the engine, i.e.

engine thrust

$$= \frac{\text{(weight of fluid flow/sec)} \times \text{(change in velocity in passing through the engine)}}{g}$$

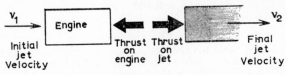

Fig. 12.4

Since we are concerned only with the change in fluid velocity, v_1 and v_2 may be either *both* relative to the engine or *both* relative to the ground. If v is the velocity of the engine in ft/sec, then the horse-power developed at the jet is—

$$\text{h.p.} = \frac{\text{thrust} \times v}{550}$$

Example. The engine of a missile ejects 200 lb of exhaust gases per second at a speed of 2,000 ft/sec relative to the engine. Calculate the thrust of the engine at a forward speed of 600 ft/sec: (a) when the missile is rocket propelled; (b) when jet propelled.

What is the horse-power developed when jet-propelled?

Solution

(a) The rocket-driven missile carries the fuel and oxygen with it so that the initial speed of the propellant relative to the rocket is zero. The final velocity is 2,000 ft/sec relative to the rocket and this is also the *change* in the velocity, i.e.

$$\text{thrust} = \text{change of momentum per second}$$

$$= \frac{200}{32\cdot2} \times 2,000$$

$$= \textbf{12,420 lb}$$

(b) The air input to a jet engine is initially at rest. The velocity of the air relative to the engine is therefore 600 ft/sec. The final relative velocity is 2,000 ft/sec and the change in relative velocity = 2,000 − 600 = 1,400 ft/sec. Therefore

$$\text{thrust} = \frac{200}{32\cdot2} \times 1,400$$

$$= \textbf{8,700 lb}$$

$$\text{h.p.} = \frac{\text{thrust} \times \text{velocity}}{550}$$

$$= \frac{8,700 \times 600}{550}$$

$$= \textbf{9,480}$$

PROBLEMS

1. An aircraft draws 100 lb of air per second into its engine and ejects it at a speed of 1,200 ft/sec relative to the engine. Find the thrust exerted by the jet, (a) when stationary, (b) at a forward speed of 500 m.p.h.

(3,730 lb; 1,450 lb)

2. A rocket ejects 40 lb of exhaust gases per second at a speed of 2,000 ft/sec relative to the rocket. Find the propulsive force.

At a given instant the weight of the rocket is 1,230 lb and it is moving vertically upwards. What is its acceleration?

(2,484 lb; 32·8 ft/sec²)

3. A jet plane discharges a jet at the rate of 60 lb/sec with a velocity of 3,000 ft/sec relative to the plane. If the forward speed of the plane is 600 m.p.h. what is the thrust on the plane and the horse-power developed at the jet?

(3,950 lb; 6,320 h.p.)

12.6. Angular Momentum and Impulse

Consider a shaft rotating with initial angular velocity ω_0, and acted upon by a torque T for time t, and let the final velocity be ω. Then the average angular acceleration α is given by—

$$\alpha = \frac{\omega - \omega_0}{t}$$

and if the shaft has moment of inertia I

$$T = I\alpha$$

$$= I\,\frac{\omega - \omega_0}{t}$$

We define the *angular impulse* by the product—

torque × time

i.e.   impulse $= T \times t$

$$= I\frac{\omega - \omega_0}{t} \times t$$

$$= I(\omega - \omega_0)$$

$$= I\omega - I\omega_0$$

The product $I\omega$ is called the *angular momentum* of the rotating body; the angular impulse is therefore measured by the change in angular momentum it produces; thus

angular impulse = change of angular momentum

The idea of angular momentum plays a similar part in considerations of changes of angular motion as does change of linear momentum in linear motion. In particular: (*a*) if there is no torque acting there is no change in angular momentum; (*b*) if two shafts are engaged by a clutch, and no external torques are brought into play (by reactions at the bearings for example), the total angular momentum of the system will remain unaltered, although kinetic energy may be lost in heat during slipping of the clutch.

Example. Two masses, each of weight 4 lb, rotate at a radius of 3 ft attached at opposite ends of a light arm, Fig. 12.5. The initial

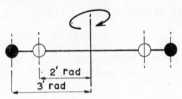

FIG. 12.5

speed of rotation is 400 rev/min. If the two masses are moved inwards along the arm to a radius of 2 ft find (*a*) the final speed of rotation, (*b*) the change in kinetic energy of rotation.

Solution

(*a*) Since there is no external torque acting on the shaft carrying the rotating masses the angular momentum remains unchanged by the change in radius of rotation. Let the final speed of rotation be N rev/min, then

final angular momentum = initial angular momentum

or $I_2 \times N = I_1 \times 400$

where I_1 and I_2 are the initial and final moments of inertia, respectively. (*Note*—It is unnecessary to convert the speeds of rotation to radians per second since the conversion factor is common to both sides of the equation and would cancel.)

Assuming each mass to be concentrated at its respective radius of rotation

$$I_1 = 2 \times 4 \times 3^2 \text{ lb-ft}^2$$

$$I_2 = 2 \times 4 \times 2^2 \text{ lb-ft}^2, \text{ for two masses}$$

Hence

$$(2 \times 4 \times 2^2) \times N = (2 \times 4 \times 3^2) \times 400$$

thus

$$N = \textbf{900 rev/min}$$

(b) Initial kinetic energy $= \dfrac{1}{2} \dfrac{W}{g} k^2 \omega^2$

$$= \frac{1}{2} \times \frac{8}{32 \cdot 2} \, 3^2 \times \left(\frac{2\pi}{60} \times 400\right)^2$$

$$= 1{,}962 \text{ ft-lb}$$

final kinetic energy $= \dfrac{1}{2} \times \dfrac{8}{32 \cdot 2} \times 2^2 \times \left(\dfrac{2\pi}{60} \times 900\right)^2$

$$= 4{,}415 \text{ ft-lb}$$

change in kinetic energy $= 4{,}415 - 1{,}962$

$$= \textbf{2,453 ft-lb}$$

This is a *gain* in kinetic energy and arises from the work done in moving the masses inwards against the radial inertia force due to rotation.

Example. A shaft has a moment of inertia of 5 slug-ft^2 and rotates clockwise at 100 rad/sec (Fig. 12.6). It is engaged, by a clutch, with

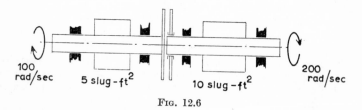

100 rad/sec   5 slug-ft^2 10 slug-ft^2 200 rad/sec

Fig. 12.6

a shaft rotating at 200 rad/sec anticlockwise about the same axis. The latter shaft has a moment of inertia of 10 slug-ft^2. After clutch slip has ceased they both rotate together with common angular velocity ω. Calculate ω.

Solution

$$\text{Initial angular momentum} = 5 \times 100 + 10 \times (-200)$$
$$= 500 - 2,000$$
$$= -1,500$$

Note that account must be taken of the sense of rotation. If the final angular velocity is ω rad/sec clockwise the final angular momentum is

$$I\omega = (5 + 10) \times \omega$$
$$= 15\,\omega$$

Since no external torque acts—

$$\text{final angular momentum} = \text{initial angular momentum}$$

thus
$$15\,\omega = -1,500$$

i.e.
$$\omega = -\mathbf{100\ rad/sec}$$

The negative sign indicates that the final common angular velocity is *anticlockwise*. If there is an external driving or friction torque acting on the shafts this is often assumed negligible compared with the impulsive torque and therefore neglected during the slipping of the clutch.

Example. A shaft carrying a load of moment of inertia 200 lb-ft² revolves at a speed of 600 rev/min and is engaged by means of a disk clutch with a shaft on the same axis having a moment of inertia of 300 lb-ft². If the second shaft is initially at rest, find: (a) the final speed of rotation of the two shafts together after slipping has ceased; (b) the time of slip if the torque is constant at 150 lb-ft during slipping.

Solution

(a) Equating the final momentum at a speed of N rev/min to the total initial momentum—

$$(200 + 300) \times N = (200 \times 600) + 0$$

The conversion factors are the same on both sides of the equations and therefore cancel. Thus

$$N = \frac{2}{5} \times 600$$
$$= \mathbf{240\ rev/min}$$

(b) For the second shaft alone, the impulse of the torque T for time t is equal to the change of angular momentum, thus since

$$\omega = 240 \times \frac{2\pi}{60} = 8\pi \text{ rad/sec}$$

then $T \times t = I\omega - 0$

or $150\, t = \dfrac{300}{32 \cdot 2} \times 8\pi$

therefore $t = 1 \cdot 56$ sec

(Note that I in lb-ft^2 units must be divided by 32·2.)

PROBLEMS

1. A light bar rotates about a perpendicular axis through its centre. Attached to each arm of the rotating bar are two similar movable weights. The plane of rotation is horizontal. If, when the weights each rotate at a radius of 3 ft, the speed of rotation is 360 rev/min, what will be their speed at a radius of 4 ft when moved radially outwards during free rotation.

If each weight weighs 3 lb what is the loss of energy due to the change in radius?

(202·5 rev/min; 520 ft-lb)

2. A scheme proposed to conserve fuel in running a vehicle consists of a flywheel connected to the engine in such a way that energy gained when running downhill may be stored and utilized when running uphill or accelerating. If the flywheel weighs 200 lb, has a radius of gyration of 1·2 ft and has a maximum speed of 30,000 rev/min calculate the corresponding angular momentum and kinetic energy of rotation.

(28,070 lb-sec; 44,000,000 ft-lb)

❸ A rotating table has a moment of inertia about a vertical axis through its centroid of 200 lb-ft^2 and turns at 360 rev/min. A servo piston of weight 3 lb rotates with the table at an initial radius of 4 ft. It then moves towards the centre of rotation a distance of 2 ft in such a way that no external torque acts on the system. Assuming the piston to be a concentrated mass determine the final speed of free rotation of the table.

(421 rev/min)

4. Two shafts, turning about the same axis of rotation, rotate at 1,200 rev/min clockwise and 720 rev/min anticlockwise, respectively. If they are then connected by a clutch find the final speed of rotation: (a) if they have the same moment of inertia about the axis of rotation; (b) if the faster shaft has one-half the moment of inertia of the slower.

(240 rev/min clockwise; − 80 rev/min anticlockwise)

5. The rotating parts of an electric motor have a moment of inertia of 300 lb-ft^2. When running at 1,200 rev/min it is connected by means of a disk clutch to another shaft at rest, which has a moment of inertia of 600 lb-ft^2. Find the common speed of rotation immediately after slip has ceased. Assume the motor torque negligible compared with the impulsive torque.

If the electric motor exerts a constant torque of 120 lb-ft find the time taken for the two shafts together to regain the initial speed of 1,200 rev/min.

(400 rev/min; 19·5 sec)

6. A shaft which, with its load, weighs 600 lb and has a radius of gyration of 2 ft, is running freely at 720 rev/min. It is then connected by a clutch to a shaft at rest which has a moment of inertia of 1,000 lb-ft^2. Find: (a) the final speed of rotation of the two shafts together after slipping has ceased; (b) the loss of energy due to the engagement.

(508 rev/min; 62,500 ft-lb)

Direct Stress and Strain

13.1. Stress

THE ability of a structural member to withstand load or transmit
force, as in a machine, depends upon its dimensions. In particular,
the cross-sectional area over which the load is distributed determines the *intensity of loading* or *average stress* in the member. If
the intensity of loading is uniform the *direct stress, f,* is defined as

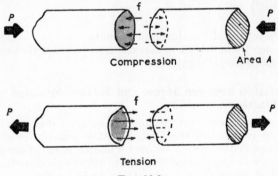

Compression   Area *A*

Tension

FIG. 13.1

the ratio of load, *P*, to cross-sectional area, *A*, *normal to the load,*
Fig. 13.1. Thus

$$stress = \frac{load}{area}$$

or

$$f = \frac{P}{A}$$

If the load is in pounds and the area in square inches the units of
stress are pounds per square inch (lb/in.²).

The direct stress may be *tensile* or *compressive* according as the load is a pull (tension), or a push (compression). It is often convenient to consider tensile stresses and loads as positive and compressive stresses and loads as negative.

13.2. Strain

A member under any loading experiences a change in shape or size. In the case of a bar loaded in tension the extension of the bar depends upon its total length. The bar is said to be strained and the *strain* is defined as the extension per unit of original length of the bar. Strain may be produced in two ways—

1. By application of a load.
2. By a change in temperature, unaccompanied by load or stress.

If l is the original length of bar, x the extension or contraction in length under load or temperature change, and e the strain, then

$$strain = \frac{change\ in\ length}{original\ length}$$

or
$$e = \frac{x}{l}$$

Strain is a ratio and has therefore no units.

Strain due to an extension is considered positive, that associated with a contraction is negative.

13.3. Relation between Stress and Strain: Modulus of Elasticity

If the extension or compression in a member due to a load disappears on removal of the load, then the material is said to be *elastic*. Most metals are elastic over a limited range of stress known as the *elastic range*. Elastic materials, with some exceptions, obey Hooke's law, which states that: *the strain is directly proportional to the applied stress*. Thus

$$\frac{stress}{strain} = constant,\ E$$

i.e.
$$\frac{f}{e} = E \quad \text{or} \quad e = \frac{f}{E}$$

where E is the constant of proportionality, known as the *modulus of elasticity* or *Young's modulus*.

Since strain is a ratio, the units of E are those of stress, i.e. pounds per square inch.

Typical values of E are as follows—

Material	E (lb/in.²)	E (ton/in.²)
Steel . . .	28–30·5 × 10⁶	12,500–13,500
Cast iron* . .	15–18 × 10⁶	6,700–8,000
Wrought iron . .	25 × 10⁶	11,000
Brass . . .	12 × 10⁶	5,350
Aluminium alloys .	10 × 10⁶	4,600
Copper . . .	17 × 10⁶	7,600
Timber . . .	1–2 × 10⁶	450–900
Spheroidal cast iron .	25 × 10⁶	11,000
Rubber* . .	56–225	—

* These materials do not obey Hooke's law, and E is an approximation only.

Example. A rubber pad for a machine mounting is to carry a load of 1,000 lb and to compress 0·2 in. under this load. If the stress in the rubber is not to exceed 40 lb/in.², determine the diameter and thickness of a pad of circular cross-section. Take E for rubber as 150 lb/in.²

Solution

$$\text{Stress} = \frac{\text{load}}{\text{area}}$$

i.e.

$$f = P/A$$

$$40 = \frac{1,000}{\pi d^2/4}$$

hence

$$d^2 = 31\cdot83 \text{ in.}^2 \quad \text{and} \quad d = 5\cdot64 \text{ in.}$$

i.e.　　　　diameter of pad = **5·64 in.**

The increase in area due to compression has been neglected.

Also　　　　$$\text{strain} = \frac{\text{reduction in length}}{\text{original length}}$$

$$\frac{f}{E} = \frac{x}{l}$$

$$\frac{40}{150} = \frac{0\cdot2}{l}$$

therefore thickness of pad is given by—

$$l = \mathbf{0\cdot75 \text{ in.}}$$

Example. Fig. 13.2 shows a steel strut with two grooves cut out along part of its length. Calculate the total compression of the strut due to a load of 24 tons. $E = 12,500$ ton/in.²

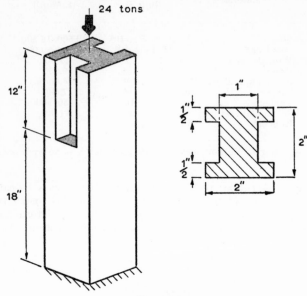

Fɪɢ. 13.2

Solution

Suffices 1 and 2 denote solid and grooved portions, respectively. The load at every section is the same, 24 tons.

For the solid length of 18 in.—

$$\text{compression, } x_1 = e_1 l = e_1 \times 18$$

$$\text{stress, } f_1 = \frac{P}{A_1} = \frac{24}{2 \times 2} = 6 \text{ tons/in.}^2$$

$$\text{strain, } e_1 = \frac{f_1}{E} = \frac{6}{E}$$

For the grooved length of 12 in.—

$$\text{compression, } x_2 = e_2 \times 12$$

$$\text{stress, } f_2 = \frac{24}{(4 - 1 \times 1)} = 8 \text{ tons/in.}^2$$

$$\text{strain, } e_2 = \frac{f_2}{E} = \frac{8}{E}$$

The total compression of the strut is equal to the sum of the compressions of the solid and grooved portions. Therefore

$$x = x_1 + x_2$$

$$= (e_1 \times 18) + (e_2 \times 12)$$

$$= \frac{6}{E} \times 18 + \frac{8}{E} \times 12$$

$$= \frac{204}{E}$$

$$= \frac{204}{12,500}$$

$$= 0.0163 \text{ in.}$$

Note—It has been assumed here that the stress distribution is uniform over all sections, but at the change in cross-section the stress distribution is actually very complex. The assumption produces little error in the calculated compression.

PROBLEMS

1. A bar of 1 in. diameter is subjected to a tensile load of 10,000 lb. Calculate the extension on a 1 ft length. $E = 30 \times 10^6$ lb/in.^{2}

(0·00509 in.)

2. A steel strut, 2 in. diameter, is turned down to 1 in. diameter for one-half its length. Calculate the ratio of the extensions in the two parts due to axial loading.

(4 : 1)

3. When a bolt is in tension the load on the nut is transmitted through the root area of the bolt which is smaller than the shank area. A bolt of 1 in. diameter (root area = 0·55 in.^{2}) carries a tensile load. Find the percentage error in the calculated value of the stress if the shank area is used instead of the root area.

(30 per cent)

4. A light alloy bar is observed to increase in length by 0·35 per cent when subjected to a tensile stress of 18 ton/in.^{2} Calculate Young's modulus for the material.

(5,140 tons/in.^{2})

5. A duralumin tie, 2 ft long, 1½ in. diameter, has a hole drilled out along its length. The hole is of 1 in. diameter and 4 in. long. Calculate the total extension of the tie due to a load of 18 tons. $E = 12 \times 10^6$ lb/in.^{2}

(0·0517 in.)

6. A steel strut of rectangular section is made up of two lengths. The first, 6 in. long, has breadth 2 in. and depth 1½ in.; the second, 4 in. long, is 1 in. square. If $E = 14,000$ tons/in.^{2}, calculate the compression of the strut under a load of 10 tons.

(0·00428 in.)

7. A solid cylindrical bar, of 1 in. diameter and 9 in. long, is welded to a hollow tube of 1 in. internal diameter, 6 in. long to make a bar of total length 15 in. Determine the external diameter of the tube if, when loaded axially by a 4-ton load, the stress in the solid bar and that in the tube are to be the same. Hence calculate the total change in length of the bar. $E = 30 \times 10^6$ lb/in.²

(1·414 in.; 0·0057 in.)

8. A steel bar of 2 in. diameter and 12 in. long is turned down to 1½ in. diameter for a length of 3 in. and reduced to 1 in. diameter for a further length of 4 in. Calculate the total extension of the bar when carrying a load of 7 tons in tension. $E = 30 \times 10^6$ lb/in.² State the stress in each portion of the bar.

(0·00438 in.; 4,980, 8,880, 19,960 lb/in.²)

13.4. Compound Bars

When two or more members are rigidly fixed together so that they *share* the same load and extend or compress the same amount, the two members form a compound bar. The stresses in each member are calculated using the following—

1. The total load is the sum of the loads taken by each member.
2. The load taken by each member is given by the product of its stress and its area.
3. The extension or contraction is the same for each member.

Consider a concrete column reinforced by two steel bars (Fig. 13.3) subjected to a compressive load P. Let A_s be the area of steel, A_c the area of concrete, f_s the stress in the steel, and f_c the stress in the concrete. Thus

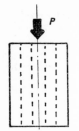

total load = load taken by steel
+ load taken by concrete

i.e. $$P = f_s A_s + f_c A_c \quad . \qquad . \ (13.1)$$

Since the column is a compound bar both steel and concrete compress the same amount, and since the original lengths are the same the strains are equal. Therefore

$$e_s = e_c$$

$$\frac{f_s}{E_s} = \frac{f_c}{E_c}. \qquad . \qquad . \ (13.2)$$

Fɪɢ. 13.3

i.e. the stresses are proportional to the moduli of elasticity.

Example. A column is made up of a steel tube, 3 in. inside diameter, filled with concrete. If the maximum stress in the concrete is not to exceed 3,000 lb/in.² and the column is to carry a compressive load of 20 tons, calculate the minimum outside diameter of the tube. For concrete, $E = 3 \times 10^6$ lb/in.^{2} For steel $E = 30 \times 10^6$ lb/in.^{2}

Solution

Let suffices c and s denote the concrete and steel, respectively.

$$A_c = \frac{\pi 3^2}{4} = 7 \cdot 06 \text{ in.}^2$$

$$A_s = \frac{\pi(d^2 - 9)}{4}$$

where d = outside diameter of the tube. Since the steel and concrete are of equal length and the compression of both is the same, the strains are equal, then

$$e_c = e_s$$

or

$$\frac{f_c}{E_c} = \frac{f_s}{E_s}$$

thus

$$f_s = \frac{E_s}{E_c} \times f_c = \frac{30}{3} \times 3{,}000 = 30{,}000 \text{ lb/in.}^2$$

Total load $P = f_c A_c + f_s A_s$

$$20 \times 2{,}240 = 3{,}000 \times 7 \cdot 06 + 30{,}000 \times \frac{\pi(d^2 - 9)}{4}$$

hence $\qquad\qquad d^2 = 10$

i.e. $\qquad\qquad d = \mathbf{3 \cdot 16 \text{ in.}}$

In practice a radial or lateral strain exists in addition to the axial strain due to the load. Unless the concrete shrinks on setting, to allow a small radial clearance, additional stresses may be set up due to interference between the steel and concrete.

Example. A steel bar of 1 in. diameter and 20 in. long, is placed concentrically inside a gun-metal tube, Fig. 13.4. The tube has inside diameter 1·1 in. and thickness 0·2 in. The length of the tube exceeds the length of the steel bar by 0·006 in. Rigid plates are placed on the ends of the tube and an axial compressive load applied to the compound assembly. Find (*a*) the load which will just make tube and bar the same length; (*b*) the stresses in the steel and gun-metal when a load of 5 tons is applied. E for steel = 13,500 tons/in.^{2}; E for gun-metal = 6,500 tons/in.^{2}

Solution

$$\text{Area of gun-metal tube} = \frac{\pi}{4}(1 \cdot 5^2 - 1 \cdot 1^2) = 0 \cdot 818 \text{ in.}^2$$

$$\text{area of steel bar} = \frac{\pi}{4} \times 1^2 = 0 \cdot 785 \text{ in.}^2$$

(a) For tube to compress 0·006 in.—

$$\text{strain} = \frac{0 \cdot 006}{20} = 0 \cdot 0003$$

thus $\qquad \dfrac{f}{E} = 0 \cdot 0003$

i.e. $\qquad f = 0 \cdot 0003 \times 6{,}500 = 1 \cdot 95 \text{ tons/in.}^2$

hence $\qquad \text{load} = 1 \cdot 95 \times 0 \cdot 818 = \mathbf{1 \cdot 59 \ tons}$

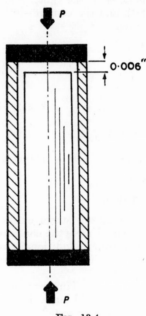

FIG. 13.4

(b) Load available to compress bar and tube as a compound bar is given by

$$P = 5 - 1 \cdot 59 = 3 \cdot 41 \text{ tons}$$

Let f_g be the *additional* stress produced in the gun-metal tube due to this load and f_s the corresponding stress in the steel bar, then

$$P = f_g A_g + f_s A_s$$

i.e. $\qquad 3 \cdot 41 = f_g \times 0 \cdot 818 + f_s \times 0 \cdot 785 \qquad . \qquad . \ (13.3)$

Since the lengths of tube and bar are initially the same when the load of 3·41 tons is applied the strains are equal, then

$$\text{strain} = \frac{f_g}{E_g} = \frac{f_s}{E_s}$$

and

$$f_g = \frac{6{,}500}{13{,}500} \times f_s \qquad . \qquad . \qquad . \quad (13.4)$$

From equations (13.3) and (13.4)—

$$f_g = 1\text{·}395 \text{ tons/in.}^2$$
$$f_s = 2\text{·}89 \text{ tons/in.}^2$$

Therefore

final stress in the steel = **2·89 tons/in.²**

final stress in gun-metal = 1·395 + 1·95 = **3·345 tons/in.²**

PROBLEMS

1. A rectangular timber tie, 7 in. by 3 in., is reinforced by a bar of aluminium of 1 in. diameter. Calculate the stresses in the timber and reinforcement when the tie carries an axial load of 30 tons. E for timber = 1,000 tons/in.²; E for aluminium = 6,000 tons/in.²

(1·167; 7 tons/in.²)

2. A concrete column having modulus of elasticity 3×10^6 lb/in.² is reinforced by two steel bars of 1 in. diameter having a modulus of 30×10^6 lb/in.² Calculate the dimensions of a square section strut if the stress in the concrete is not to exceed 1,000 lb/in.² and the load is to be 40 tons.

(8·6 in. square)

3. A cylindrical mild steel bar of $1\frac{1}{2}$ in. diameter and 6 in. long, is enclosed by a bronze tube of the same length having an outside diameter of $2\frac{1}{2}$ in. and inside diameter of $1\frac{1}{2}$ in. This compound strut is subjected to an axial compressive load of 20 tons. Find: (a) the stress in the steel rod; (b) the stress in the bronze tube; (c) the shortening of the strut. For steel E = 13,000 tons/in.² For bronze E = 6,500 tons/in.²

(Steel 6 tons/in.²; bronze 3 tons/in.²; 0·00277 in.)

4. A compound assembly is formed by brazing a brass sleeve on to a solid steel bar of 2 in. diameter. The assembly is to carry a tensile axial load of 25 tons. Find the cross-sectional area of the brass sleeve so that the sleeve carries 30 per cent of the load. Find for this composite bar the stresses in the brass and steel. E for brass = 12×10^6 lb/in.²; E for steel = 30×10^6 lb/in.²

(3·365 in.²; steel 5·57 tons/in.²; brass 2·23 tons/in.²)

5. A compound assembly is made up as shown in Fig. 13.5. The outside bars are of bronze each 2 in. wide and 0·3 in. thick. The middle bar is of steel 2 in. wide and x in. thick. Assuming the assembly to act as a single bar when loaded in tension find the value of x to limit the maximum stress in the steel

to 10 tons/in.² What is then the stress in the bronze? The axial load is 20 tons. For bronze $E = 7,200$ tons/in.² For steel $E = 13,400$ tons/in.²

(0·678 in., 5·37 tons/in.²)

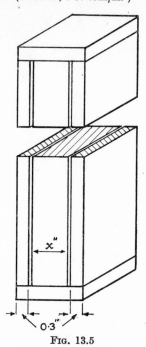

FIG. 13.5

6. A duralumin rod of 2 in. diameter is a loose fit inside a mild steel tube of 2½ in. outside diameter. If the steel tube is turned down to 2¼ in. diameter over one-half its length calculate the stress in the duralumin rod and the stress in each portion of the tube due to an axial load of 2 tons. Both rod and tube are of the same length. E for steel $= 28 \times 10^6$ lb/in.²; E for duralumin $= 18 \times 10^6$ lb/in.² (*Hint:* strains are not equal; to solve, equate the compressions.)

(913 lb/in.²; 915 lb/in.²; 1,930 lb/in.²)

13.5. Thermal Strain

Change in temperature of a material gives rise to a thermal strain. For example, a rise in temperature t in a bar of length l will cause it to extend by an amount

$$x = \alpha t l$$

where α is the coefficient of linear thermal expansion of the material. The thermal strain is given by—

$$e = \frac{x}{l}$$

$$= \alpha t$$

There is no stress associated with this strain unless the bar is prevented from extending. In this case the load produced in the bar would be the same as the load required to compress the bar a distance equal to the free expansion of the bar. Typical values of the coefficients of linear expansion are as follows—

carbon steel	$6{\cdot}7 \times 10^{-6}/°F$
austenitic stainless steel	$10 \ \times 10^{-6}/°F$
aluminium	$13{\cdot}5 \times 10^{-6}/°F$
copper	$9{\cdot}5 \times 10^{-6}/°F$
cast iron	$5{\cdot}6 \times 10^{-6}/°F$
brass	$9 \ \times 10^{-6}/°F$
bronze	$10 \ \times 10^{-6}/°F$
nickel steels	$7 \ \times 10^{-6}/°F$

For example, carbon steel expands $0{\cdot}0000067$ in. per in. length per °F rise in temperature.

The magnitude of the temperature strain is of the same order as the elastic strain in a metal due to stress and is therefore of importance. For example, the elastic strain at a tensile stress of 30,000 lb/in.^{2} for a carbon steel having an elastic modulus E of 30×10^6 lb/in.^{2} is—

$$e = \frac{f}{E} = \frac{30,000}{30 \times 10^6} = 0{\cdot}001$$

A temperature rise of 150°F in the same steel gives a thermal strain

$$e = \alpha t = 6{\cdot}7 \times 10^{-6} \times 150 = 0{\cdot}001$$

If the extension of a bar due to this temperature rise were completely prevented, a *compressive* stress of 30,000 lb/in.^{2} would be set up in the bar, since it would require this stress to return the bar to its original length.

For large temperature changes, α and E vary with temperature; however, it will be assumed here that the temperature changes are sufficiently small for α and E to be taken as constants.

Both the thermal strain αt and the elastic strain f/E may exist together. The total strain e is the sum of the two, thus—

$$e = \alpha t + \frac{f}{E}$$

and $$\text{extension} = e \times l$$

$$= \left(\alpha t + \frac{f}{E}\right) l$$

13.6. Sign Convention

In tension, strain e and stress f are positive, in compression they are negative; and t is positive for a rise in temperature. When a stress is unknown f is assumed positive, a negative answer therefore implies that it is compressive.

Fig. 13.6 shows a clamped bar restrained against extension or contraction. If the bar is subjected to a change in temperature the

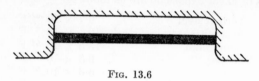

FIG. 13.6

total strain is zero, i.e. the elastic strain must be equal and opposite to the thermal strain, thus

$$\text{total strain, } e = 0$$

therefore

$$\alpha t + \frac{f}{E} = 0$$

or

$$\frac{f}{E} = -\alpha t$$

The stress in the clamped bar is therefore compressive for a rise in temperature (t positive).

13.7. Effects of Thermal Strain

Thermal strain may be of engineering importance because of the deformation it produces or because, if the deformation is resisted, thermal stresses result.

Thermal expansion of a metal is utilized when a collar is shrunk on to a shaft. The collar is bored out to a diameter slightly smaller than that of the shaft, it is then heated so that when expanded it may be slipped into position on the shaft. When cooled the collar grips the shaft firmly and the collar and shaft remain stressed after cooling. Again, a thermostat switch may be actuated by a rise in temperature deforming a bimetal strip. For example, when strips of copper and steel are riveted together a rise in temperature causes the copper to expand more than the steel, the strip bends and the resulting deflexion can be used to operate the switch.

The expansion of a metal must be allowed for in high temperature piping. A straight pipe will produce high loads at the pipe end connexions if not allowed to expand freely along its length. In order to overcome this a loop is inserted in the pipe-line. The flexibility of the loop permits the expansion to be taken up. Similarly special arrangements are made to allow free expansion of long exposed pipe-lines in hot climates; the pipes may be looped or the lines staggered (see Plate IV). Gaps are often left in rail tracks to permit free expansion in hot weather without buckling of the tracks. Present-day practice, however, is to weld the joints for considerable lengths and to rely on the clamping effect of sleepers and ballast to prevent buckling.

When dissimilar metals are bonded together each tends to resist the change in length of the other and high stresses may be induced. If two parts of the same structure are at different temperatures, or if a body of non-uniform thickness is subject to a sudden change in temperature, again high stresses or excessive deformation may result. Many examples of these effects will come to mind: cold water poured into a hot cylinder block may crack it; foundry castings of complex shapes allowed to cool too quickly may shatter; tools may be cracked by the process of quench-hardening.

Finally it may be remarked that when the change of temperature is large the properties of metals change also and this may have to be taken into account. A rise in temperature is usually accompanied by a drop in the values of the modulus of elasticity, the ultimate tensile stress and the yield stress. The ductility of the metal may increase (*see* Chapter 14). The reverse is true for a drop in temperature; in particular, at low temperatures mild steel may become relatively brittle.

Example. A steel bar 1 ft long, 1 in. diameter, is turned down to $\frac{3}{4}$ in. diameter for one-third of its length. It is heated 60° above room temperature, clamped at both ends and then allowed to cool to room temperature. If the distance between the clamps is unchanged find the maximum stress in the bar. $\alpha = 7 \times 10^{-6}/°F$; $E = 28 \times 10^6 \text{ lb/in.}^2$

Solution

If allowed to contract freely without constraint the contraction of the whole length is given by—

$$\alpha \times t \times l = 7 \times 10^{-6} \times 60 \times 12$$
$$= 0·00504 \text{ in.}$$

Contraction is prevented by a tensile force P exerted by the clamps, Fig. 13.7.

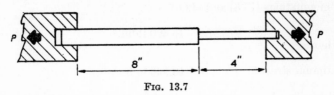

Fɪɢ. 13.7

Each portion of the bar carries the total load P but the extension of each portion is different since the lengths and section areas are different. The load is the same throughout and the maximum stress will therefore occur in the portion of smaller diameter. Since

$$\frac{f}{E} = e \quad \text{and} \quad e = \frac{x}{l}$$

then, for the longer portion, using suffix 1

$$x_1 = e_1 l_1 = \frac{f_1 l_1}{E}$$

and for the shorter portion

$$x_2 = \frac{f_2 l_2}{E}$$

As the load on each portion is the same, then

$$P = f_1 A_1 = f_2 A_2$$

i.e.
$$f_1 = \frac{A_2}{A_1} f_2$$

$$= \frac{0 \cdot 75^2}{1^2} f^2$$

$$= 0 \cdot 562 \, f_2 \qquad . \qquad . \qquad . \qquad . \quad (13.5)$$

As the total length remains unchanged, then

total extension due to load = contraction due to temperature drop

thus
$$x_1 + x_2 = 0 \cdot 00504 \text{ in.}$$

$$\frac{f_1 l_1}{E} + \frac{f_2 l_2}{E} = 0 \cdot 00504$$

therefore $f_1 \times 8 + f_2 \times 4 = 0 \cdot 00504 \times 28 \times 10^6$

$$2 f_1 + f_2 = 0 \cdot 03528 \times 10^6 \qquad . \qquad . \qquad . \quad (13.6)$$

From equations (13.5) and (13.6)—

$$f_2 = 16{,}600 \text{ lb/in.}^2$$

Hence

maximum stress in the bar = **16,600 lb/in.²**

Example. A narrow steel strip, $\frac{1}{2}$ in. thick, is clad by two magnesium plates of the same width, each $\frac{1}{8}$ in. thick. Calculate the change in stress in the steel and magnesium for each Fahrenheit degree rise in temperature of the compound strip. Assume perfect bonding of the strips along their length, Fig. 13.8.

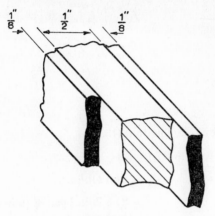

$\frac{1''}{8}$ $\frac{1''}{2}$ $\frac{1''}{8}$

FIG. 13.8

For steel, $\alpha = 6\cdot7 \times 10^{-6}/°\text{F}$; $E = 29 \times 10^6$ lb/in.^{2} For magnesium, $\alpha = 15 \times 10^{-6}/°\text{F}$; $E = 6\cdot5 \times 10^6$ lb/in.^{2}

Solution

The criteria for solving this problem are—

1. Since the magnesium cladding tends to extend more than the steel it will be restrained by the latter and will therefore be in compression. The steel is correspondingly stretched by the magnesium and is in tension.

2. Since there is perfect bonding the final extension of each strip is the same and, since the original lengths are equal, the total strains are equal.

3. There is no *external* load on the compound strip.

For a temperature rise of $t°\text{F}$, taking tensile strains as positive—

total strain in steel = total strain in magnesium

thus $\qquad\qquad \alpha_1 t + \dfrac{f_1}{E_1} = \alpha_2 t + \dfrac{f_2}{E_2}$

or $\qquad\qquad f_1 - f_2 \times \dfrac{E_1}{E_2} = (\alpha_2 - \alpha_1)t \times E_1$

i.e. $\qquad f_1 - f_2 \times \dfrac{29}{6\cdot5} = (15 - 6\cdot7) \times 10^{-6} \times 29 \times 10^6 \times t$

therefore $\qquad f_1 - 4\cdot47 f_2 = 241\, t$.   .   .   .   . (13.7)

Also

total load on compound strip = 0

thus
$$f_1 A_1 + f_2 A_2 = 0$$

i.e.
$$f_2 = -f_1 \frac{A_1}{A_2}$$

$$= -f_1 \times \frac{1/2}{2 \times 1/8}$$

$$= -2f_1$$

Substituting for f_2 in equation (13.7)—

$$f_1 - 4{\cdot}47(-2f_1) = 241 \times t$$

therefore
$$f_1 = 24{\cdot}3\,t\ \text{lb/in.}^2$$

$$= \mathbf{24{\cdot}3\ lb/in.^2\ per\ °F}\ \text{(tension)}$$

and
$$f_2 = \mathbf{-\,48{\cdot}6\ lb/in.^2\ per\ °F}\ \text{(compression)}$$

Note—These results are not accurate at the end of the strip. Further, they apply strictly only to narrow strips where restriction of expansion across the width may be neglected. The various temperature changes to which a clad strip such as this may be subjected during manufacture will often leave it in a state of stress at room temperature. Such a state of stress is termed *residual stress*. In this case it can be removed only by over-stretching beyond the yield point and cannot be removed by annealing.

Example. A stainless steel rod is placed inside, and concentric with, a mild steel tube. There is a large radial clearance between rod and tube but the tubes are welded together at each end to form a compound bar of length 20 in. For the rod, $E = 24 \times 10^6$ lb/in.^{2}, and $\alpha = 10 \times 10^{-6}/°F$.

(*a*) If, when the temperature of the compound bar is raised 50°F the extension is found to be 0·008 in., find the stress in the rod.

(*b*) If the cross-sectional area of the rod is 1·1 in.^{2} and that of the tube is 2·4 in.^{2}, find the stress in the tube.

(*c*) If E for the mild steel tube is 30×10^6 lb/in.^{2} find its coefficient of linear expansion.

Solution

(*a*) Total extension of the compound bar equals total strain times length, thus

$$0{\cdot}008 = \left(\alpha t + \frac{f}{E}\right) l\ \text{in.} \qquad . \qquad . \qquad . \quad (13.8)$$

Applying this equation to the stainless steel rod, denoting stress in rod by f_R—

$$0{\cdot}008 = \left(10 \times 10^{-6} \times 50 + \frac{f_R}{24 \times 10^6}\right) \times 20$$

thus $\qquad f_R = -2{,}400 \text{ lb/in.}^2$

The negative sign signifies compression. Therefore, stress in the rod is **2,400 lb/in.²** compression.

(b) Since there is no external load on the compound bar, the loads in the rod and tube must be equal and opposite. Therefore

$$f_R A_R = -f_T A_T$$

i.e. $\qquad -2{,}400 \times 1{\cdot}1 = -f_T \times 2{\cdot}4$

$$f_T = +1{,}100 \text{ lb/in.}^2 \text{ (tension)}$$

Therefore stress in the tube is **1,100 lb/in.²** tension.

(c) Applying equation (13.8) to the tube—

$$0{\cdot}008 = \left(\alpha \times 50 + \frac{1{,}100}{30 \times 10^6}\right) \times 20$$

thus $\qquad \alpha = 7{\cdot}27 \times 10^{-6}/°\text{F}$

Therefore the coefficient of linear expansion of the mild steel tube is **$7{\cdot}27 \times 10^{-6}/°\text{F}$**.

PROBLEMS

1. A brittle steel rod of 1 in. diameter is heated to 300°F and then suddenly clamped at both ends. It is then allowed to cool and breaks at a temperature of 200°F. Calculate the breaking stress of the steel. $E = 30 \times 10^6 \text{ lb/in.}^2$; $\alpha = 7 \times 10^{-6}/°\text{F}$.

(21,000 lb/in.²)

2. A steel bar of 4 in. diameter is rigidly clamped at both ends so that all axial extension is prevented. A hole of 1·5 in. diameter is drilled out for one-third of the length. If the bar is raised in temperature by 50°F above that of the clamps calculate the maximum axial stress in the bar. $E = 30 \times 10^6 \text{ lb/in.}^2$; $\alpha = 0{\cdot}000007/°\text{F}$.

(11,600 lb/in.²)

3. Two steel bars are connected together so as to form a rod of total length 25 in. One, of mild steel, is 9 in. long and 1 in. diameter; the other, of stainless steel, is 16 in. long and ½ in. diameter. If the bar is heated to 100°F above room temperature, clamped rigidly at both ends and then allowed to cool to room temperature calculate the stress in each part of the rod. For stainless steel, $E = 25 \times 10^6 \text{ lb/in.}^2$; $\alpha = 10 \times 10^{-6}/°\text{F}$. For mild steel, $E = 30 \times 10^6$ lb/in.²; $\alpha = 6{\cdot}7 \times 10^{-6}/°\text{F}$.

(Mild steel, 7,700 lb/in.²; stainless steel, 30,800 lb/in.²)

4. A steel bar of 2 in. diameter is placed between two stops, with an end clearance of 0·002 in. The temperature of the bar is raised 100°F and the stops are found to have been forced apart a distance of 0·002 in. Calculate the maximum stress in the bar if its total length is 10 in. and there is a hole

of 1 in. diameter drilled along its length for a distance of 4 in. $E = 30 \times 10^6$ lb/in.²; $\alpha = 7 \times 10^{-6}$/°F.

(10,600 lb/in.²)

5. A compound tube is formed by a stainless steel outer tube of 2 in. outside diameter and 1·875 in. inside diameter, together with a concentric mild steel inner tube of wall thickness ¼ in. The radial clearance between inner and outer tubes is $\frac{1}{16}$ in. The two tubes are welded together at their ends, the compound tube being free to expand when heated. Calculate the stress in each tube due to a temperature rise of 100°F. For stainless steel, $E = 25 \times 10^6$ lb/in.²; $\alpha = 10 \times 10^{-6}$/°F. For mild steel, $E = 30 \times 10^6$ lb/in.²; $\alpha = 6·7 \times 10^{-6}$/°F.

(Mild steel, 2,100 lb/in.² tensile; stainless steel, 6,510 lb/in.² compressive)

6. A stainless steel rod of 1 in. diameter is placed inside, and concentric with, a mild steel tube of 1¼ in. inside diameter and 2 in. outside diameter. The tube and bar are welded together at the ends but are otherwise free to expand. Calculate the stress in each part of the compound bar so formed due to a temperature rise of 40°F. If the length of the compound bar is 10 in. what is the extension? For stainless steel $E = 24 \times 10^6$ lb/in.²; $\alpha = 10 \times 10^{-6}$/°F. For mild steel $E = 28 \times 10^6$ lb/in.²; $\alpha = 7 \times 10^{-6}$/°F.

($-$ 2,130, 874 lb/in.²; 0·00311 in.)

7. A compound bar is made up of steel plate 2 in. wide, 0·4 in. thick clad on both sides by copper plates 2 in. wide, each 0·2 in. thick. The plates are bonded together along their length and at room temperature the original length is 48 in. Find the load taken by *each* plate and the increase in length when the temperature rises 200°F. For steel, $E = 13,200$ tons/in.²; $\alpha = 7 \times 10^{-6}$/°F. For copper, $E = 16 \times 10^6$ lb/in.²; $\alpha = 10 \times 10^{-6}$/°F.

(Steel, $+$ 4,990 lb; copper, $-$ 2,495 lb; 0·0774 in.)

8. In the arrangement shown in Fig. 13.9 the steel bar has 1·2 in. diameter and the bronze bar 2 in. diameter. The bars are of equal length and just

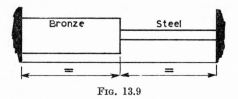

FIG. 13.9

fit between the end fixings at room temperature. The distance between the fixings cannot change. Calculate the stresses produced in the steel and bronze by a temperature rise of 100°F. For steel, $E = 13,500$ tons/in.²; $\alpha = 6·5 \times 10^{-6}$/°F. For bronze, $E = 7,000$ tons/in.²; $\alpha = 10 \times 10^{-6}$/°F.

(Steel, $-$ 13·12 tons/in.²; bronze, $-$ 4·72 tons/in.²)

13.8. Strain Energy: Resilience

Work is done in stretching or compressing a bar of material. If the bar is elastic this work is stored as *strain energy* or energy of deformation, and is recoverable on removal of the load. The bar behaves exactly like a spring.* The energy stored per unit volume in a strained bar is also called the *resilience*.

* The strain energy of springs is dealt with on p. 179.

If a force P stretches a bar a small distance $\mathrm{d}x$, then the work done is $P\mathrm{d}x$. When the force P varies with the extension x the total work done in stretching the bar a distance x is

$$\int_0^x P\mathrm{d}x$$

and this is the area enclosed by the load–extension graph and the x-axis. It is also the total strain energy U in the elastic bar. If the

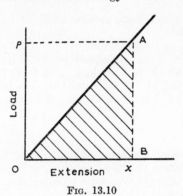

FIG. 13.10

bar obeys Hooke's law the load–extension graph is a straight line, Fig. 13.10, hence

$$U = \text{work done}$$

$$= \text{area OAB}$$

therefore $\qquad\qquad U = \tfrac{1}{2} Px$. $\qquad$. $\qquad$. $\qquad$. $\qquad$. (13.9)

where P is the maximum force. The factor $\tfrac{1}{2}$ represents the fact that the force increases uniformly from zero to a maximum value P during the extension of the bar. Alternatively

$$U = \text{work done}$$

$$= \text{average force} \times \text{extension}$$

$$= \tfrac{1}{2} Px$$

It is convenient to write the strain energy in terms of the maximum stress f produced by the force P. If A is the cross-sectional area of the bar and l its length, then

$$P = fA$$

and $\qquad\qquad\qquad x = fl/E$

thus $U = \frac{1}{2} Px$

$$= \frac{1}{2} \times (fA) \times \frac{fl}{E}$$

$$= \frac{f^2}{2E} \times Al$$

i.e. $U = \frac{f^2}{2E} \times$ ***volume of bar***   .   . (13.10)

The units of strain energy are those of work, i.e. inch-pounds (in.-lb) or foot-pounds (ft-lb).

Example. A steel strut is of square section, 4 in. by 4 in. over the middle portion, which is 6 in. long, and 3 in. by 3 in. over the remainder of its length. If the total length is 10 in. and the load 80 tons, calculate the total strain energy in the bar. $E = 12,000$ tons/in.^{2}

Solution

Since the cross-sectional areas of the two portions of the bar are different, the stresses produced in these portions differ and the strain energy for each portion must be calculated separately.

Middle portion—

$$f = \frac{80}{4 \times 4} = 5 \text{ tons/in.}^2$$

$$\text{volume} = 4 \times 4 \times 6 = 96 \text{ in.}^3$$

$$\text{strain energy} = \frac{f^2}{2E} \times \text{volume}$$

$$= \frac{5^2}{2 \times 12,000} \times 96$$

$$= 0 \cdot 1 \text{ in.-ton}$$

End portions—

$$f = \frac{80}{3 \times 3} = 8 \cdot 89 \text{ tons/in.}^2$$

$$\text{volume} = 3 \times 3 \times 4 = 36 \text{ in.}^3$$

$$\text{strain energy} = \frac{8 \cdot 89^2}{2 \times 12,000} \times 36$$

$$= 0 \cdot 1185 \text{ in.-ton}$$

$$\text{Total strain energy} = 0 \cdot 1 + 0 \cdot 1185 = 0 \cdot 2185 \text{ in.-ton}$$

$$= \textbf{490 in.-lb}$$

PROBLEMS

1. A steel bar 5 ft long is of 2 in. diameter for 3 ft of its length and 1 in. diameter for the remainder. What is the strain energy stored in the bar under a load of 10,000 lb? $E = 12,500$ tons/in.^{2}

(75·1 in.-lb)

2. Compare the strain energy stored in a loaded bar, 10 in. long and 2 in. diameter, with that stored in a similar bar which is turned down to 1·5 in. diameter for one-half its length. The maximum direct stress in each bar is to be the same.

(2·28 : 1)

3. A bar of steel is 3 ft long and of $\frac{1}{2}$ in. diameter. Calculate the strain energy stored in the bar when a tensile load of 6,000 lb is applied.

Find also the additional strain energy that can be stored before the material exceeds its elastic limit stress of 21 tons/in.^{2} $E = 13,500$ tons/in.^{2}

(109 in.-lb; 149 in.-lb)

13.9. Application of Strain Energy to Impact and Suddenly Applied Loads

Impact Loads

If a load is suddenly applied to a bar, as in an impact, the bar stretches and behaves as a spring, oscillating about a mean position.

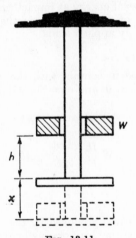

Fig. 13.11

The strain energy stored in the bar is greatest when the bar and load are instantaneously at rest at the position of maximum displacement. At this point the total energy of the load has been absorbed as strain energy. For example, assume that a load of weight W falls through a height h on to a collar at the end of a vertical bar of length l, Fig. 13.11. Let x be the maximum instantaneous extension of the bar and f the corresponding maximum stress. Then

$$x = \frac{fl}{E}$$

At the point of maximum extension

initial potential energy of load = strain energy in bar

$$W(h + x) = \frac{f^2}{2E} \times Al$$

or $$W\left(h + \frac{f}{E}l\right) = \frac{f^2}{2E} \times Al \qquad . \qquad . \qquad (13.11)$$

This gives a quadratic in f.

There are two answers therefore for the stress f; the negative answer is the compressive stress produced in the bar on rebound if the load were to lock to the collar after impact. The assumptions involved are as follows—

1. All connexions except the bar are completely rigid.
2. The limit of proportionality of stress is not exceeded.
3. There is no loss of energy at impact (mass of bar negligible).
4. The modulus of elasticity, E, is the same for impulsive loading as for steadily applied loads.

SUDDENLY APPLIED LOADS

If the load is placed in contact with the collar without impact and suddenly let go, $h = 0$, and equation (13.11) gives

$$Wx = \frac{f^2}{2E} \times Al$$

i.e. $$W\frac{fl}{E} = \frac{f^2}{2E} \times Al$$

$$f = 2\frac{W}{A}$$

Hence the maximum stress produced by the suddenly applied load is *twice* that due to the same load gradually applied. The maximum instantaneous extension will also be *twice* that for the gradually applied load.

Example. A load of weight 100 lb falls $\frac{1}{8}$ in. on to a collar at the end of a bar of $\frac{1}{16}$ in. diameter and 2 in. long. The rod is made of an alloy having a modulus of elasticity of 15×10^6 lb/in.^{2} Calculate the maximum tensile force in the rod.

Solution

$$\text{Area of section} = \frac{\pi}{4}\left(\frac{1}{16}\right)^2 = 0\!\cdot\!00307 \text{ in.}^2$$

If P lb is the maximum tensile force produced and f the corresponding stress, then

$$f = \frac{P}{0\!\cdot\!00307} \text{ lb/in.}^2$$

and maximum extension is given by—

$$x = e \times l$$
$$= \frac{f}{E} \times l$$
$$= \frac{P \times 2}{0\!\cdot\!00307 \times 15 \times 10^6}$$
$$= \frac{P}{23,000}$$

Loss of potential energy of load equals gain of strain energy of rod. Therefore, using equation (13.9).

$$W(h + x) = \tfrac{1}{2} Px$$
$$100 \left(\frac{1}{8} + \frac{P}{23,000}\right) = \frac{1}{2} P \times \frac{P}{23,000}$$

thus $P^2 - 200\,P - 575,000 = 0$

and $P = 100 \pm 765$
$$= + 865 \quad \text{or} \quad - 665 \text{ lb}$$

The negative answer may be disregarded if the falling weight does not become fixed to the collar.

Maximum force in the rod = **865 lb**

Example. A rapidly moving free piston having a kinetic energy of 30 ft-lb suddenly seizes in the cylinder shown, Fig. 13.12. Calculate the maximum tensile and compressive stresses in the cylinder

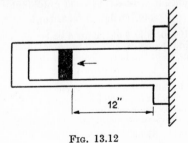

Fig. 13.12

due to impact. Effective length of cylinder to point of seizure, 1 ft; inside diameter, 3 in.; outside diameter, 3·5 in.; modulus of elasticity, 30×10^6 lb/in.²

Solution

$$\text{Kinetic energy lost} = \text{strain energy gained}$$

$$= \frac{f^2}{2E} \times \text{volume}$$

$$\text{volume of material stressed} = \frac{\pi}{4}(3 \cdot 5^2 - 3^2) \times 12 = 30 \cdot 7 \text{ in.}^3$$

$$\text{kinetic energy lost} = 30 \times 12 = 360 \text{ in.-lb}$$

therefore

$$360 = \frac{f^2}{2 \times 30 \times 10^6} \times 30 \cdot 7$$

and

$$f^2 = 704 \times 10^6$$

i.e.

$$f = \pm \, \mathbf{26{,}500 \ lb/in.^2}$$

The positive answer represents the maximum tensile stress, and the negative answer the maximum compressive stress on elastic rebound, provided that the piston remains firmly fixed to the cylinder.

PROBLEMS

1. A load of weight 50 lb falls through a height of 2 in. and then starts to stretch a steel bar of $\frac{1}{2}$ in. diameter and 2 ft long. If $E = 30 \times 10^6$ lb/in.², calculate the maximum stress induced.

(36,800 lb/in.²)

2. A load of 1 ton is placed on a collar at the end of a vertical tie rod of $\frac{1}{2}$ in. diameter. Calculate the static stress induced.

If the load is dropped from a height of 3 in. calculate the maximum instantaneous stress induced in the rod. Length of rod $= 4$ ft, $E = 15,000$ tons/in.²

What is the maximum instantaneous stress if the load is not dropped but applied suddenly without impact?

(5·1, 100·3, 10·2 tons/in.²)

3. A collar is turned at the end of a bar, $\frac{1}{4}$ in. diameter, 2 ft long. The bar is hung vertically with the collar at the lower end. A load of weight 1,000 lb is placed just above the collar so as to be in contact but leave the bar unloaded. Calculate the maximum instantaneous stress and extension of the bar if the load is suddenly released. $E = 30 \times 10^6$ lb/in.²

(40,760 lb/in.², 0·0326 in.)

4. A weight of 100 lb falls 6 in. on to a collar attached to the end of a vertical rod of 2 in. diameter and 72 in. long. Calculate the maximum instantaneous extension of the bar. $E = 30 \times 10^6$ lb/in.²

(0·0303 in.)

5. A load of 500 lb falls $\frac{3}{4}$ in. on to a vertical cylindrical column, thereby compressing it. The column is 30 in. long and 2 in. diameter. Find the maximum instantaneous stress produced by the impact and the total strain energy stored by the column at the instant of maximum compression.

(15,600 lb/in.²; 382 in.-lb)

6. A load of 10,000 lb is to be dropped a height of 2 in. on to a cast-iron column of 3 in. diameter. What is the minimum length of column if the energy of impact is to be absorbed without raising the maximum instantaneous stress above 30,000 lb/in.²? E for cast iron $= 16 \times 10^6$ lb/in.²

(9·27 ft)

7. A load of weight 20 lb falls through a height of 6 in. and then starts to stretch a steel bar of $\frac{1}{2}$ in. diameter and 3 ft long. If the bar is turned down to $\frac{3}{8}$ in. diameter for 1 ft of its length calculate the maximum stress induced in the bar. $E = 30 \times 10^6$ lb/in.²

(50,500 lb/in.²)

8. What is the maximum height a weight of 2,000 lb can be dropped on to a steel column of 1 in. diameter and 1 ft long, if the maximum instantaneous stress is not to exceed 40,000 lb/in.²? $E = 30 \times 10^6$ lb/in.²

(0·1096 in.)

THIN-WALLED PRESSURE VESSELS

13.10. Hoop Stress in a Cylinder

A cylinder containing fluid under pressure is subjected to a uniform radial pressure normal to the walls, Fig. 13.13. Since the

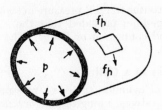

FIG. 13.13

cylinder tends to expand radially there will be a tensile or *hoop stress* f_h set up in the circumferential direction, i.e. tangent to the shell wall. This stress may be found by considering the equilibrium

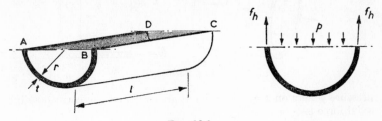

FIG. 13.1

of forces acting on one-half of the shell. Imagine the cylinder to be cut across a diameter, Fig. 13.14. Then there is a uniform downward pressure p acting on the diametral surface section ABCD shown;

this is balanced by the upward force due to the hoop stress f_h along the two edges.

Force due to radial pressure on area ABCD $= p \times$ area ABCD

$$= p \times \text{AB} \times \text{BC}$$
$$= p \times 2\,r \times l \quad .(13.12)$$

where r is the cylinder internal radius and l the length. If the thickness t of the shell wall is small compared to the internal radius r (e.g. if t is less than $r/10$), then the hoop stress may be taken as uniform across the wall section. Then the upward force on the two edges due to f_h is

$$= 2 \times f_h \times \text{area of one edge}$$
$$= 2 f_h \times t \times l \quad . \qquad . \qquad . \qquad . \qquad (13.13)$$

Equating the forces given by equations (13.12) and (13.13)—

$$2 f_h t l = 2\,prl$$

therefore $$\boldsymbol{f_h = \frac{pr}{t}} \qquad . \qquad . \qquad . \qquad (13.14)$$

This is the only stress due to fluid pressure in an open ended seamless cylinder (e.g. a pipe-line) provided that the section considered is distant from an end connexion or flange. The weight of the fluid has been neglected.

13.11. Axial Stress in a Cylinder

In a closed pipe or cylinder, such as a pressure vessel there is, in addition to the hoop stress, a longitudinal or *axial stress* arising from the force due to pressure on the closed ends. Imagine the cylinder to be cut by a plane normal to the axis, Fig. 13.15. Then the

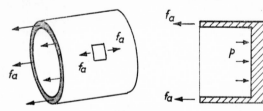

FIG. 13.15

pressure p acts on a cross-sectional area πr^2 and the corresponding axial force is—

$$p \times \pi r^2$$

This force is balanced by the force due to the axial stress f_a acting on the area of the shell rim, which is approximately—

$$\text{circumference} \times \text{thickness} = 2\pi r \times t$$

Hence $\qquad\qquad f_a \times 2\pi r t = p \times \pi r^2$

$$f_a = \frac{pr}{2t} \qquad . \qquad . \qquad . \qquad . \quad (13.15)$$

Thus from (13.14) $\qquad f_a = \tfrac{1}{2} f_h$

i.e. the axial stress is one-half the hoop stress.

13.12. Tangential Stress in a Spherical Shell

If a thin spherical shell is subject to internal pressure p, a tensile stress is set up in the shell wall due to the tendency of the shell to expand under pressure. Imagine the spherical shell to be cut

FIG. 13.16

across a diameter and consider the forces acting on one-half of the shell, Fig. 13.16; these are—

1. The diametral force due to the pressure

$$= p \times \pi r^2$$

2. The resisting force due the tangential stress f_t acting on the section of the rim. If t is small compared with the internal radius r, then f_t is nearly uniform and the area of the rim section is approximately $2\pi r t$, i.e.

$$\text{resisting force} = f_t \times 2\pi r t$$

Equating these two forces

$$f_t \times 2\pi r t = p \times \pi r^2$$

$$f_t = \frac{pr}{2t}$$

This applies to any diametral section of the sphere and hence at any point there is a tangential stress f_t acting in all directions tangent to the wall.

13.13. Effect of Joints on Stresses in Thin Shells

In many cases cylindrical shells are not seamless but are jointed, the joints being along a circumferential or longitudinal seam. The distribution of stress in a riveted joint is complex and the strength of such joints cannot be calculated with any great accuracy. The design of riveted joints is largely empirical and cannot be dealt with properly here. It is possible, however, to arrive at more accurate values for the stresses by making allowances for the efficiencies of the joints. The efficiency of a joint may be defined as the ratio—

$$\frac{\text{strength of joint of given width}}{\text{strength of solid plate of same width}}$$

For example, if the efficiency of a joint is 70 per cent it means in effect that the effective area of the perforated plate is 0·7 of that of the solid plate. The average stresses calculated using the thin cylinder formulae would therefore have to be increased in the ratio 1/0·7.

A circumferential joint has to resist the axial tension whereas the longitudinal joint has to resist the hoop tension. The axial tension is one-half the hoop tension so that the longitudinal joint is potentially the weakest part of the cylinder. Circumferential joints, therefore, do not have to be of the same efficiency as the longitudinal joint and are often permitted to have a much lower efficiency.

Example. Calculate the required thickness of the shell of an experimental pressure vessel of spherical shape and 18 in. diameter, which has to withstand an internal fluid pressure of 1,000 lb/in.^{2} without the stress in the material of the shell exceeding 10,000 lb/in.^{2} If the shell is to be made by bolting together two flanged halves using sixteen bolts what should be the root area of each bolt? The tensile stress in the bolts must not exceed 10 tons/in.^{2}

Solution

$$f_t = \frac{pr}{2t}$$

thus
$$t = \frac{pr}{2f_t} = \frac{1,000 \times 9}{2 \times 10,000} = \mathbf{0 \cdot 45 \text{ in.}}$$

$$\text{Diametral bursting force} = p \times \pi r^2$$

$$= 1,000 \times \pi \times 9^2$$

$$= 255,000 \text{ lb}$$

$$\text{force per bolt} = \frac{255,000}{16}$$

$$= 15,935 \text{ lb}$$

therefore   15,935 = stress in bolt × root area

                                = 10 × 2,240 × A

thus   A = **0·71 in.²**

(1 in. diameter bolts would be required.)

Example. A thin tube contains oil at a pressure of 800 lb/in.²
Each end is closed by a piston, the two pistons being free to move
in the tube but rigidly connected by a rod as shown, Fig. 13.17.

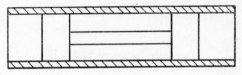

Fig. 13.17

(a) Calculate the stresses in the tube if it has an inside diameter of
2 in. and a wall thickness 0·1 in. (b) Calculate the tensile stress in
the rod joining the pistons if it is of 1 in. diameter.

Solution

(a) The axial force due to oil pressure is taken by the connecting-
rod. There is therefore no axial force or stress in the tube. The
hoop stress in the tube is given by—

$$f_h = \frac{pr}{t}$$

$$= \frac{800 \times 1}{0 \cdot 1}$$

$$= \textbf{8,000 lb/in.}^2$$

(b) Inside area of piston $= \frac{\pi}{4} \times 2^2 - \frac{\pi}{4} \times 1^2$

$$= 2 \cdot 356 \text{ in.}^2$$

axial force on piston $= 800 \times 2 \cdot 356$

$$= 1{,}882 \text{ lb}$$

area of rod $= \frac{\pi}{4} \times 1^2 = 0 \cdot 7854 \text{ in.}^2$

tensile stress in rod $= \dfrac{1{,}882}{0 \cdot 7854}$

$$= \textbf{2,400 lb/in.}^2$$

Example. A boiler shell is 6 ft 6 in. internal diameter and is made of plate 0·8 in. thick. If the working pressure is 250 lb/in.² and the efficiency of the longitudinal joint is 75 per cent find the average hoop stress in the plate at the joint.

Solution

For the solid plate

$$\text{hoop stress} = \frac{pr}{t}$$

$$= \frac{250 \times 39}{0\cdot 8}$$

$$= 12{,}190 \text{ lb/in.}^2$$

For the riveted plate

$$\text{average hoop stress} = \frac{12{,}190}{0\cdot 75}$$

$$= \mathbf{16{,}230 \ lb/in.}^2$$

Example. A cylindrical pressure vessel has an internal diameter of 5 ft and is subject to an internal fluid pressure of 400 lb/in.² The plate is $\frac{1}{2}$ in. thick with an ultimate tensile stress of 40 tons/in.² The efficiencies of the circumferential and longitudinal joints are 55 and 70 per cent, respectively. Determine the factor of safety.

Solution

For the solid plate

$$\text{hoop stress} = \frac{pr}{t}$$

$$= \frac{400 \times 30}{0\cdot 5}$$

$$= 24{,}000 \text{ lb/in.}^2$$

At the longitudinal joint

$$\text{hoop stress} = \frac{24{,}000}{0\cdot 7}$$

$$= 34{,}300 \text{ lb/in.}^2$$

For the solid plate

$$\text{axial stress} = \frac{24{,}000}{2} = 12{,}000 \text{ lb/in.}^2$$

At the circumferential joint

$$\text{axial stress} = \frac{12,000}{0\cdot55}$$

$$= 21,800 \text{ lb/in.}^2$$

thus $\qquad \text{factor of safety*} = \dfrac{\text{ultimate tensile stress}}{\text{maximum stress}}$

$$= \frac{40 \times 2,240}{34,300}$$

$$= 2\cdot61$$

Therefore the factor of safety for the vessel is **2·61**.

* The ultimate tensile stress is discussed in Chapter 14. It is the tensile stress at which a bar in tension will break. In practice, the maximum stress allowed is a fraction of this value. The ratio

$$\frac{\text{ultimate tensile stress}}{\text{allowable stress}}$$

is called the *factor of safety*.

PROBLEMS

1. Calculate the maximum allowable pressure in a boiler shell of 8 ft diameter 1 in. thick if the tensile stress is not to exceed 4 tons/in.^{2} Assume a joint efficiency of 60 per cent.

$$(112 \text{ lb/in.}^2)$$

2. What is the minimum shell thickness required for a Lancashire boiler of 8 ft inside diameter for a pressure of 200 lb/in.^{2} if the allowable stress is not to exceed 3·33 tons/in.^{2}? Allow for a joint efficiency of 65 per cent.

$$(1\cdot98 \text{ in.})$$

3. Calculate the maximum allowable diameter for a spherical pressure vessel for a nuclear reactor if it is to contain carbon dioxide at a pressure of 150 lb/in.^{2} The tensile stress in the shell wall is to be 5 tons/in.^{2} and the maximum thickness of vessel shell that can be manufactured is 3 in.

$$(74\cdot66 \text{ ft})$$

4. A spherical copper shell is 2 ft in internal diameter and is to withstand an internal pressure of 300 lb/in.^{2} without the stress in the copper exceeding 4 tons/in.^{2} Find the thickness of shell required assuming a joint efficiency of 80 per cent.

$$(0\cdot251 \text{ in.})$$

5. An air receiver for a compressor is 6 ft in internal diameter and made of plate 0·6 in. thick. If the hoop stress is not to exceed 6 tons/in.^{2} and the axial stress is not to exceed 4 tons/in.^{2} find the maximum safe air pressure.

$$(224 \text{ lb/in.}^2)$$

6. A bronze sleeve of 3 in. internal diameter and $\frac{1}{4}$ in. thick is force fitted on to a solid steel shaft. The force fitting of the sleeve on to the shaft subjects it to an internal radial pressure. A measurement of hoop strain in the sleeve shows that the corresponding hoop stress is 6·4 tons/in.^{2} Find the radial pressure between sleeve and shaft.

$$(2,390 \text{ lb/in.}^2)$$

7. A thin spherical vessel is to contain 3,000 ft³ of gas at a pressure of 200 lb/in.² The stress in the material must not exceed 8 tons/in.² Find the internal diameter of the vessel and the thickness of plate required.

(17·9 ft; 0·6 in.)

8. A metal tube of 1·5 in. mean diameter and 0·08 in. thick is tested in tension and fails at a load of 15,000 lb. A similar tube is used to contain fluid under pressure. Find the safe internal pressure allowing a factor of safety of 4.

(106·2 lb/in.²)

9. A dumb-bell piston forming part of a hydraulic control valve slides freely in the cylinder shown, Fig. 13.18. The pressure in the cylinder at A is 600

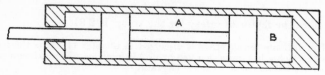

Fɪɢ. 13.18

lb/in.² and that in B is 100 lb/in.² Calculate the largest hoop and axial stresses in the cylinder. Internal diameter of cylinder is 2 in., wall thickness $\frac{1}{16}$ in.

(9,600, 800 lb/in.²)

13.14. Rotating Rims

A circular thin ring rotating about an axis through its centre O with angular velocity ω rad/sec is subject to an inertia force acting

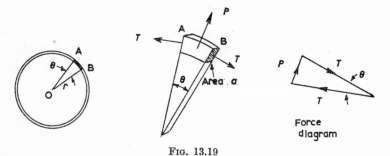

Fɪɢ. 13.19

radially outwards on every element. For any small arc AB (Fig. 13.19) subtending an angle θ rad at the centre, the inertia (centrifugal) force is

$$P = \frac{W}{g}\,\omega^2 r$$

where W is the weight of the element AB.

If w is the specific weight of the material and a the cross-sectional area of the ring section, then

$$W = w \times \text{AB} \times a$$
$$= w \times r\theta \times a$$

hence

$$P = \frac{wr\theta a}{g} \times \omega^2 r$$

$$= \frac{w\theta a\omega^2 r^2}{g}$$

The element is maintained in equilibrium by the inertia force P and by the tangential forces T at A and B exerted by the material of the ring at these points. Thus a tensile force is set up in the ring, as in a thin cylinder under internal pressure. From the force diagram, since θ is *small*—

$$T\theta = P = \frac{w\theta a\omega^2 r^2}{g}$$

thus

$$T = \frac{wa\omega^2 r^2}{g}$$

If f is the stress set up due to T, then

$$f \times a = T$$

$$= \frac{wa\omega^2 r^2}{g}$$

thus

$$f = \frac{w\omega^2 r^2}{g}$$

The tensile stress in the ring is therefore independent of the area of section of the ring. The effect of radial spokes or a disk connecting the ring to its axis of rotation has been neglected.

Example. A thin cylindrical spring steel tube of $\frac{1}{8}$ in. mean radius is required to rotate at 500,000 rev/min when used in a machine for spinning nylon. Calculate the maximum tensile stress in the tube. Specific weight of steel, 460 lb/ft³.

Solution

$$r = \tfrac{1}{8} \text{ in.}$$

$$w = \frac{460}{12^3} = 0 \!\cdot\! 266 \text{ lb/in.}^3$$

$$g = 32 \!\cdot\! 2 \times 12 = 386 \!\cdot\! 4 \text{ in./sec}^2$$

$$\omega = \frac{2\pi \times 500,000}{60} = 52,400 \text{ rad/sec}^2$$

$$\text{maximum tensile stress} = \frac{w\omega^2 r^2}{g}$$

$$= \frac{0\cdot266 \times 52{,}400^2 \times (\tfrac{1}{8})^2}{386\cdot4}$$

$$= \mathbf{29{,}500 \ lb/in.^2}$$

Example. A flywheel may be taken as a thin ring having a rim section 2 in. by 2 in. The flywheel is to rotate at 420 rev/min. Find the least value of the mean diameter to satisfy the following conditions: (a) the tensile stress in the material must not exceed 1 ton/in.²; (b) the total weight of the flywheel must be less than 250 lb. Specific weight of material = 0·25 lb/in.³

Solution

$$\omega = \frac{2\pi \times 420}{60} = 44 \ \text{rad/sec}$$

If the tensile stress is limited to 1 ton/in.² then

$$w = 0\cdot25 \ \text{lb/in.}^3$$

$$f = \frac{w\omega^2 r^2}{g}$$

thus

$$r^2 = \frac{fg}{\omega^2 w}$$

$$= \frac{1 \times 2{,}240 \times 32\cdot2 \times 12}{44^2 \times 0\cdot25}$$

$$= 1{,}790$$

therefore $\qquad r = 42\cdot3 \ \text{in.}$

and   mean diameter $\leqslant 84\cdot6$ in. or 7·05 ft

If total weight is limited to 250 lb, then

weight = area of section × mean circumference × density

i.e. $250 = (2 \times 2) \times \pi d \times 0\cdot25$

hence, mean diameter is given by

$$d \leqslant 79\cdot6 \ \text{in.} \quad \text{or} \quad 6\cdot63 \ \text{ft}$$

Hence the least diameter to satisfy both conditions = **6·63 ft.**

PROBLEMS

1. Calculate the tensile stress in a thin rim of mean diameter 3 ft rotating at 600 rev/min, if the material used weighs 0·26 lb/in.³

(864 lb/in.²)

2. Calculate the maximum allowable speed of rotation of a cast-iron ring 4 ft diameter if the design stress is 1·6 ton/in.^{2} and cast iron weighs 0·25 lb/in.^{3}

(935 rev/min)

3. What is the required mean diameter of a flywheel which has to rotate at a maximum speed of 2,165 rev/min with a maximum permissible stress of 5 tons/in.^{2}? Specific weight of material = 0·26 lb/in.^{3}

(3·06 ft)

4. A cast-steel flywheel has a rim of square cross-section 3 in. × 3 in. The wheel has to rotate at 900 rev/min. Find the value of the least mean diameter to satisfy the following conditions: (a) the total weight of the wheel must be less than 500 lb; (b) the stress in the steel must not exceed 2 tons/in.^{2} Specific weight of steel = 0·28 lb/in.^{3}

(4·4 ft)

5. A thin steel tube of ½ in. mean diameter and 0·02 in. thick rotates at 19,000 rev/min and carries an internal pressure of 100 lb/in.^{2} Calculate the maximum hoop stress in the tube wall if its specific weight is 0·26 lb/in.^{2}

(1,417 lb/in.^{2})

6. A thin steel drum is required to rotate at 4,200 rev/min whilst the pressure inside the drum is 200 lb/in.^{2} If the drum is to be made from ¼ in. plate find the maximum diameter for a limiting tensile stress of 5 tons/in^2. Specific weight of steel = 0·28 lb/in.^{3}

(13·06 in.)

14

Properties of Materials

14.1. Black Mild Steel in Tension

BLACK mild steel is a low-carbon steel in a hot-rolled or annealed condition. A tension test on a typical specimen would give the graph of load against extension shown in Fig. 14.1.

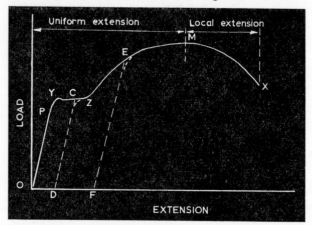

FIG. 14.1. BLACK MILD STEEL IN TENSION

ELASTIC STAGE

In the initial stage of the test the steel is elastic, i.e. when unloaded the test piece returns to its original unstretched length. This is represented by the line OP, Fig. 14.1. Over the major portion of this stage the material obeys Hooke's law, i.e. the extension is proportional to the load and the strain is proportional to the stress.

LIMIT OF PROPORTIONALITY

The point P represents the *limit of proportionality*. Beyond P the metal no longer obeys Hooke's law.

ELASTIC LIMIT

The stress at which a permanent extension occurs is the *elastic limit stress*. The metal is no longer elastic. In black mild steel the limit of proportionality and elastic limit are very close together and often cannot be distinguished.

PERMANENT SET

If the metal is loaded beyond the point P representing the elastic limit, and then unloaded, a permanent extension remains, called the *permanent set*.

YIELD STRESS

At Y the metal stretches without further increase in load. Y is termed the *yield point* and the corresponding stress is the *yield stress*. This sharp yield is typical of mild carbon steel and occurs with few other metals.

PLASTIC STAGE

Beyond Y the steel is said to be *plastic*. If the test piece is unloaded from any point C beyond Y the permanent extension would be OD, approximately, where CD represents the unloading line (approximately parallel to PO). If the specimen is reloaded immediately the load–extension graph would tend to traverse first the line DC and then continue from near C as before.

WORK HARDENING

At the point Z further extension requires an increase in load and the steel is said to *work harden* or increase in strength. If unloaded from any point E between Z and M the unloading graph would be approximately the line EF. If reloaded immediately the graph would trace out approximately the same elastic line from F to E, after which it continues from E to M, as it would have done if not unloaded. The process of *cold working*, i.e. cold drawing or rolling, represents a work hardening or strengthening of this nature.

During the stage Z to M the mill scale on an unmachined specimen of black mild steel is seen to flake off from the stretched metal. Furthermore, the extension is now no longer small but could be measured roughly with a simple rule.

WAISTING

M represents the *maximum load* which the test piece can carry. At this point the extension is no longer uniform along the length of the specimen but is localized at one portion. The test piece begins to *neck down* or *waist*, the area at the waist decreasing rapidly. Local extension continues with a decrease of load until fracture occurs at point X.

Ultimate Tensile Stress

The *ultimate tensile stress* (U.T.S.) is defined as—

$$\frac{\text{maximum load}}{\text{original area}}$$

Breaking Stress

The *nominal fracture* or *breaking stress* is—

$$\frac{\text{load at fracture}}{\text{original area}}$$

and this is less than the U.T.S. in a metal which necks down before fracture.

True Fracture Stress

The *true* or *actual fracture stress* is—

$$\frac{\text{load at fracture}}{\text{final area at fracture}}$$

and this is greater than either the nominal fracture stress or the U.T.S. in a metal which necks down, due to the reduced area at

fracture. The true stress may be as much as 100 per cent higher than the U.T.S. for mild steel. Also, it may be noted that the true stress is found to be roughly constant for a given material whereas the U.T.S. varies with the treatment of the specimen before testing.

Fracture

The appearance of the fracture is shown in Fig. 14.2. It is described as a cup-and-cone fracture and is typical of a *ductile* material such as mild steel.

Ductility

Fig. 14.2   A material is said to be ductile if it can be drawn out and undergo a considerable plastic deformation before fracture. Ductility in a member of a structure permits it to "give" slightly under load, which is useful where errors in workmanship or non-uniform stresses occur. Ductility is of importance in manufacture where material is to be bent or formed to shape. Ductility is measured in two ways—

1. By the *percentage reduction in area*, which is

$$\frac{\text{reduction in area}}{\text{original area}} \times 100 \text{ per cent}$$

where the reduction in area is the difference between the original area and the least area at the point of fracture.

2. By the *percentage elongation in length*. If a gauge length l is marked on the test piece before testing and the extension of this length after fracture found to be x, then, provided fracture occurred between the gauge points,

$$\text{percentage elongation} = \frac{x}{l} \times 100$$

The percentage elongation depends on the dimensions of the test piece so that, for the purposes of comparison, the dimensions have been standardized. It is found that for cylindrical test pieces, if the ratio of gauge length to diameter is kept constant, the percentage elongation is constant for a given material. Gauge lengths of 2 in. and 8 in. are normally used. The standard test piece for a round

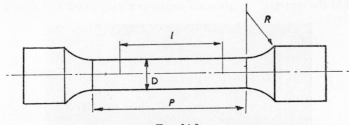

FIG. 14.3

bar in tension (BSS. 18) is shown in Fig. 14.3. The dimensions are shown below.

Gauge length, l (in.)	2
Diameter, D (in.)	0·564
Radius, R, minimum (in.)	0·5
Area (in.²)	0·25
P, minimum (in.)	2·25

There appears to be no simple relation between percentage elongation and percentage reduction in area for steels. To estimate ductility both ratios should be found as some steels show a high percentage elongation with a low percentage reduction in area.

STRESS–STRAIN CURVE

Since the nominal stress is

$$\frac{\text{load}}{\text{original area}}$$

and the strain is

$$\frac{\text{extension}}{\text{original gauge length}}$$

the curve of (nominal) stress against strain will be of the same shape as the load–extension graph up to the maximum load. Beyond this point the extension is non-uniform and the ratio of extension to gauge length no longer measures the true strain at any point. Similarly the area of the test piece has been reduced so much as to make the ratio of load to original area an inaccurate measure of the *true stress* at the waist. Nevertheless it is convenient to sketch a *stress–strain curve* which illustrates some of the properties of the material independent of the size of the specimen.

14.2. Modulus of Elasticity

The modulus of elasticity E is the ratio of stress to strain taken from a point on the initial straight-line portion of the stress–strain curve. Its value may be affected by the previous treatment or working of the material. It gives the engineer a very quick and accurate

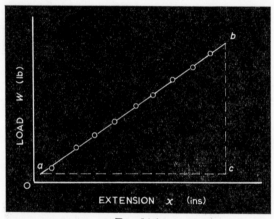

FIG. 14.4

indication of the stiffness of the material since the greater the value of E the greater the slope of the stress–strain graph, and hence the greater the load for a given extension.

Fig. 14.4 represents, for a metal obeying Hooke's law, the best straight line connecting load W and extension x obtained from the plotted experimental points. The modulus of elasticity E is determined directly from the slope of the load–extension graph as follows: If A is the cross-sectional area of the test-piece and l the gauge length, then

$$\text{strain, } e = \frac{x}{l}$$

and

$$\text{stress, } f = \frac{W}{A}$$

and
$$E = \frac{f}{e}$$
$$= \frac{W/A}{x/l}$$
$$= \frac{l}{A} \times \frac{W}{x}$$

But W/x is the slope of the load–extension graph, i.e. bc/ac. Therefore

$$E = \frac{l}{A} \times \frac{bc}{ac}$$

The load–extension graph does not usually pass through the point of zero load for two reasons—

1. The specimen is lightly loaded on first gripping in the testing machine.

2. Initial extensometer readings are slightly inaccurate at light loads.

However, since only the slope of the graph is required the zero error is unimportant when calculating the elastic modulus.

14.3. Black Mild Steel in Compression

Up to the limit of proportionality, tension and compression tests on black mild steel give roughly similar stress–strain graphs, the

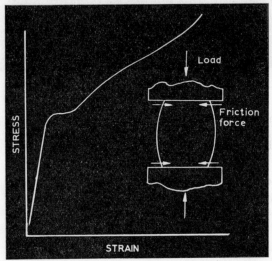

Fig. 14.5. Black Mild Steel in Compression

value of the modulus of elasticity being approximately the same in compression as in tension. A well-defined yield point occurs after which the stress continues to rise with increasing strain, no maximum load or stress being reached. The test specimen can be compressed almost indefinitely. Owing to friction at the surfaces of contact between specimen and compression plattens the metal does not deform uniformly but develops a barrel shape, Fig. 14.5. To avoid buckling under load the length of a cylindrical test piece is usually less than twice the diameter.

14.4. Bright Drawn Mild Steel

Bright drawn mild steel is again low carbon steel, but has been previously worked by cold drawing. The material is stronger but less ductile than the same steel in the form of black mild steel. A typical stress–strain curve in tension would follow the curve OPMX, Fig. 14.6 (*a*). The sharp yield point has disappeared but a limit of proportionality may be determined. If sufficiently cold-worked,

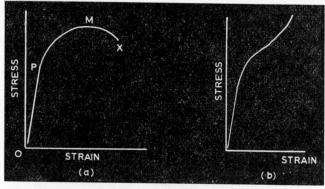

Fig. 14.6. (*a*) Bright Mild Steel in Tension.
(*b*) Bright Mild Steel in Compression

fracture may occur without necking. In compression the stress rises continuously and there is no fracture, Fig. 14.6 (*b*). Bright drawn mild steel when annealed shows the same properties as black mild steel.

14.5. Ductile Metals

Most alloys of aluminium or copper give a stress–strain curve of a similar shape to Fig. 14.6 (*a*).

Hard alloy steels usually have a stress–strain curve as in Fig. 14.6 (*a*), but with fracture occurring between P and M, without prior necking.

Soft metals such as aluminium and copper are more ductile than steel and a tensile test of these materials would give a stress–strain curve of the form shown in Fig. 14.7. The limit of proportionality and yield point are not clearly defined.

14.6. Proof Stress

For engineering purposes it is desirable to know the stress to which a highly ductile material such as aluminium can be loaded safely before a large permanent extension takes place. This stress is known as the *proof* or *offset stress* and is defined as the stress at which a specified permanent extension has taken place in the tensile test. The extension specified is usually 0·1, 0·2 or 0·5 per cent of gauge length.

The proof stress is found from the stress–strain curve, Fig. 14.7, as follows. From the point on the strain axis representing 0·1 per

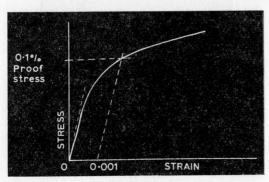

FIG. 14.7

cent strain draw a line parallel to the initial slope of the stress–strain diagram at O. The stress at the point where this line cuts the curve is the 0·1 per cent proof stress. The 0·2 per cent proof stress is found in a similar manner by starting from the point on the strain axis representing 0·2 per cent extension. The larger the value taken for the percentage extension the less the variation in the proof stress for any given material since the effect of errors in the slope of the curve are minimized.

14.7. Brittle Materials

TENSION

Fig. 14.8 shows the stress–strain curve for cast iron, which is a typical brittle material. The metal is elastic almost up to fracture, but does not obey Hooke's law. A metal such as this, which has little plasticity or ductility and does not neck down before fracture is termed *brittle*. The total strain and elongation before fracture occurs is very small. Cast iron fractures straight across the specimen and the cup-and-cone fracture of a ductile material does not occur. The modulus of elasticity for cast iron is not a constant but depends on the portion of the curve from which it is calculated.

COMPRESSION

The stress–strain curve for cast iron is similar to that for a tension test. The metal fractures across planes making 55° with the axis of the specimen, except when the specimen is very short when fracture occurs across several planes.

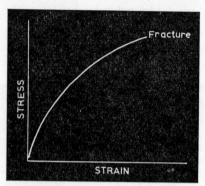

FIG. 14.8. CAST IRON IN TENSION

The brittleness of a material is often best measured by the energy which it will absorb before fracture in an impact test; the lower the energy absorbed by a standard specimen of a given material the greater the brittleness.

14.8. Fatigue

A metal subjected to repeated loading fails at a stress level below the ultimate tensile stress. The term *fatigue failure* is applied to such a fracture. The *fatigue strength* is measured by the number of repetitions of stress before fracture occurs and depends upon the level of both the mean stress and the range of stress. Fatigue is particularly important when the stress is tensile and in the presence of sharp corners, holes or notches. The greatest number of fatigue failures are probably due to reversed bending stresses.

Fatigue failure in a metal causes a slow spreading fracture which has an appearance not unlike that of the fine granulated texture of cast iron. There is usually no sign of plastic deformation so that a fatigue failure may be mistaken for the fracture of a brittle material. On the other hand a brittle-type fracture does not necessarily mean fatigue failure has occurred. A fatigue fracture may show two areas of quite different appearance, Fig. 14.9. The first is crescent-shaped, smooth textured and may have "beach" type markings. This represents the spreading of the fatigue crack. The remaining area is rough and jagged and represents the final tensile fracture after the metal has been greatly weakened with the spread of the fatigue crack.

Most ferrous metals have a "safe" range of stress and a certain stress known as the fatigue limit below which fracture does not occur even after a very large number of cycles of repetition of stress. Non-ferrous metals do not appear to have either a "safe" range or a "fatigue limit."

14.9. Hardness

Hardness is the term used to describe the resistance the surface of a metal offers to indentation, wear or abrasion. Tests for wear

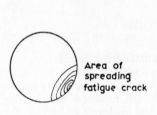

Area of spreading fatigue crack

FIG. 14.9. TYPICAL FATIGUE
FRACTURE IN BENDING

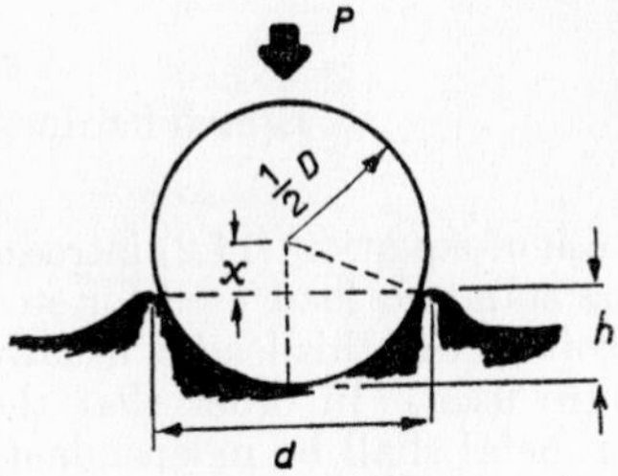

FIG. 14.10

and indentation are quite different and only indentation will be considered.

14.10. The Brinell Hardness Test

This test is performed by pressing a hardened steel ball into the metal for 15 sec with a load great enough to form a permanent indentation. The average diameter of the impression is measured and used to calculate the curved surface area of the impression. The *Brinell hardness number* is defined by the expression—

$$\text{Brinell hardness number} = \frac{\text{load (kg)}}{\text{curved surface area (mm}^2)}$$

Let P be the load (kg), D the diameter of ball (mm), d the diameter of impression (mm), h the depth of impression (mm). Then from Fig. 14.10—

$$h = \tfrac{1}{2} D - x$$

where

$$x^2 = D^2/4 - d^2/4$$

i.e.

$$x = \tfrac{1}{2} \sqrt{(D^2 - d^2)}$$

hence

$$h = \tfrac{1}{2} D - \tfrac{1}{2} \sqrt{(D^2 - d^2)}$$

The curved surface area of a spherical cap is given by—

$$A = \pi D h$$
$$= \tfrac{1}{2}\pi D\{D - \sqrt{(D^2 - d^2)}\}$$
$$= \tfrac{1}{2}\pi D^2\{1 - \sqrt{(1 - d^2/D^2)}\} \qquad . \qquad . \quad \text{(14.1)}$$

Expanding the square root by the binomial theorem

$$A = \tfrac{1}{2}\pi D^2 \left\{1 - \left(1 - \frac{d^2}{2D^2} - \frac{d^4}{8D^4} - \cdots\right)\right\}$$

and neglecting higher powers of d/D

$$A \simeq \tfrac{1}{4}\pi d^2 \left(1 + \frac{d^2}{4D^2}\right) \qquad . \qquad . \qquad . \quad (14.2)$$

Hence

$$\text{Brinell hardness number} = \frac{P}{A}$$

The use of equation (14.2) introduces little error in practice.

The standard load used for steel is 3,000 kg, with a 10 mm ball. For soft metals this load is usually too large and a smaller load and ball are used. In order that the Brinell hardness number for a given metal shall be independent of the load and diameter of ball used it has been shown that the load P should be varied with the diameter D according to the relation—

$$\frac{P}{D^2} = \text{constant}$$

This constant takes the following values—

Steel and cast iron . .	30
Copper alloys . . .	10
Aluminium alloys . . .	10
Copper and aluminium . .	5

For example, if a 2 mm ball is to be used on steel the load P is given by

$$\frac{P}{2^2} = 30$$

i.e.
$$P = 120 \text{ kg}$$

Similarly if a load of 3,000 kg produces an indentation of 4 mm diameter with a 10 mm diameter ball, the indentation diameter d produced by a 120 kg load and a 2 mm ball is found from the principle of geometric similarity to be given by

$$\frac{d}{2} = \frac{4}{10}$$

thus
$$d = 0 \cdot 8 \text{ mm}$$

The following points should be noted—

1. Ordinary steel balls are used up to a Brinell number of about 400; tungsten–carbide balls being used for harder metals up to 700.

2. The Brinell test compares the hardness of the same metal in different conditions of cold work and can be used to compare different materials of a similar hardness number. But the relative hardness of different materials of very different Brinell numbers cannot be ascertained by comparison of the numbers.

3. The test is most useful for metals having a Brinell number of up to about 400 but is generally inadequate for harder metals.

4. The test cannot be used for very thin specimens nor for surface-hardened specimens.

5. There is a useful relation between the Brinell hardness number and the ultimate tensile strength of steel. For most carbon and alloy steels

$$\text{U.T.S.} = 0.23 \times \text{Brinell number, roughly}$$

6. When carrying out the test the following precautions should be taken.

(a) The thickness of the test specimen should be at least ten times the depth of the impression.

(b) The surface should be ground flat and polished.

(c) The centre of the impression should be at least two and a half times the indentation diameter from the edge of the specimen.

14.11. Mechanical Properties

Table 14.1 gives typical values of percentage elongation, yield or 0.1 per cent proof stress and ultimate tensile strength for common

TABLE 14.1

	Percentage elongation (total)	Yield stress (tons/in.^{2})	0.1% proof stress (tons/in.^{2})	Ultimate tensile stress (tons/in.^{2})
Copper, annealed	60	—	4	14
Copper, hard	4	—	21	25
Aluminium, soft	35	—	2	6
Aluminium, hard	5	—	9	10
Black mild steel	25–26	15–18	—	23–25
Bright mild steel	14–17	—	—	28
Structural steel	20	14–16	—	28–33
Stainless steel	60	15	—	38
Cast iron	—	—	—	18–22
Spheroidal graphite cast iron (annealed)	10–25	20–25	—	27–35

engineering materials. These values vary widely, however, for alloys and reference should be made to the corresponding specification or manufacturer's data; for example, "British Standards for Steel and Steel Products," BS. Handbook No. 10.

Example. In a tensile test on a specimen of black mild steel of 0·5 in. diameter the following results were obtained for a gauge length of 8 in.

Load (lb) . .	1,000	2,000	3,000	4,000	5,000	6,000	7,000	8,000
Extension (10^{-3} in.) .	1·4	2·72	4·1	5·4	6·76	8·12	9·6	11·2

When tested to destruction, maximum load = 13,000 lb; load at fracture = 10,000 lb, diameter at fracture = 0·3 in., total extension on gauge length = 2·3 in. Find Young's modulus, ultimate tensile stress, breaking stress, true stress at fracture, limit of proportionality, percentage elongation, percentage reduction in area.

Solution

The load extension graph is plotted in Fig. 14.11 and the slope of the straight line portion determined from the initial part of the best straight line drawn through the experimental points. The gradient of the straight line portion is found to be 732,000 lb/in. Since

$$E = \frac{f}{e} = \frac{P}{A} \times \frac{l}{x} = \frac{l}{A} \times \frac{P}{x}$$

and $\dfrac{P}{x} = 732,000$ lb/in., $l = 8$ in., $A = \dfrac{\pi}{4}\left(\dfrac{1}{2}\right)^2 = 0{\cdot}1965$ in.^{2}

then
$$E = \frac{8}{0{\cdot}1965} \times 732,000$$

$$= \mathbf{29{\cdot}8 \times 10^6 \ lb/in.^2}$$

$$\text{Ultimate tensile stress} = \frac{\text{maximum load}}{\text{area}}$$

$$= \frac{13,000}{0{\cdot}1965}$$

$$= \mathbf{66,200 \ lb/in.^2}$$

$$\text{Breaking stress} = \frac{10,000}{0{\cdot}1965}$$

$$= \mathbf{50,900 \ lb/in.^2}$$

Area at fracture $= \dfrac{\pi}{4}(0\cdot3)^2$

$= 0\cdot0708 \text{ in.}^2$

true stress at fracture $= \dfrac{\text{load at fracture}}{\text{area at fracture}} = \dfrac{10,000}{0\cdot0708}$

$= \mathbf{141,500 \ lb/in.^2}$

Percentage elongation $= \dfrac{\text{extension}}{\text{gauge length}} = \dfrac{2\cdot3}{8} \times 100 \text{ per cent}$

$= \mathbf{28\cdot7 \text{ per cent}}$

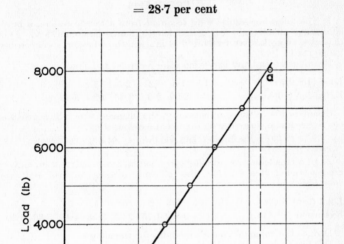

Gradient $\dfrac{P}{x} = \dfrac{ab}{bc} = \dfrac{7750-500}{(10\cdot6-0\cdot7)\times10^{-3}}$

$= \dfrac{7250\times10^3}{9\cdot9}$

$= 732,000 \text{ lb/in}$

Fig. 14.11

$$\text{Percentage reduction in area} = \frac{0\cdot1965 - 0\cdot0708}{0\cdot1965} \times 100 \text{ per cent}$$

$$= \textbf{64 per cent}$$

The load at the limit of proportionality = 6,000 lb approximately

$$\text{limit of proportionality} = \frac{6,000}{0\cdot1965}$$

$$= \textbf{30,500 lb/in.}^2$$

PROBLEMS

1. The following results were recorded from a tensile test on a mild steel specimen: diameter $\frac{1}{2}$ in., gauge length 8 in., maximum load, 13,000 lb, diameter of neck after fracture 0·31 in., length of broken specimen between gauge marks 10·29 in.

Readings of load and extension were recorded as follows:

Load (10^3 lb) .	.	.	1	1·5	2	2·5	3	4	5	6	6·5
Extension (10^{-3} in.)		.	1·40	2·00	2·69	3·60	4·00	5·40	6·81	8·20	8·80

Calculate the modulus of elasticity, the ultimate tensile strength, the percentage reduction in area and the percentage elongation.

$$(30 \times 10^6 \text{ lb/in.}^2; \ 662,000 \text{ lb/in.}^2; \ 61\cdot5\%; \ 28\cdot62\%)$$

2. In a tensile test on an alloy specimen, of gauge length 2 in. and original cross-sectional area 0·25 in.^{2}, the following readings of load and extension were obtained:

Load (ton)	.	.	.	1	2	3	4	5	6	7	8
Extension (10^{-3} in.)	.		.	0·85	1·75	2·65	3·55	4·45	5·35	6·30	7·40

Deduce the value of Young's modulus for the alloy.

In a test to destruction the maximum load recorded was 9·6 ton, the diameter of the neck was 0·42 in., and the length between the gauge marks was 2·65 in. Deduce the ultimate tensile strength, percentage elongation and percentage reduction of area.

$$(9,140 \text{ ton/in.}^2; \ 38\cdot4 \text{ ton/in.}^2; \ 32\cdot5\%; \ 44\cdot5\%)$$

3. In a Brinell hardness test on a steel specimen the following data were recorded: Load 3,000 kg; dia of ball 10 mm; dia of impression 4·2 mm. Deduce the Brinell hardness number for the specimen.

Shear and Torsion

15.1. Shear Stress

IF two equal and opposite parallel forces Q, not in the same straight line, act on parallel faces of a member (Fig. 15.1) then it is said to

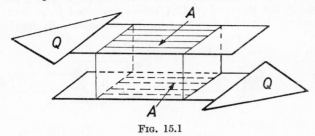

FIG. 15.1

be loaded in *shear*. If the shaded area of cross-section parallel to the applied load is A then the *average shear stress* on the section is—

$$q = \frac{Q}{A}$$

The shear stress, or intensity of shear force, is tangential to the area over which it acts. For example in cutting plate by a guillotine (Fig. 15.2) Q is the total force exerted by the blade and is balanced by an equal and opposite force provided at the edge of the table. The area resisting shear is measured by the plate thickness multiplied by the length of the blade. In a punching operation (Fig. 15.3) the area resisting shear would be the plate thickness multiplied by the perimeter of the hole punched. The ultimate strength in shear of a metal is measured in practice by a punching operation of this type.

The *ultimate shear stress or strength* is defined as

$$\frac{\text{maximum punch load}}{\text{area resisting shear}}$$

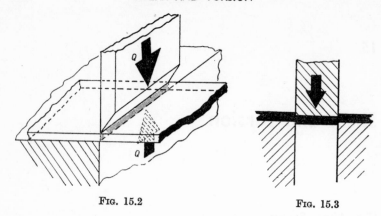

FIG. 15.2   FIG. 15.3

15.2. Riveted Joints

A structural member commonly loaded in shear, but seldom in tension, is the rivet. Fig. 15.4 shows a riveted joint loaded in *single-shear*; Fig. 15.5 shows a joint in *double-shear*. In single-shear

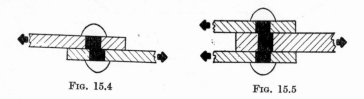

FIG. 15.4   FIG. 15.5

the area resisting shear is the cross-sectional area of the rivet, $\pi d^2/4$, where d is the diameter of the rivet. In double-shear the resisting area is twice the area of section of the rivet, and the load which can be carried is theoretically twice that in single-shear.

Example. A load P of $\frac{1}{2}$ ton is applied to the tensile member shown in Fig. 15.6 and is carried at the joint by a single rivet. The

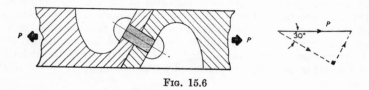

FIG. 15.6

angle of the joint is 60° to the axis of the load. Calculate the tensile and shear stresses in a 1 in. diameter rivet.

Solution

The axis of the rivet is at 30° to the line of action of the load P.

$$\text{Area of rivet} = \frac{\pi}{4} \times 1^2 = 0.7854 \text{ in.}^2$$

direct pull on rivet = component of P along axis of rivet
$$= \tfrac{1}{2} \times \cos 30°$$
$$= \tfrac{1}{2} \times 0.866$$
$$= 0.433 \text{ ton}$$

Therefore

$$\text{direct stress on rivet} = \frac{0.433}{0.7854} = \mathbf{0.552 \text{ ton/in.}^2}, \text{ tensile}$$

Shear force on rivet equals component of P transverse to rivet, i.e. along joint face.

$$\text{Shear force} = \tfrac{1}{2} \times \sin 30°$$
$$= 0.25 \text{ ton}$$

thus $$\text{shear stress on rivet} = \frac{0.25}{0.7854} = \mathbf{0.318 \text{ ton/in.}^2}$$

Note—In this case, where the stress is predominantly tensile rather than shear, the rivet would be replaced by a bolt.

Example. A solid coupling transmits 100 h.p. at 120 rev/min through eight equally spaced bolts (Fig. 15.7). If the bolts are $\tfrac{1}{2}$ in.

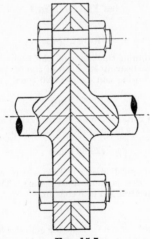

Fig. 15.7

diameter and are on a pitch circle of 6 in. diameter calculate the average shear stress in each bolt.

Solution

$$\text{Horse-power} = \frac{2\pi N T}{33,000}$$

Thus the torque is

$$T = \frac{\text{h.p.} \times 33,000}{2\pi N}$$

$$= \frac{100 \times 33,000}{2\pi \times 120}$$

$$= 4,380 \text{ lb-ft} \quad \text{or} \quad 52,600 \text{ lb-in.}$$

Total shear load at radius of 3 in. is

$$\frac{52,600}{3} = 17,530 \text{ lb}$$

Since bolts are *ductile* it may be assumed that this load is equally distributed among the eight bolts. Therefore

$$\text{load per bolt} = \frac{17,530}{8} = 2,190 \text{ lb}$$

$$\text{area of bolt} = \frac{\pi}{4} \times \left(\frac{1}{2}\right)^2 = 0 \cdot 1963 \text{ in.}^2$$

thus $\qquad$ $$\text{shear stress } q = \frac{2,190}{0 \cdot 1963}$$

$$= \mathbf{11,150 \ lb/in.^2}$$

PROBLEMS

1. Calculate the maximum thickness of plate which can be sheared on a guillotine if the ultimate shearing strength of the plate is 16 tons/in.^{2} and the maximum force the guillotine can exert is 20 tons. The width of the plate is 3 ft.

$$(0 \cdot 0347 \text{ in.})$$

2. A rectangular hole 2 in. by 2·5 in. is punched in a steel plate $\frac{1}{4}$ in. thick. The ultimate shearing stress of the plate is 13 tons/in.^{2} Calculate the load on the punch.

$$(29 \cdot 25 \text{ tons})$$

3. Calculate the maximum diameter of hole which can be punched in $\frac{1}{16}$ in. plate if the punching force is limited to 4 tons. The plate is aluminium having an ultimate shear strength of 6 tons/in.^{2}

$$(3 \cdot 4 \text{ in.})$$

4. A boiler is to be made of a 6 ft diameter cylinder having a riveted single-lap seam. Calculate the minimum number of $\frac{1}{2}$ in. diameter rivets required per foot length of longitudinal seam if the boiler pressure is 20 lb/in.^{2} The ultimate shear stress of each rivet is 21 tons/in.^{2} and a factor of safety of 7 is to be used.

$$(65 \cdot 3, \text{ say, } 7)$$

5. A bar is cut at 45° to its axis and joined by two $\frac{1}{2}$ in. diameter bolts, Fig. 15.8. If the pull in the bar is 8 tons calculate the direct and shear stresses in each bolt.

(14·4 tons/in.²; 14·4 tons/in.²)

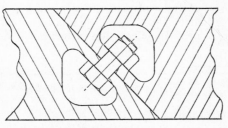

Fig. 15.8

6. A solid coupling is to transmit 300 h.p. at 600 rev/min. The coupling is fastened with six bolts on a pitch circle diameter of 8 in. If the ultimate shear stress is 20 tons/in.² calculate the bolt diameter required. The factor of safety is to be 4.

(0·386 in.)

7. A shaft is to transmit 250 h.p. at 600 rev/min through solid coupling flanges. There are four coupling bolts, each of $\frac{1}{2}$ in. diameter. If the shear stress in each bolt is to be limited to 2·5 tons/in.² calculate the minimum diameter of the circle at which the bolts are to be placed.

(11·92 in.)

8. A gear wheel 1 in. thick is shrunk on to a 2 in. diameter shaft so that the radial pressure at the circle of contact is 1,000 lb/in.² The coefficient of friction between gear wheel and shaft is 0·2 and they are also prevented from relative rotation by a key $\frac{1}{4}$ in. wide, 1 in. long. If the shaft transmits 20 h.p. at 100 rev/min calculate the shear stress in the key.

(45,380 lb/in.²)

9. In a flexible coupling transmitting 40 h.p. at 1,200 rev/min the pins transmitting the drive are set at a radius of 4 in. If there are four pins and all pins transmit the drive equally, calculate the pin diameters. Allow a safe shear stress of 4,000 lb/in.²

If, due to faulty machining, one pin is ahead of its correct position and may be assumed to take the whole drive, what should be the pin diameter?

(0·2 in.; 0·4 in.)

10. A shaft is to be fitted with a flanged coupling having 8 bolts on a circle of diameter 6 in. The shaft may be subject *either* to a direct tensile load of 40 ton *or* to a twisting-moment of 13,000 lb-ft. If the maximum direct and shearing stresses permissible in the bolt material are 8 ton/in.² and 3·5 ton/in.² respectively find the minimum diameter of bolt required. Assume each bolt takes an equal share of the load or torque. Using this bolt diameter and assuming only one bolt to carry the full torque what would then be the shearing stress in the bolt?

(1·027 in., using torque data; 28 ton/in.²)

15.3. Shear Strain

Fig. 15.9 shows an element of material rigidly fixed at one face DC and subject to a shearing stress q on the parallel face AB. The element will deform, and the deformation may be taken as similar to that which would take place if the element were made up of a number of thin independent layers, each layer slipping relative to its neighbour below. In effect, the element will deform to the

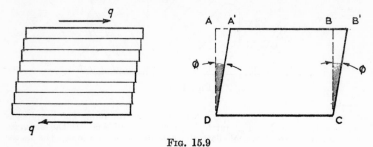

Fig. 15.9

rhombus DA'B'C. The *shear strain* is defined as the angle of deformation ADA' (or BCB') in radians. Since shear strain is small

$$\phi = \angle ADA'$$

$$\simeq \frac{AA'}{AD} \text{ rad}$$

15.4. Relation between Shear Stress and Shear Strain: Modulus of Rigidity

By analogy with the tensile stress–strain relation for an elastic material we write for shear—

$$\frac{\text{shear stress}}{\text{shear strain}} = \text{constant}, G$$

i.e.

$$\frac{q}{\phi} = G$$

where the constant G is known as the modulus of rigidity of the material. The units of G are those of stress, i.e. pounds per square inch (lb/in.²).

For most carbon steels the value of G is about 12×10^6 lb/in.² or 5,350 tons/in.² For cast-iron and ductile materials such as copper, aluminium, bronze, G lies between 4 and 6×10^6 lb/in.²

15.5. Torsion of a Thin Tube

Consider the thin tube shown in Fig. 15.10. The mean radius is r, and the thickness of wall, t, is very small compared with r. If a

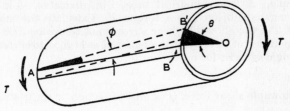

Fig. 15.10

twisting moment T is applied to both ends of the tube, one end will twist *relative* to the other. A strip AB parallel to the tube axis will distort to AB′. If it is assumed that the displacement BB′ is small compared with the length of tube AB, then AB′ will be approximately straight. Then angle $\angle$BOB′ is the *angle of twist* θ of the length AB. The *shear strain* is

$$\phi \simeq \frac{BB'}{AB} = \frac{r\theta}{l} \text{ rad} \qquad . \qquad . \qquad . \qquad (15.1)$$

since BB′ $= r\theta$, and AB $=$ length of tube, l.

The shear force on the cross-section of the tube is

$$Q = \frac{\text{torque}}{\text{radius}} = \frac{T}{r}$$

This force acts on area $2\pi rt$, since the tube is thin. Therefore

$$\text{shear stress } q = \frac{\text{shear force}}{\text{area}} = \frac{Q}{2\pi rt}$$

$$= \frac{T/r}{2\pi rt}$$

$$= \frac{T}{2\pi r^2 t} \qquad . \qquad . \qquad . \qquad . \qquad (15.2)$$

Also from $q/\phi = G$, the modulus of rigidity, substituting for ϕ from equation (15.1)—

$$\frac{q}{r\theta/l} = G$$

hence $\qquad\qquad\qquad \frac{q}{r} = \frac{G\theta}{l} \qquad . \qquad . \qquad . \qquad (15.3)$

Note—(a) for a given torque the angle of twist varies directly with the length; (b) in these formulae the twist θ must be in radians.

Example. A *thin* cylindrical tube, 1 in. diameter, $\frac{1}{16}$ in. thick, 12 in. long, is subjected to a torque T. Calculate the maximum value of T if the allowable shear stress is not to exceed 5,000 lb/in.² If the modulus of rigidity of the material is $11\cdot5 \times 10^6$ lb/in.² what is the angle of twist for maximum torque?

Solution

Allowable shear force, Q = area of section $\times$ shear stress

$$= 2\pi rt \times q = 2\pi \times \tfrac{1}{2} \times \tfrac{1}{16} \times 5{,}000$$

$$= 982 \text{ lb}$$

Maximum torque, $T = Q \times r = 982 \times \tfrac{1}{2}$

$$= \mathbf{491 \text{ lb-in.}}$$

Since
$$\frac{G\theta}{l} = \frac{q}{r}$$

then
$$\theta = \frac{ql}{rG} = \frac{5{,}000}{1/2} \times \frac{12}{11\cdot5 \times 10^6}$$

$$= 0\cdot01043 \text{ rad}$$

$$= \mathbf{0\cdot597°}$$

PROBLEMS

1. A *thin* steel tube 3·5 in. inside diameter is subject to a torque of 2 ton-in. (a) If the shear stress is not to exceed 4,000 lb/in.² calculate the tube thickness. (b) If the twist is not to exceed 0·1 in. of arc on a 2 ft length what would be the thickness required? $G = 12 \times 10^6$ lb/in.²

$$(0\cdot0582 \text{ in.}; \quad 0\cdot00466 \text{ in.})$$

2. A *thin* tube $\frac{1}{16}$ in. thick, 3 in. mean diameter is subjected to a torque of 3,000 lb-in. Calculate (a) the shear stress in the tube, (b) the twist on a 3 ft length. $G = 12 \times 10^6$ lb/in.²

$$(3{,}400 \text{ lb/in.}^2; \quad 0\cdot0068 \text{ rad or } 0\cdot39°)$$

15.6. Twisting of Solid Shafts

To derive the relation between torque, angle of twist and shear stress for a solid shaft of diameter d we make the following assumptions—

1. The shaft is composed of a succession of thin concentric tubes.

2. Each thin tube carries shear force independent of, and without interfering with, its neighbours.

3. Lines which are radial before twisting are assumed to remain radial after twisting.

4. The shaft is not stressed beyond the elastic limit.

For any elementary thin tube of thickness dr at radius r (Fig. 15.11)—

$$\text{area of section} = 2\pi r \times dr$$

If q is the shear stress at radius r, then

$$\text{shear force on tube} = 2\pi r \, dr \times q$$

thus

$$\text{torque carried by tube} = 2\pi r q \, dr \times r$$

$$= 2\pi r^2 q \, dr$$

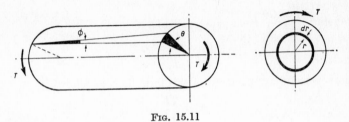

FIG. 15.11

If θ is the angle of twist of the tube in a length l, then from the results of paragraph 15.5—

$$q = \frac{G\theta}{l} r$$

therefore

$$\text{torque carried by tube} = 2\pi r^2 q \, dr$$

$$= 2\pi r^2 \times \frac{G\theta}{l} r \times dr$$

$$= 2\pi \frac{G\theta}{l} r^3 \, dr$$

The whole torque T carried by the solid shaft is the sum of all the elementary torques, i.e.

$$T = \int_0^{d/2} 2\pi \frac{G\theta}{l} r^3 \, dr$$

Since radial lines before twisting remain radial after twisting θ is therefore the same for all the thin tubes making up the shaft. Also G and l are constant, therefore—

$$T = \frac{G\theta}{l} \int_0^{d/2} 2\pi r^3 \, dr \qquad . \qquad . \qquad . \quad (15.4)$$

$$= \frac{G\theta}{l} J$$

where
$$J = \int_0^{d/2} 2\pi r^3 \, dr$$

$$= \frac{\pi d^4}{32}$$

which is the *polar second moment of area* of a shaft of circular section. Hence, rearranging equation (15.4)—

$$\frac{T}{J} = \frac{G\theta}{l}$$

and, since $\dfrac{q}{r} = \dfrac{G\theta}{l}$ from paragraph 15.5—

$$\frac{T}{J} = \frac{G\theta}{l} = \frac{q}{r} \qquad . \qquad . \qquad . \qquad . \quad (15.5)$$

Another useful arrangement of this formula is as follows—

$$\theta = \frac{Tl}{GJ} . \qquad . \qquad . \qquad . \qquad . \quad (15.6)$$

Some important points should be noted—

1. The angle of twist θ varies *directly* with length l.
2. Since $q = Tr/J$, for a given torque T the shear stress q is proportional to the radius r. Thus the maximum shear stress occurs at the outside surface where $r = d/2$, and the shear stress at the centre of the shaft is zero. Fig. 15.12 shows the variation of q across a diameter.

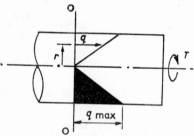

FIG. 15.12. VARIATION OF q WITH RADIUS

15.7. Twisting of Hollow Shafts

If d_2, d_1 are the outside and inside diameters of a hollow shaft subject to a twisting moment T then equation (15.4) becomes

$$T = \frac{G\theta}{l} \int_{d_1/2}^{d_2/2} 2\pi r^3 \, dr$$

$$= \frac{G\theta}{l} J$$

as before, where now—

$$J = \int_{d_1/2}^{d_2/2} 2\pi r^3 \, dr$$

$$= \frac{\pi(d_2{}^4 - d_1{}^4)}{32}$$

Since, from equation (15.5) $q = \dfrac{T}{J} \cdot r$

the maximum shear stress for a given torque is again at the outside fibres of the shaft, where $r = d_2/2$.

Note—For a very thin tube of thickness t, radius r

$$J = \text{area of section} \times r^2$$

$$= 2\pi r t \times r^2$$

$$= 2\pi r^3 t$$

and substituting for J in equation (15.5)—

$$\frac{T}{2\pi r^3 t} = \frac{q}{r} = \frac{G\theta}{l}$$

which agrees with the result of paragraph 15.5.

15.8. Stiffness and Strength

The *stiffness* or *torsional rigidity* of a shaft is the torque to produce unit angle of twist. Thus if a torque T produces a twist θ then

$$\text{stiffness} = \frac{T}{\theta} = \frac{GJ}{l}$$

The *strength* of a shaft is measured by the torque it can transmit for a given permissible value of the maximum shear stress. For a given shear stress therefore the strengths of two shafts are in the ratio of the corresponding torques. Alternatively, for a given torque, the strengths are in the ratio of the maximum allowable shear stresses produced.

15.9. Horse-power and Torque

If a shaft transmits horse-power at N rev/min, the torque T in pound-feet (lb-ft) carried by the shaft is given by

$$\text{horse-power} = \frac{\text{work done by torque per minute}}{33,000}$$

$$= \frac{\text{torque (lb-ft)} \times \text{speed (rad/min)}}{33,000}$$

$$= \frac{2\pi N T}{33,000}$$

since speed $= 2\pi N$ rad/min.

Example. Compare the torsional stiffness of a solid shaft 2 in. diameter, 12 in. long, with that of a hollow shaft of the same material having diameters 3 in., 2 in. and length 8 in.

Solution

$$\text{Torsional stiffness} = \frac{T}{\theta} = \frac{GJ}{l}$$

which is proportional to J/l since G is constant.

For the solid shaft—

$$J = \frac{\pi}{32} \times 2^4 = \frac{\pi}{2} \text{ in.}^4$$

thus

$$\frac{J}{l} = \frac{\pi/2}{12} = \frac{\pi}{24} \text{ in.}^3$$

For the hollow shaft—

$$J = \frac{\pi(3^4 - 2^4)}{32} = 2 \cdot 03\pi \text{ in.}^4$$

therefore

$$\frac{J}{l} = \frac{2 \cdot 03\pi}{8} = 0 \cdot 254\pi \text{ in.}^3$$

thus ratio of stiffnesses—

$$\frac{\text{hollow shaft}}{\text{solid shaft}} = \frac{0 \cdot 254\pi}{\pi/24}$$

$$= \mathbf{6 \cdot 1 : 1}$$

i.e. the hollow shaft is 6·1 times as stiff in torsion as the solid shaft.

Example. A shaft used in an aircraft engine is of 2 in. diameter. The maximum allowable shear stress is 12,000 lb/in.² Find the torsional strength of the shaft. If the shaft now has a hole bored in it find the percentage reductions in strength and weight, (*a*) if the hole is 1½ in. diameter, (*b*) if the hole is 1 in. diameter. The hole is concentric with the shaft axis.

Solution

The strength of the shaft is the torque it can transmit for the given shear stress—

$$J = \frac{\pi}{32} \times 2^4 = \frac{\pi}{2} \text{ in.}^4$$

$$\frac{T}{J} = \frac{q}{d/2}$$

therefore

$$T = \frac{12,000 \times \pi/2}{1}$$

$$= \mathbf{18,850 \text{ lb-in.}}$$

(a) When a hole $1\frac{1}{2}$ in. diameter is bored—

$$J = \frac{\pi(2^4 - 1\cdot5^4)}{32} = 0\cdot342\pi \text{ in.}^4$$

$$T = \frac{qJ}{\frac{1}{2}d_1}$$

$$= \frac{12,000 \times 0\cdot342\pi}{1}$$

$$= 12,860 \text{ lb-in.}$$

thus percentage reduction in strength is given by—

$$\left(\frac{18,850 - 12,860}{18,850}\right) \times 100 = \mathbf{31\cdot8 \text{ per cent}}$$

For a given length the weight of shaft varies with the cross-sectional area. Therefore percentage reduction in weight equals percentage reduction in area, i.e.

$$\frac{(\pi/4) \times 2^2 - (\pi/4)(2^2 - 1\cdot5^2)}{(\pi/4) \times 2^2} \times 100 = \mathbf{56\cdot25 \text{ per cent}}$$

(b) When a hole of 1 in. diameter is bored—

$$J = 0\cdot469\pi \text{ in.}^4$$

$$T = 17,700 \text{ lb-in.}$$

percentage reduction in strength = **6·1 per cent**

percentage reduction in weight = **25 per cent**

Example. A solid shaft is to transmit 1,000 h.p. at 200 rev/min. If the shaft is not to twist more than 1° on a length of twelve diameters, and the shear stress is not to exceed 3 tons/in.², calculate the minimum shaft diameter required. $G = 12 \times 10^6 \text{ lb/in.}^2$

Solution

$$\text{Torque } T = \frac{\text{h.p.} \times 33,000}{2\pi N}$$

$$= \frac{1,000 \times 33,000}{2\pi \times 200}$$

$$= 26,300 \text{ lb-ft} \quad \text{or} \quad 315,500 \text{ lb-in.}$$

There are two independent conditions to be satisfied in this problem The torque is limited by *both* the twist *and* the shear stress.

For condition of twist—

$$1° = \frac{\pi}{180} \text{ rad}$$

$$l = 12 \, d$$

and

$$\frac{T}{J} = \frac{G\theta}{l}$$

thus

$$\frac{315,000}{\pi d^4/32} = \frac{12 \times 10^6 \times \pi/180}{12 \, d}$$

and

$$d^3 = 184$$

i.e.

$$d = 5\!\cdot\!7 \text{ in.}$$

For condition of maximum shear stress—

$$q = 3 \text{ tons/in.}^2$$

$$\frac{T}{J} = \frac{q}{\frac{1}{2} d}$$

therefore

$$\frac{315,000}{\pi d^4/32} = \frac{3 \times 2,240}{\frac{1}{2} d}$$

$$d^3 = 239$$

and

$$d = 6\!\cdot\!2 \text{ in.}$$

The *least* diameter to satisfy both conditions is therefore $d = \mathbf{6\!\cdot\!2}$ **in.**

Example. A phosphor–bronze shaft of 2 in. diameter and 24 in. long is bored for part of its length to a diameter of 1 in. and subjected to a twisting moment. (*a*) If the angle of twist in the length of 1 in. bore is to equal that in the length of solid shaft find the length which has to be bored. (*b*) What is the total angle of twist when the shaft transmits 25 h.p. at 420 rev/min? (*c*) Compare the maximum shear stresses produced in the two portions of shaft. $G = 6 \times 10^6 \text{ lb/in.}^2$

Solution

(*a*) Fig. 15.13 shows the shaft, *l* being the unknown length of bored shaft in inches. Since

$$\theta = \frac{Tl}{GJ}$$

then for solid shaft

$$J = \frac{\pi}{32} \times 2^4 = 1\!\cdot\!57 \text{ in.}^4$$

therefore

$$\theta = \frac{T \times (24 - l)}{G \times 1\!\cdot\!57} \qquad . \qquad . \qquad . \quad (15.7)$$

for hollow shaft

$$J = \frac{\pi(2^4 - 1^4)}{32} = 1 \cdot 47 \text{ in.}^4$$

thus

$$\theta = \frac{Tl}{G \times 1 \cdot 47} \qquad . \qquad . \qquad . \qquad . \qquad (15.8)$$

equating the two values of θ—

$$\frac{Tl}{G \times 1 \cdot 47} = \frac{T(24 - l)}{G \times 1 \cdot 57}$$

hence

$$l = \textbf{11·6 in.}$$

(b)

$$T = \frac{25 \times 33{,}000}{2\pi \times 420}$$

$$= 312 \cdot 5 \text{ lb-ft}$$

$$= 3{,}750 \text{ lb-in.}$$

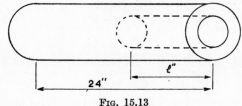

FIG. 15.13

From equation (15.8)—

$$\theta = \frac{Tl}{G \times 1 \cdot 47} = \frac{3{,}750 \times 11 \cdot 6}{6 \times 10^6 \times 1 \cdot 47}$$

$$= 0 \cdot 00494 \text{ rad or } 0 \cdot 283°$$

thus   total angle of twist for whole shaft $= 2 \times 0 \cdot 283° = \textbf{0·566}°$

(c) The maximum shear stress occurs at the outside surface for both portions. Since

$$\frac{T}{J} = \frac{q}{r}$$

then for the solid shaft

$$\frac{3{,}750}{1 \cdot 57} = \frac{q}{1}$$

therefore

$$q = \textbf{2,390 lb/in.}^2$$

for the hollow shaft

$$\frac{3{,}750}{1 \cdot 47} = \frac{q}{1}$$

thus

$$q = \textbf{2,550 lb/in.}^2$$

PROBLEMS

1. A hollow shaft, of 2 in. internal diameter and $\frac{1}{2}$ in. thick, twists through an angle of $1\cdot 2°$ in a length of 8 ft when subjected to a torque of 746 lb-ft. Calculate the modulus of rigidity for the material.

$$(2,870 \text{ tons/in.}^2)$$

2. The propeller shaft of an aircraft engine is steel tubing of 3 in. external and 2·5 in. internal diameter. The shaft is to transmit 200 h.p. at 1,650 rev/min. The failing stress in shear for this shaft is 20,000 lb/in.^{2} What is the factor of safety?

$$(7\cdot 17)$$

3. An aluminium alloy bar was tested in tension and torsion. The tension test on one portion of 0·8 in. diameter showed an extension of 0·0136 in. with a load of 4 tons measured on a gauge length of 8 in. The torsion test on a second portion of 0·564 in. diameter showed an angle of twist of 0·125 rad on a gauge length of 10 in. when the torque was 26 lb-ft. Find E and G for the material.

$$(4,680 \text{ tons/in.}^2; \ 1,120 \text{ tons/in.}^2)$$

4. A hollow shaft is to transmit 2,600 h.p. at 2,400 rev/min. The external diameter is to be 1·3 times the internal diameter. The maximum torque may be taken as 20 per cent greater than the average value and the maximum shear stress is limited to 10 tons/in.^{2} Find the external diameter of the shaft.

$$(3\cdot 06 \text{ in.})$$

5. For phosphor-bronze the relation between the moduli of elasticity and rigidity may be taken as

$$E = 2\cdot 6\,G$$

A tensile specimen of this material, of diameter 0·8 in., extended by 0·003 in. on a gauge length of 2 in. when the load applied was 11,000 lb. What would be the angle of twist per foot length on a shaft of the same material (0·8 in. diameter) due to a torque of 10 lb-ft?

$$(0\cdot 00647 \text{ rad or } 0\cdot 37°)$$

6. A brass shaft of $\frac{1}{4}$ in. diameter is tested in torsion. At the limit of proportionality the torque is 5 lb-in. and the angle of twist 1·13° on a gauge length of 10 in. Calculate G for the brass.

$$(6\cdot 63 \times 10^6 \text{ lb/in.}^2)$$

7. Calculate the maximum shear stress in a $\frac{1}{4}$ in. diameter bolt when tightened by a force of 10 lb at the end of a 6 in. spanner. What would be the corresponding stress in a $\frac{3}{8}$ in. diameter bolt?

$$(19,600 \text{ lb/in.}^2; \ 5,800 \text{ lb/in.}^2)$$

8. A gear wheel is keyed to a 2 in. diameter shaft by a square section key of width w in. and length 2 in. The load on the wheel teeth amounts to 1,000 lb at a radius of 6 in. If the shear stress in the key is to be twice the maximum shear stress in the shaft calculate the width w.

$$(0\cdot 393 \text{ in.})$$

9. A solid circular shaft is connected to the drive shaft of an electric motor by a solid flanged coupling, the drive being taken through eight bolts, of $\frac{1}{2}$ in. diameter, on a pitch circle diameter of 9 in. The bolts carry the whole driving torque and are loaded in shear only. Calculate the shaft diameter if the maximum shear stress in the shaft is to be equal to the shear stress in the bolts.

$$(3\cdot 3 \text{ in.})$$

10. A length of hollow steel shaft is used to drill a hole 10,000 ft deep in rock. The horse-power exerted is 240 h.p. and the speed of rotation of the drill is 60 rev/min. If the inner and outer diameters of the shaft are 6 in. and 7 in., respectively, calculate: (a) the maximum shear stress in the shaft; (b) the twist of one end relative to the other, in revolutions. $G = 12 \times 10^6$ lb/in.²

(8,140 lb/in.²; 3·7 rev)

11. A length of hollow steel shaft transmits 1,200 h.p. at 165 rev/min. The maximum shear stress is not to exceed 8,000 lb/in.² and the inside diameter is to be 0·6 times the outside diameter. Determine (a) the shaft diameters, (b) the shear stress at the *inner* surface of the shaft.

(4·17 in., 6·95 in.; 4,800 lb/in.²)

12. A turbine shaft is to transmit power at 240 rev/min. If the shaft is 40 in. external diameter and 1 in. thick and the maximum shear stress permitted is 10,000 lb/in.² find the horse-power transmitted.

What is the diameter of the equivalent solid shaft and what is the percentage saving in weight of the hollow shaft over the solid?

(88,600; 22·73 in.; 60·5 per cent)

13. Compare the torsional stiffness of a 1 in. diameter solid shaft with that of a hollow shaft of 1½ in. diameter externally. Both shafts are to have the same length, same modulus of rigidity, and same weight. What is the internal diameter of the hollow shaft?

(1 : 3·5; 1·12 in.)

14. Calculate the horse-power which will be transmitted at 220 rev/min by a hollow shaft of 6 in. inside diameter and 2 in. thick, if the maximum shear stress is 10,000 lb/in.² Find the percentage by which the shaft will be stronger if made solid instead of hollow and the external diameter is the same.

(5,980; 14·84 per cent)

15. A hollow shaft driving a ship's screw is to carry a torque of 10,000 lb-ft and is to be of 6 in. diameter externally. Calculate the inside diameter if the maximum shear stress is not to exceed 6,000 lb/in.² Calculate the angle of twist in degrees on an 18 ft length and the *minimum* shear stress. $G = 12 \times 10^6$ lb/in.²

(5·12 in.; 2·06°; 5,120 lb/in.²)

16. For the coupled shaft shown in Fig. 15.4, find (a) diameter d to make the maximum shear stress in the solid and hollow portions the same; (b) the length L to make the angle of twist in both portions the same.

(2·75 in.; 18 in.)

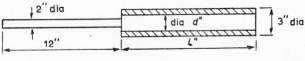

Fɪɢ. 15.14

17. A hollow shaft of alloy steel is 6 in. outside diameter and ½ in. thick. It is to be coupled to a solid shaft of the same material, 5 in. diameter. If the length of the hollow shaft is 48 in. find the length of solid shaft to limit the *total* angle of twist to 2·7° under a torque of 18,000 lb-ft. $G = 10 \times 10^6$ lb/in.²

(89·7 in.)

Shear Force and Bending Moment

16.1. Shear Force

THE *shear force* in a beam at any section is the force transverse to the beam tending to cause it to shear across the section. Fig. 16.1

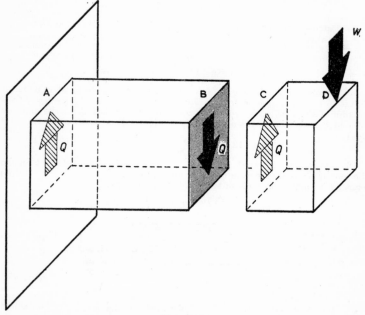

FIG. 16.1

shows a beam under a transverse load W at the free end D; the other end A is built in to the wall. Such a beam is called a *cantilever* and the load W, which is assumed to act at a point, is called a *concentrated* or *point load*.

Consider the equilibrium of any portion of beam CD. At section C for balance of forces there must be an upward force Q equal and opposite to the load W at D. This force Q is provided by the resistance of the beam to shear at the plane B; this plane being coincident with the plane section at C. Q is the shear force at B and in this case is the same magnitude for any section in AD. Consider now the equilibrium of the portion of beam AB. There is a downward force $Q = W$, exerted on plane B, so for balance there must be an upward force Q at A. This latter force being exerted *on* the beam by the wall.

SIGN CONVENTION

The shear force at any section is taken *positive* if the right-hand side tends to slide downwards relative to the left-hand portion, Fig. 16.2. A *negative* shear force tends to cause the right-hand portion to slide upward relative to the left.

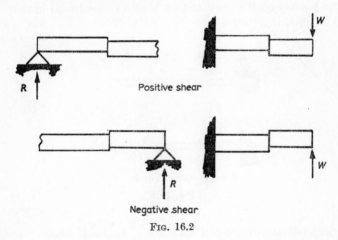

FIG. 16.2

If several loads act on the beam to the right-hand side of section C the shear force at C is the resultant of these loads. Thus *the shear force at any section of a loaded beam is the algebraic sum of the loads to one side of the section.* It does not matter which side of the section is considered provided all loads on that side are taken into account —including the forces exerted by fixings and props.

16.2. Shear Force Diagram

The graph showing the variation of shear force along a beam is known as the *shear force diagram*. For the beam of Fig. 16.1 the shear force was $+ W$, uniform along the beam. Fig. 16.3 shows the shear force diagram for this beam, O–O being the axis of zero shear force.

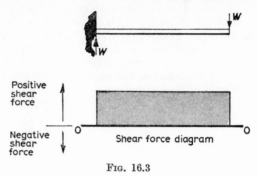

Fɪɢ. 16.3

16.3. Bending Moment

The *bending effect* at any section X of a concentrated load W at D, Fig. 16.4, is measured by the applied moment Wx, where x is

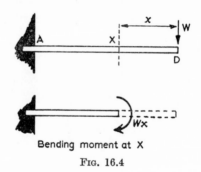

Bending moment at X

Fɪɢ. 16.4

the perpendicular distance of the line of action of W from section X. This moment is called the *bending moment* and is balanced by an equal and opposite moment M exerted by the material of the beam at X, called the *moment of resistance*.

Sɪɢɴ Cᴏɴᴠᴇɴᴛɪᴏɴ

A bending moment is taken as *positive* if its effect is to tend to make the beam *sag* at the section considered, Fig. 16.5. If the moment tends to make the beam bend upward or *hog* at the section it is *negative*.

When more than one load acts on a beam *the bending moment at any section is the algebraic sum of the moments due to all the loads on one side of the section.* It does not matter which side of the section is considered but all loads to that side must be taken into account, including any moments exerted by fixings.

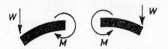

Negative bending moment
Beam hogs

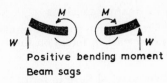

Positive bending moment
Beam sags

W = Load
M = Moment of resistance

Fig. 16.5

16.4. Bending Moment Diagram

The variation of bending moment along the beam is shown in a *bending moment diagram.* For the cantilever beam of Fig. 16.1 the bending moment at any section X is given by—

bending moment $= - Wx$ (negative, since the beam hogs at X)

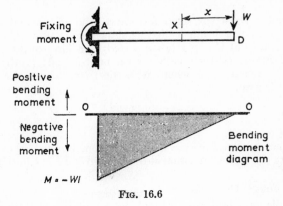

Fig. 16.6

Since there is no other load on the beam this expression for the bending moment applies for the whole length of beam from $x = 0$ to $x = l$. The moment is proportional to x and hence the bending moment diagram is a straight line. Hence the diagram can be drawn by calculating the moment at two points and joining the two corresponding points on the graph by a straight line.

$$\text{At D,} \quad x = 0 \quad \text{and} \quad \text{bending moment} = 0$$
$$\text{at A,} \quad x = l \quad \text{and} \quad \text{bending moment} = -Wl$$

Since the bending moment is everywhere negative the graph is plotted below the line O–O of zero bending moment, Fig. 16.6. At the fixed end A the wall exerts a moment Wl anticlockwise *on* the beam; this is called a *fixing moment*.

16.5. Calculation of Beam Reactions

When a beam is fixed at some point, or supported by props, the fixings and props exert *reaction* forces on the beam. To calculate these reactions the procedure is—

    (*a*) equate the net vertical force to zero;
    (*b*) equate the total moment about any convenient point to zero.

Note—Distinguish carefully between "taking moments" and calculating a "bending moment"—

    1. The Principle of Moments states that the algebraic sum of the moments of all the forces about any point is zero, i.e. when forces *on both sides* of a beam section are considered.
    2. The bending moment is the algebraic sum of the moments of forces *on one side* of the section about that section.

Example. Draw the shear force and bending moment diagrams for the cantilever beam loaded as shown, Fig. 16.7. The vertical load of 2 tons at C is partly supported by a force of 3 tons at the prop B. State: (*a*) the reaction at the built-in end; (*b*) the greatest bending moment and where it occurs; (*c*) where the bending moment is zero.

Solution

REACTION

The net external load $= 3 - 2 = 1$ ton, upward. For balance therefore the vertical reaction at the built-in end A is **1 ton** *downward*.

SHEAR FORCE DIAGRAM

The diagram is drawn by making use of the fact that on any unloaded portion of the beam the shear force is uniform and the graph between loads is a horizontal line. Starting at the left-hand end draw a line to scale from the zero line O–O of length and

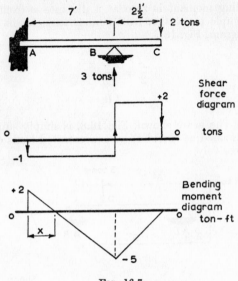

Fig. 16.7

direction corresponding to that of the reaction at A, i.e. 1 ton downward.

Between A and B the shear force is uniform and of amount -1 ton (using the sign convention given). At B it changes by $+3$ tons. The shear force just to the right of B, in BC, is therefore—

$$-1 + 3 = 2 \text{ ton}$$

The shear force is uniform from B to C and changes by -2 tons at C. At C it is therefore zero, as it should be at a free end; (just to the left of C the shear force is of course $+2$ tons). The complete shear force diagram is shown in Fig. 16.7.

BENDING MOMENT DIAGRAM

The diagram is drawn by making use of the fact that on unloaded portions of the beam the bending moment is represented by straight lines. The bending moment is therefore calculated at the load and reaction points; the corresponding points on the diagram are then joined by straight lines.

At B, bending moment $= -2 \times 2\frac{1}{2} = -5$ ton-ft

At A, bending moment $= -2 \times 9\frac{1}{2} + 3 \times 7 = 2$ ton-ft

At C, bending moment $= 0$ (at the free end)

The greatest bending moment is at B and is **5 ton-ft.**

The bending moment is zero at a distance x from the end A found by simple proportion from similar triangles in the bending moment diagram, Fig. 16.7.

i.e.
$$\frac{x}{2} = \frac{7-x}{5}$$

thus
$$x = 2 \text{ ft}$$

Example. The beam shown, Fig. 16.8, is simply supported at C and B, and loaded at A and D by concentrated loads of 1 ton and 3 tons, respectively.

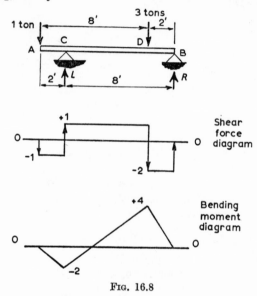

Fig. 16.8

Determine the reactions L and R at C and B and draw the shear force and bending moment diagrams.

Solution

REACTIONS

A "simple support" is one in which the beam is rested as on a knife-edge. The reaction exerted by the support is assumed to act at a point and is vertical. The reaction at B is found by taking moments about C for *all* the loads on the beam, i.e. equating clockwise and anticlockwise moments about C—

$$1 \times 2 + R \times 8 = 3 \times 6$$

therefore
$$R = 2 \text{ tons}$$

Similarly, taking moments about B—

$$L \times 8 = 3 \times 2 + 1 \times 10$$

therefore $\qquad L = \textbf{2 tons}$

Alternatively,

$$L + R = 3 + 1$$

thus $\qquad L = 4 - 2$

$$= 2 \text{ tons, as before}$$

SHEAR FORCE DIAGRAM

The diagram is drawn by remembering—

(a) the shear force changes abruptly at a concentrated load;
(b) the shear force is uniform on an unloaded portion of the beam.

Using the given sign convention we may start at the *left-hand end* and draw the diagram by following the arrows representing the loads and reactions, thus we draw—

at A, 1 ton down, then a horizontal line to C;
at C, 2 tons up, then a horizontal line to D;
at D, 3 tons down, then a horizontal line to B;
at B, 2 tons up to the zero line again.

Note that in this method we have followed the *changes* in shear force along the beam.

BENDING MOMENT DIAGRAM

At the free ends A and B, the bending moment is zero. At C, considering the left-hand portion AC—

$$\text{bending moment} = -1 \times 2 = -2 \text{ ton-ft}$$

(negative, since the 1 ton load at A tends to make the beam hog at C). At D, considering the left-hand portion AD—

$$\text{bending moment} = -1 \times 8 + L \times 6$$
$$= -8 + 2 \times 6, \quad \text{since } L = 2 \text{ tons}$$
$$= +4 \text{ ton-ft}$$

This is the greatest bending moment in the beam. The values of the bending moment at A, B, C and D are plotted in Fig. 16.8 and the bending moment diagram completed by joining the resulting points by straight lines.

Example. Draw the shear force and bending moment diagrams for the beam ABC, Fig. 16.9. The beam is pin-jointed at A and is supported by a cable at B.

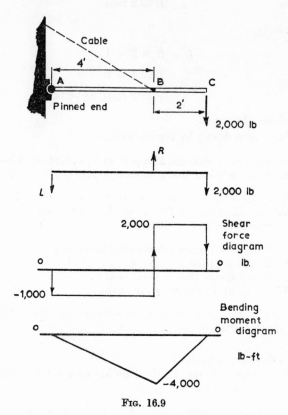

Fig. 16.9

Solution

REACTIONS

The joint at the pinned end A may be assumed frictionless and therefore carries no bending moment. We are interested only in forces transverse to the horizontal beam, hence only *vertical* components of the tension in the cable and the reaction at A need be considered.

Let L and R be the vertical forces at A and B, respectively. To find R take moments about A—

$$R \times 4 = 2,000 \times 6$$

therefore $$R = 3,000 \text{ lb (upward)}$$

Since the net vertical force is zero

$$- L + R - 2,000 = 0$$

thus
$$L = + 3,000 - 2,000$$
$$= + 1,000 \text{ lb (downward)}$$

SHEAR FORCE DIAGRAM

The shear force diagram is drawn by starting at A and the *changes* in shear force plotted by following each load at A, B and C in turn as in the previous example.

BENDING MOMENT DIAGRAM

The bending moment is zero at pin A and at the free end C. At B, considering the right-hand portion BC—

$$\text{bending moment} = - 2,000 \times \text{BC}$$
$$= - 2,000 \times 2$$
$$= - 4,000 \text{ lb-ft}$$

This is negative since the load at C tends to cause the beam to hog at B. The bending moments at A, B and C are plotted in the diagram and, since AB and BC are unloaded, the bending moment diagram may be completed by joining the plotted points by straight lines as shown.

PROBLEMS

1. Draw the shear force and bending moment diagrams for the cantilever beams shown in Fig. 16.10. State in each case: (i) the shear force between points A and B; (ii) the bending moment at points A and B.

((*a*) 6 tons; 54 ton-ft; 24 ton-ft; (*b*) 1·73 tons; 17·3 ton-ft; 0 ton-ft;
(*c*) 4·33 tons; 30 ton-ft; 0 ton-ft; (*d*) 30 tons; 0 ton-ft; 30 ton-ft)

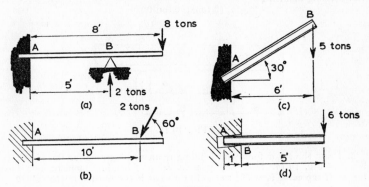

FIG. 16.10

2. Draw the shear force and bending moment diagrams for the simply supported beams shown in Fig. 16.11. State in each case: (i) the reactions

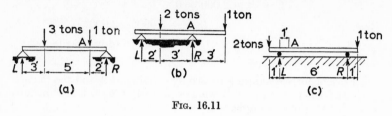

Fig. 16.11

L and R; (ii) the greatest shear force in the beam; (iii) the bending moment at point A.

((a) L, 2·3 tons; R, 1·7 tons; 2·3 tons; 3·4 ton-ft; (b) L, 0·6 tons; R, 2·4 tons; 1·4 tons; 3 ton-ft; (c) L, 2·167 tons; R, 0·833 ton; 2 tons; 1·833 ton-ft)

3. For the cantilever beam shown in Fig. 16.12, determine the greatest value of the bending moment and the upward reaction at the built-in end. Draw the shear force and bending moment diagrams.

(10 ton-ft; 2 tons)

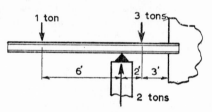

Fig. 16.12

4. Draw the shear force and bending moment diagrams for the simply supported beam shown in Fig. 16.13. State the values of the greatest shear force and bending moment.

(2 tons; 6 ton-ft)

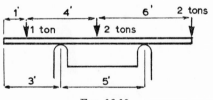

Fig. 16.13

5. Draw the shear force and bending moment diagrams for the pin-ended beam of Fig. 16.14. State the greatest value of bending moment and shear force. If the cable is at 30° to the beam what is the tension in the cable?

($\frac{10}{7}$ ton-ft; $\frac{5}{7}$ ton; $\frac{10}{7}$ tons)

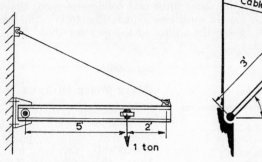

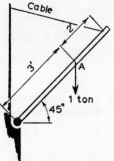

FIG. 16.14   FIG. 16.15

6. Draw the shear force and bending moment diagrams for the pin-ended jib crane shown in Fig. 16.15. State the bending moment at the point A, and calculate the shear force in the beam at the pin-joint. If the cable is at 60° to the beam what is the tension in the cable?

(0·849 ton-ft; 0·283 ton; 0·49 ton)

16.6. Uniformly Distributed Loads

When a load is not concentrated at a point but spread uniformly over a portion of the beam the load is said to be *uniformly distributed*. The loading is usually given as an intensity of loading per unit length of the beam, i.e. lb/ft run. Suppose a beam to carry a load

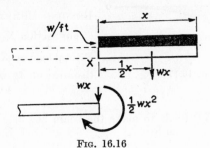

FIG. 16.16

of intensity w over a length x as shown in Fig. 16.16. Then the shear force at section X due to this load is the total load $w \times x$, i.e.

$$\text{shear force at } X = wx$$

The distance of the centroid of the load wx from section X is $\frac{1}{2}x$. Therefore the bending moment at X due to this load is

$$wx \times \tfrac{1}{2}x$$
$$= \tfrac{1}{2}wx^2$$

Example. Draw the shear force and bending moment diagrams for the uniformly loaded cantilever shown, Fig. 16.17. The loading is 4 tons/ft run. State the values of the greatest shear force and bending moment.

Solution

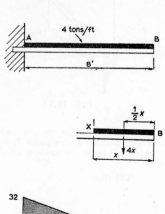

SHEAR FORCE DIAGRAM

For section X, distant x from B; total load on $BX = 4\,x$ tons. This load tends to push XB downwards relative to AX, hence shear force at X is $4\,x$ tons. The shear force is proportional to x, hence *the shear force graph is a straight line.*

At B, shear force = 0.

At A, shear force = 4×8

$= 32$ tons

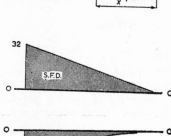

Joining the corresponding points on the shear force diagram completes the diagram. The greatest shear force is at A, and is **32 tons.**

BENDING MOMENT DIAGRAM

For section X—

total load on $XB = 4\,x$ tons

distance of its centroid from X

$= \frac{1}{2}\,x$ ft

FIG. 16.17

The load on XB tends to make the beam hog at X, thus bending moment at X is given by—

$$-4\,x \times \tfrac{1}{2}\,x$$

$$= -2\,x^2 \text{ ton-ft}$$

The calculated values of the bending moment are shown in the following table—

x (ft)	0	2	4	6	8
Bending moment (ton-ft) .	0	-8	-32	-72	-128

The bending moment graph is a parabola and the greatest value of the bending moment occurs at A, i.e.

$$\text{greatest bending moment} = -\ 128 \text{ ton-ft}$$

Example. Draw the shear force and bending moment diagrams for the uniformly-loaded, simply-supported beam of Fig. 16.18.

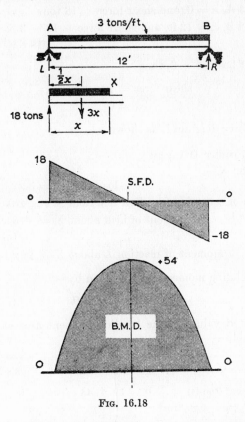

Fig. 16.18

The load intensity is 3 tons/ft. State the value of the maximum bending moment and where it occurs.

Solution

REACTIONS

$$\text{Total load} = 3 \times 12 = 36 \text{ tons}$$

From symmetry $L = R = 18 \text{ tons}$

SHEAR FORCE DIAGRAM

For section X, distant x ft from A—

$$\text{shear force} = L - \text{load on AX}$$
$$= 18 - 3\,x \text{ tons}$$

which gives a straight line graph.

$$\text{At A, } x = 0, \text{ and shear force} = 18 \text{ tons}$$
$$\text{At B, } x = 12 \text{ ft, and shear force} = 18 - 3 \times 12$$
$$= -18 \text{ tons}$$

At centre of beam $x = 6$, thus

$$\text{shear force} = 18 - 3 \times 6$$
$$= 0$$

The shear force diagram is as shown.

BENDING MOMENT DIAGRAM

For section X—

$$\text{load on AX} = 3\,x$$
$$\text{distance of centroid of load on AX from X} = \tfrac{1}{2}\,x \text{ ft}$$
$$\text{moment of load about X} = -3\,x \times \tfrac{1}{2}\,x$$
$$= -1\cdot5\,x^2 \text{ ton-ft}$$
$$\text{moment of reaction } L \text{ about X} = 18\,x \text{ ton-ft}$$

The total bending moment at X is given by—

$$18\,x - 1\cdot5\,x^2 \text{ ton-ft}$$

The calculated values of the bending moment are set out in the following table—

x (ft)	0	2	4	6	8	10	12
Bending moment (ton-ft) .	0	30	48	54	48	30	0

The bending moment diagram is a parabola and symmetrical about the middle of the beam. The maximum bending moment is at the middle, therefore

$$\text{maximum bending moment} = \textbf{54 ton-ft}$$

16.7. Combined Loading

When a beam carries both concentrated and uniformly distributed loads it is necessary to consider the beam and its loading in convenient portions and obtain expressions for the shear force and bending moment in each portion separately. This is because the formula for bending moment and shear force changes at each concentrated load.

Example. Draw the shear force and bending moment diagrams for the beam shown, Fig. 16.19 (*a*). The beam is simply supported at A and D.

Solution

REACTIONS

To determine the support reactions L and R the distributed load over AC may be taken as acting at its centroid, 2 ft from A.

$$\text{Total distributed load} = 0.5 \times 4 = 2 \text{ tons}$$

Moments about A—

$$R \times 8 = 1 \times 3 + 2 \times 2 + 2 \times 9$$

thus $\qquad R = 3.125 \text{ tons}$

Moments about D—

$$L \times 8 = 2 \times 6 + 1 \times 5 - 2 \times 1$$

therefore $\qquad L = 1.875 \text{ tons}$

(Check: $L + R = 1.875 + 3.125$

$\qquad\qquad = 5 \text{ tons}$

$\qquad\qquad = \text{net downward load.}$)

SHEAR FORCE DIAGRAM

For section AB, Fig. 16.19 (*b*). Consider shear force at section X due to load on left-hand portion of beam AX—

$$\text{load on AX} = 0.5\,x$$

The shear force at X is—

$$L - 0.5\,x$$
$$= 1.875 - 0.5\,x \text{ ton}$$

This gives a straight line graph.

At A, $x = 0$, $\qquad$ shear force $= 1.875$ tons
At B, $x = 3$ ft, $\qquad$ shear force $= 1.875 - 0.5 \times 3$
$\qquad\qquad\qquad\qquad\qquad = 0.375$ ton

These values are plotted in Fig. 16.19 (*c*). The shear force diagram is completed for portion AB by joining the plotted points by a straight line as shown.

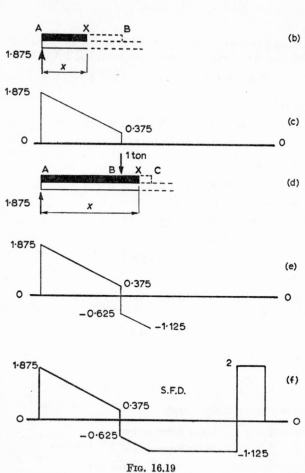

Fig. 16.19

For section BC, Fig. 16.19 (*d*). Consider shear force at X in BC due to loads on left-hand portion of beam AX. Shear force at X is—

$$1 \cdot 875 - 1 - 0 \cdot 5\, x$$
$$= 0 \cdot 875 - 0 \cdot 5\, x \text{ ton}$$

At B, $x = 3$ ft, shear force $= 0 \cdot 875 - 0 \cdot 5 \times 3 = -0 \cdot 625$ ton.

At C, $x = 4$ ft, shear force $= 0 \cdot 875 - 0 \cdot 5 \times 4 = -1 \cdot 125$ ton

These values are plotted in Fig. 16.19 (*e*) and the shear force diagram completed as far as point C.

For section CD. The portion CD is unloaded, hence the shear force is uniform at $-1 \cdot 125$ tons.

For section DE, Fig. 16.19 (*f*). At support D the shear force changes abruptly due to the reaction *R* upwards, i.e.

$$\text{shear force to right of D} = -1 \cdot 125 + 3 \cdot 125$$
$$= 2 \text{ tons}$$

The shear force is uniform at 2 tons along DE since this portion of the beam is unloaded. The complete shear force diagram is shown in Fig. 16.19 (*f*). Since it is made up of straight lines it could have been drawn by calculating the shear force at the principal points and joining the plotted points by straight lines.

BENDING MOMENT DIAGRAM

Section AB, Fig. 16.20 (*b*). Consider bending moment at X due to load on portion AX—

bending moment due to reaction $L = 1 \cdot 875\, x$ ton-ft

bending moment due to load on AX $= -0 \cdot 5\, x \times \frac{1}{2} x$
$$= -0 \cdot 25\, x^2 \text{ ton-ft}$$

Total bending moment at X $= 1 \cdot 875\, x - 0 \cdot 25\, x^2$ ton-ft

Calculated values of the bending moment are tabulated below—

x (ft)	0	1	2	3
Bending moment (ton-ft) .	0	1·625	2·75	3·375

The bending moment diagram for section AB is shown in Fig. 16.20 (*c*).

Section BC, Fig. 16.20 (*d*). Consider the bending moment at X in BC due to load on portion AX.

bending moment due to 1 ton at B $= -1 \times \text{BX}$
$$= -1(x - 3) \text{ ton-ft}$$

Total bending moment at X $= 1 \cdot 875\, x - 0 \cdot 5\, x \times \frac{1}{2} x - (x - 3)$
$$= 3 + 0 \cdot 875\, x - 0 \cdot 25\, x^2 \text{ ton-ft}$$

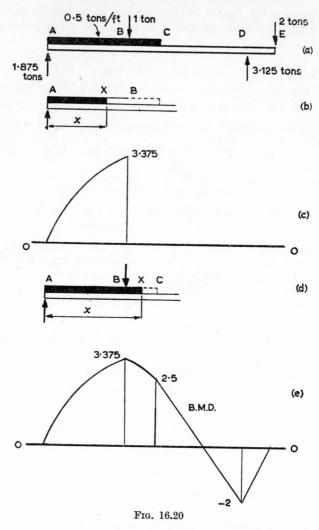

Fig. 16.20

Values of the bending moment in BC are given below—

x (ft)	.	.	.	.	3	3·5	4
Bending moment (ton-ft)			.		3·375	3·0	2·5

The bending moment diagram for length BC is shown in Fig. 16.20 (e).

Sections CD and DE. In the lengths CD and DE there are no distributed loads and the bending moment diagram is therefore completed by calculating the bending moment at D and E, plotting these values and joining these points by straight lines. At D, considering portion DE—

$$\text{bending moment} = -2 \times 1 = -2 \text{ ton-ft}$$

At E,   bending moment $= 0$

The completed bending moment diagram is shown in Fig. 16.20 (*e*). Often only a sketch may be required, in which case the values of the bending moment at the principal points should be marked as indicated. The maximum bending moment is at B and is **3·375 ton-ft.**

PROBLEMS

1. Draw the shear force and bending moment diagrams for the cantilever beams shown in Fig. 16.21. State the greatest value of shear force and bending moment in each case.

    ((*a*) 1·5 ton;   7·75 ton-ft;   (*b*) 5 tons;   19·5 ton-ft;   (*c*) 2·5 tons; 13·75 ton-ft)

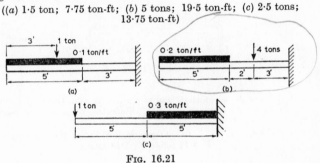

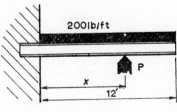

Fɪɢ. 16.21

2. The cantilever beam shown in Fig. 16.22 is partially supported by a load *P* exerted by a prop distant *x* ft from the built-in end. Calculate the value of *P* if *x* is 8 ft, in order that the bending moment at the built-in end shall be zero.

If the load in the prop is 2,000 lb and the bending moment at the built-in end is to be zero, what is the value of *x* required?

(1,800 lb;   7·2 ft)

Fɪɢ. 16.22

3. Draw shear force and bending moment diagrams for the simply supported beams shown in Fig. 16.23. State the values of the reactions L and R and the bending moments at the points A and B, in each case.

((a) L, 1·43 tons; R, 2·17 tons; 5 ton-ft, 4·34 ton-ft; (b) L, 1·354 tons; R, 1·146 tons; 2·708 ton-ft, 5·73 ton-ft; (c) L, 0·81 ton; R, 0·59 ton; 0·84 ton-ft, 0·87 ton-ft)

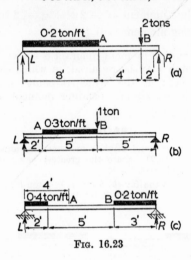

Fig. 16.23

4. For the simply supported beams shown in Fig. 16.24, determine the greatest value of the bending moment. State the values of the reactions L and R.

((a) 1·45 ton-ft; L, 0·725 ton; R, 0·475 ton; (b) 4 ton-ft; L, 2·72 tons; R, 1·48 tons)

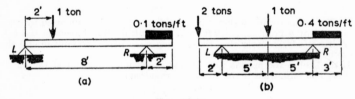

Fig. 16.24

16.8. Condition for a Maximum Bending Moment

Consider an element of a beam cut off by transverse sections A and B (Fig. 16.25) such that AB = dx. For simplicity let AB be unloaded, although the remainder of the beam may be loaded.

Let shear force at A = Q, upwards. Then since element AB is not loaded the shear force at B is Q, downwards.

Let the bending moment at A = M, clockwise. Then owing to

the effect of the length dx there must be a change in bending moment dM between A and B, thus

bending moment at B $= M + \mathrm{d}M$, anticlockwise

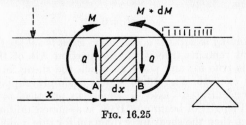

FIG. 16.25

The element is in equilibrium, therefore, taking moments about point A—

$$M + Q \times \mathrm{d}x = M + \mathrm{d}M$$

i.e.
$$\mathrm{d}M = Q\,\mathrm{d}x$$

or
$$\frac{\mathrm{d}M}{\mathrm{d}x} = Q$$

Therefore, if the bending moment is expressed as a function of x and this expression differentiated with respect to x, the shear force is obtained.

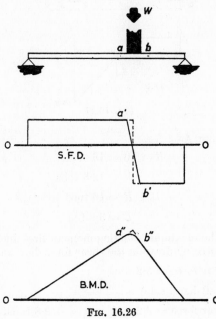

FIG. 16.26

Now, the condition that the bending moment M shall be a mathematical maximum is that

$$\frac{dM}{dx} = 0$$

i.e. $$Q = 0$$

Hence the bending moment is a maximum when the shear force is zero.

This result remains true when the portion AB of the beam is loaded. It is true for any point at which the shear force has zero value. For example Fig. 16.26 shows a simply supported beam under a "concentrated" load W which, in practice, is distributed over a small length of beam ab. If W is assumed uniformly distributed over ab then the shear force diagram for this region is the line $a'b'$ and the bending moment curve is $a''b''$. At the mid-point of ab the shear force is zero, and the bending moment therefore takes a mathematical maximum value under the load.

Example. Calculate the position and magnitude of the maximum bending moment in the simply supported beam loaded as shown in Fig. 16.27.

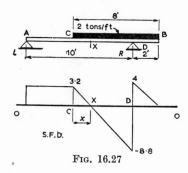

Fɪɢ. 16.27

Solution

Moments about A—

$$R \times 10 = 16 \times 8$$

therefore $$R = 12{\cdot}8 \text{ tons}$$

and $$L + R = 16 \text{ tons}$$

thus $$L = 3{\cdot}2 \text{ tons}$$

To determine the maximum bending moment first find the positions of zero shear force by drawing the shear force diagram.

At C, shear force = 3·2 tons

At D (just to left-hand side)—

shear force = $3{\cdot}2 - 2 \times 6 = -8{\cdot}8$ tons

At D (just to right-hand side)—

$$\text{shear force} = 3\cdot2 - 2 \times 6 + 12\cdot8 = 4 \text{ tons}$$

The shear force diagram is shown in Fig. 16.27. The shear force is zero at D and at X, distant x from C.

At X, by simple proportion

$$\frac{\text{CX}}{\text{CD}} = \frac{3\cdot2}{3\cdot2 + 8\cdot8} = 0\cdot267$$

thus

$$x = \text{CX}$$
$$= 0\cdot267 \times \text{CD}$$
$$= 0\cdot267 \times 6$$
$$= 1\cdot6 \text{ ft}$$

Hence at X,

$$\text{bending moment} = L \times \text{AX} - \tfrac{1}{2} \times 2 \times x^2$$
$$= 3\cdot2 \times 5\cdot6 - \tfrac{1}{2} \times 2 \times 1\cdot6^2$$
$$= 15\cdot34 \text{ ton-ft}$$

The greatest value of the bending moment therefore is at X, distant **1·6 ft** from C between C and D, and its magnitude is **15·34 ton-ft.**

PROBLEMS

1. Draw the shear force and bending moment diagrams for the beams shown in Fig. 16.28. State the maximum values of bending moment and shear force and where they occur.

((*a*) 1·25 ton-ft, 5 ft from l.h. end; 0·5 ton, 5 ft from l.h. end; (*b*) 3,067 lb-ft, 10 ft from l.h. end; 1,033 lb, 2 ft from l.h. end; (*c*) 14·5 ton-ft, 8 ft from l.h. end; 5·8 ton, 13 ft from l.h. end)

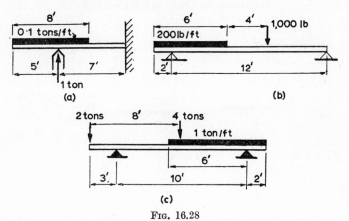

FIG. 16.28

2. For the simply supported beam shown in Fig. 16.29 find where the shear force is zero and hence obtain the maximum bending moment.

(4·2 ft from l.h. end; 1·764 ton-ft)

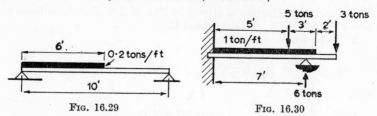

FIG. 16.29   FIG. 16.30

3. Fig. 16.30 shows a loaded cantilever beam propped at a point 7 ft from its left-hand end. Draw to scale the shear force and bending moment diagrams. Find the maximum bending moment and state where it occurs.

(45 ton-ft, at the built-in end)

4. Draw to scale the shear force and bending moment diagrams for the pin-ended beam shown in Fig. 16.31. State the maximum values of the shear force and bending moment. If the cable is at 40° to the beam what is the tension in the cable?

(11·4 tons; 18·5 ton-ft at 4·3 ft from pin-end; 31·7 tons)

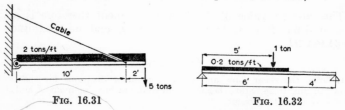

FIG. 16.31   FIG. 16.32

5. Determine the maximum shear force and bending moment in the beam shown in Fig. 16.32. Where does the maximum bending moment occur?

(1·34 tons; 4·2 ton-ft, at the 1 ton load)

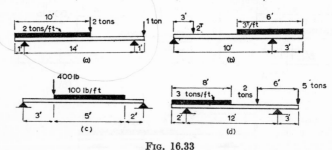

FIG. 16.33

6. State the position and magnitude of the maximum bending moment in each of the simply supported beams shown in Fig. 16.33.

((a) 7·46 ft from l.h. end, 40·6 ton-ft; (b) 10 ft from l.h. end, 13·5 ton-ft; (c) 4·05 ft from l.h. end, 1,570 lb-ft; (d) 6·41 ft from l.h. end, 23·3 ton-ft)

Bending of Beams

17.1. Pure Bending of an Elastic Beam

THE beam AB (Fig. 17.1) loaded by equal and opposite couples M at A and B, is said to be subjected to pure or *simple* bending, that is, bending without shear force. At any section X–X the bending moment is M. For equilibrium of any portion XB the couple must be balanced by an equal and opposite couple exerted by internal forces within the beam. Thus M at B is balanced by the couple represented by the pair of equal and opposite parallel forces P shown. These are internal forces exerted by the portion AX on the portion XB at X–X. The upper force represents a tension in XB, the lower a corresponding compression. Thus the top layers are stretched and lower layers are compressed.

The internal forces are not actually point loads as shown in Fig. 17.1, but are distributed across the depth of the beam as tensile

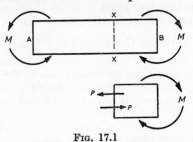

FIG. 17.1

and compressive stresses in the upper and lower portions of the section, respectively. These stresses are not uniform, however, and in order to calculate them it is necessary to make the following *assumptions*—

1. The beam is initially straight.

2. Bending takes place in the plane of the applied bending moment (the plane of the paper).

3. The cross-section of the beam is symmetrical about the plane of bending. If not symmetrical the beam would twist as well as bend. In Fig. 17.2 Y–Y is the plane of bending and the

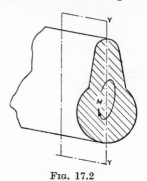

FIG. 17.2

section shown is symmetrical about, and normal to, the plane of bending.

4. The stresses are uniform across the width.

5. The material of the beam is elastic and obeys Hooke's law.

6. The stresses do not exceed the limit of proportionality.

7. The moduli of elasticity in tension and compression are the same.

8. A plane transverse section of the beam remains a plane section after bending.

9. Each layer of the beam is free to carry stress without interference from adjacent layers.

These assumptions are justified since they are found to give substantially correct values for the stresses due to bending.

17.2. Relation between Curvature and Strain

Consider the initially straight portion of beam ABCD shown, Fig. 17.3 (*a*). After bending the beam takes up the arc shape shown in Fig. 17.3 (*b*). Plane cross-sections remain plane, hence straight lines BA, CD remain straight after bending and meet at some point O. Lines such as EF and SN form part of circular arcs with a common centre at O. Since the top layers are stretched and the bottom layers are compressed there is a layer, the *neutral surface*, which is neither stretched nor compressed. The lines S′N′ and N′N′ represent the trace of the neutral surface, the line N′–N′ normal to the plane of bending being known as the *neutral axis*. The *radius of curvature* R of the bent beam is measured from O to the neutral surface.

If θ is the angle in radians subtended by the arc S′N′ at O then, since the neutral layer remains unchanged in length—

$$\text{line SN} = \text{arc S'N'} = R\theta$$

Consider the thin layer EF, distant y from the neutral surface—

initial length of EF $= \text{SN} = R\theta$

final length of EF $= \text{E'F'}$

$$= (R + y)\theta$$

thus   extension of EF $= (R + y)\theta - R\theta$

$$= y\theta$$

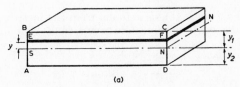

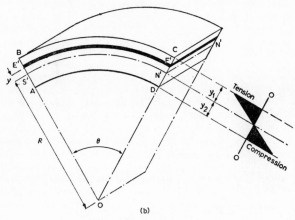

(b)

FIG. 17.3

therefore   strain in EF, $e = \dfrac{y\theta}{R\theta}$

$$= \frac{y}{R}$$

The stress in the layer EF, normal to the beam section, is given by—

$$f = E \times e$$

$$= \frac{Ey}{R}$$

or $\dfrac{f}{y} = \dfrac{E}{R}$ $\quad\cdot\qquad\cdot\qquad\cdot\qquad\cdot\quad$ (17.1)

Since E is constant for the beam and R is constant for the portion considered, the stress f *varies across the depth with the distance y from the neutral axis*. The distribution of stress across the depth of the beam is sketched in Fig. 17.3 (*b*), tensile stress being plotted to the left of the base O–O, compressive stress to the right. The *maximum* stress occurs at the *outside* surfaces such as AD and BC where y takes its largest values y_2 and y_1.

17.3. Position of the Neutral Axis

The position of the neutral axis is found from the fact that there is no net axial force on the beam. Consider a small strip of width

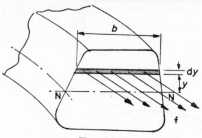

FIG. 17.4

b, thickness dy, Fig. 17.4. Let dP be the axial load on the strip due to the bending stress, then

$$dP = \text{stress} \times \text{area}$$
$$= f \times b\,dy$$

but $$f = \frac{Ey}{R}, \text{ from equation (17.1)}$$

thus $$dP = \frac{Ey}{R} \times b\,dy$$

The total load on the section is the sum of the elementary loads, therefore

$$P = \int dP$$
$$= \int \frac{Ey}{R} \times b\,dy$$

and, since the total axial load is zero

$$\int \frac{Ey}{R} \times b\,dy = 0$$

and thus $$\int y \times b\,dy = 0$$

since E and R are constants. But $y \times b\,dy$ is the moment of area $b\,dy$ about the neutral axis N–N. Hence $\int yb\,dy$ represents the moment of the whole area about the neutral axis and *this is zero only if the neutral axis passes through the centroid of the cross-section.* This result is true for any shape of cross-section.

Note—(a) The above results do not apply completely to a strip which is wide compared with its depth; (b) In a symmetrical section $y_1 = y_2$, and the maximum tensile and compressive stresses are therefore equal.

In a non-symmetrical section the *numerically largest* bending stress will occur at the outer layer most distant from the neutral axis, and may be tensile *or* compressive.

Example. Calculate the maximum stress in a coil of steel rod $\frac{1}{8}$ in. diameter due to coiling it on a drum of 6 ft diameter. $E = 30 \times 10^6$ lb/in.^{2}

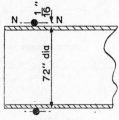

FIG. 17.5

Solution

Radius of curvature $= 36$ in. approx.

The greatest distance of outside surface from the neutral axis N–N is $\frac{1}{16}$ in. The maximum stress due to bending is

$$f = \frac{E}{R}y$$

$$= \frac{30 \times 10^6}{36} \times \frac{1}{16}$$

$$= 52{,}100 \text{ lb/in.}^2$$

PROBLEMS

1. A steel strip forming a bandsaw is wrapped round a 1 ft diameter drum. If the strip thickness is $\frac{1}{32}$ in., calculate the maximum stress due to bending. $E = 28 \times 10^6$ lb/in.^{2}

(72,900 lb/in.^{2})

2. Aluminium alloy tube of 1 in. diameter is wound on a drum of 10 ft diameter. Calculate the maximum bending stress in the tube. $E = 10 \times 10^6$ lb/in.^{2}

(82,700 lb/in.^{2})

3. Calculate the minimum diameter of drum on which copper strip 0·1 in. thick may be wound if the maximum bending stress is not to exceed 50,000 lb/in.² $E = 15 \times 10^6$ lb/in.²

(2·5 ft)

4. A steel strip of rectangular cross-section $\frac{1}{2}$ in. thick is bent to the arc of a circle until the steel just yields at the top surface. Find the radius of curvature of the neutral surface if the yield stress of the material is 18 ton/in.² $E = 12,500$ ton/in.²

(14·45 ft)

17.4. Moment of Resistance

The *moment of resistance* of a beam is the moment about the neutral axis of the internal forces resisting the applied bending moment. For equilibrium, the internal moment of resistance must be equal and opposite to the applied bending moment. Fig. 17.6

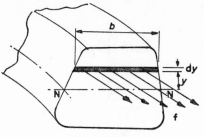

Fig. 17.6

shows the section of a beam on which the bending moment is M. Let f be the stress produced in a thin strip at a distance y from the neutral axis N–N then, if dy is the thickness of the strip

$$\text{load on strip} = dP = \text{stress} \times \text{area}$$

$$= f \times b \, dy$$

The moment of this load about the neutral axis is—

$$dM = dP \times y$$

$$= fb \, dy \times y$$

but

$$f = \frac{E}{R} y$$

thus

$$dM = \frac{E}{R} y \times by \, dy$$

$$= \frac{E}{R} by^2 \, dy$$

Hence total moment of resistance is—

$$M = \int dM$$

$$= \int \frac{E}{R} by^2 \, dy$$

$$= \frac{E}{R} \int by^2 \, dy$$

$$= \frac{E}{R} I$$

where $I = \int by^2 \, dy$, is the *second moment of area of the section about the neutral axis.* Hence

$$\frac{M}{I} = \frac{E}{R}$$

and since

$$\frac{f}{y} = \frac{E}{R}$$

then

$$\frac{M}{I} = \frac{E}{R} = \frac{f}{y} \qquad . \qquad . \qquad . \qquad (17.2)$$

17.5. *I* of Rectangular and Circular Sections

For a rectangular section of width b in. depth d in. (Fig. 17.7) the second moment of area about an axis through the centroid parallel to the width is

$$I_G = \frac{bd^3}{12} \text{ in.}^4$$

 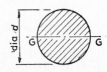

Fig. 17.7

For a circular section, diameter d in. the second moment of area about any axis through the centre, i.e. a diametral axis, is

$$I_G = \frac{\pi d^4}{64} \text{ in.}^4$$

Example. A rectangular section beam has a depth of 4 in., width 1 in., and is subjected to a bending moment of 100 ton-in. Calculate (a) the maximum stress in the beam and (b) the radius of curvature of the neutral surface. $E = 13,400$ tons/in.²

Solution

(a) The axis of bending is the axis through the centroid parallel to the 1 in. side, therefore

$$I = \frac{bd^3}{12} = \frac{1 \times 4^3}{12} = 5\cdot33 \text{ in.}^4$$

$$f = \frac{M}{I}\, y = \frac{100}{5\cdot33} \times y = 18\cdot75\, y \text{ tons/in.}^2$$

where y is in inches. Now the bending stress f takes its greatest value at the outside surface where

$$y = \pm \frac{d}{2} = \pm\, 2 \text{ in.}$$

hence $f_{\max} = \pm\, 18\cdot75 \times 2 = \pm\, 37\cdot5 \text{ tons/in.}^2$

The positive answer denotes a tensile stress at one outer surface, the negative a compressive stress at the other outer surface.

(b) $$R = \frac{I}{M}\, E = \frac{5\cdot33 \times 13,400}{100}$$

$$= 715 \text{ in.   or   } 59\cdot5 \text{ ft}$$

Example. A beam of symmetrical I-section has the following dimensions: flange 6 in. wide, 1 in. thick; web 1 in. thick; total depth of beam 8 in. Calculate the second moment of area of the beam section about an axis through the centroid parallel to the flange face.

Solution

The beam section is symmetrical about the centroidal axis G–G, Fig. 17.8. Hence I is given by the difference between I for the rectangle ABCD and I for the two cross-hatched rectangles shown. For whole rectangle ABCD—

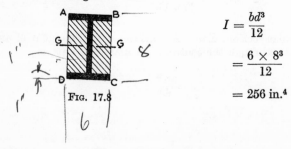

Fig. 17.8

$$I = \frac{bd^3}{12}$$

$$= \frac{6 \times 8^3}{12}$$

$$= 256 \text{ in.}^4$$

For each cut-out rectangle

$$b = 2{\cdot}5$$
$$d = 6 \text{ in.}$$

therefore

$$I = \frac{2{\cdot}5 \times 6^3}{12}$$

$$= 45 \text{ in.}^4$$

For the I-section, by difference

$$I_G = 256 - 2 \times 45$$
$$= 166 \text{ in.}^4$$

Note—This method of calculation does not apply when the I-section is not symmetrical about G–G (*see* paragraph 17.7).

Example. A symmetrical I-section beam has the dimensions shown in Fig. 17.9. It is simply supported over a length of 8 ft and

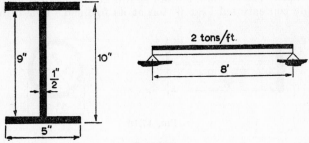

FIG. 17.9

carries a uniformly distributed load of 2 tons/ft run. Calculate the maximum bending stress in the beam.

Solution

MAXIMUM BENDING MOMENT

$$\text{Total load on beam} = 2 \times 8 = 16 \text{ tons}$$

thus

$$\text{reaction at each support} = \frac{16}{2} = 8 \text{ tons}$$

The maximum bending moment occurs at the middle of the beam; therefore

$$\text{maximum bending moment } M_{\max} = 8 \times 4 - 8 \times 2$$
$$= 16 \text{ ton-ft}$$
$$= 192 \text{ ton-in.}$$

Since the beam section is symmetrical the neutral axis N–N passes through the mid-point of the section.

$$I = \frac{5 \times 10^3}{12} - 2 \times \frac{2 \cdot 25 \times 9^3}{12}$$

$$= 143 \cdot 3 \text{ in.}^4$$

MAXIMUM BENDING STRESS

The maximum bending stress occurs at the outside surface of the section of maximum bending moment, therefore

$$\text{maximum bending stress, } f_{max} = \frac{M}{I} \, y_{max}$$

$$= \frac{192 \times 5}{143 \cdot 3}$$

$$= 6 \cdot 7 \text{ tons/in.}^2$$

Example. The cantilever beam shown in Fig. 17.10 is loaded by a single concentrated load W ton at its free end. It is of hollow

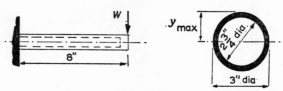

FIG. 17.10

section 3 in. outside diameter, 2·75 in. inside diameter. Calculate the maximum value of W if the bending stress is not to exceed 4 tons/in.²

Solution

Since the beam cross-section is symmetrical about the neutral axis the second moment of area is found by subtracting that of the inner circle area from that of the second moment for the whole area. For a circular section—

$$I = \frac{\pi d^4}{64}$$

therefore for hollow section

$$I = \frac{\pi \times 3^4}{64} - \frac{\pi \times 2 \cdot 75^4}{64}$$

$$= 1 \cdot 17 \text{ in.}^4$$

Allowable moment, $M = \dfrac{f}{y_{max}} I$

$$= \frac{4}{1\cdot5} \times 1\cdot17$$

$$= 3\cdot12 \text{ ton-in.}$$

The maximum bending moment on the cantilever is $W \times 8$ ton-in. Therefore

$$W \times 8 = 3\cdot12$$

i.e. $$W = \textbf{0·39 ton}$$

PROBLEMS

1. Timber beams 9 in. deep, 4 in. wide rest on supports 12 ft apart and carry a floor load of 200 lb/ft of length. Calculate the maximum bending stress in the timber.

(800 lb/in.²)

2. A light wooden bridge is supported by six parallel timber beams, each 1 ft deep, and 8 in. wide. Each beam may be considered as simply supported over a 15 ft span. If the allowable bending stress in the timber is 800 lb/in.² calculate the greatest uniformly distributed load the bridge can support.

(18·3 tons)

3. A cast-iron bracket is of rectangular section 6 in. deep and 2 in. wide. It is rigidly built in at one end and is required to carry an end load of 8 cwt. Calculate the maximum length of beam if the tensile stress in the cast iron is not to exceed $\frac{1}{2}$ ton/in.²

(15 in.)

4. The crane beam shown in Fig. 17.11 is made up of two 1 in. thick steel plates each 16 in. deep at the middle section. Calculate the maximum allow-

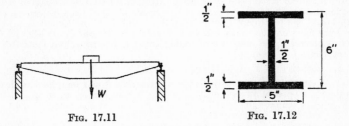

FIG. 17.11   FIG. 17.12

able central load W if the span is 15 ft and the ultimate tensile stress of the steel is 24 ton/in.² Allow a factor of safety of 6.

(7·6 tons)

5. Calculate the maximum bending moment which may be applied to the cast-iron section shown in Fig. 17.12 if the ultimate tensile stress of the material is 40,000 lb/in.² and a factor of safety of 10 is to be used.

($I = 43\cdot12$ in.⁴; 57,490 lb-in.)

6. Calculate the maximum allowable uniformly distributed load on a British Standard channel which is used as a cantilever of length 8 ft. The channel is to be loaded along its whole length and the maximum bending stress permitted is 10,000 lb/in.² Depth of channel section = 12 in.; relevant I of section about centroid = 221 in.⁴

(958 lb/ft)

7. The bar of section shown in Fig. 17.13 is simply supported over a span of 3 ft and carries a central load of 2 tons. Find the maximum bending moment and the maximum bending stress in the material.

($I = 4\cdot84$ in.⁴; $1\cdot5$ ton-ft; $5\cdot58$ tons/in.²)

8. Fig. 17.14 shows a section of a light alloy cantilever beam 4 ft long which is to carry a load of 2 tons at its free end. Calculate the second moment

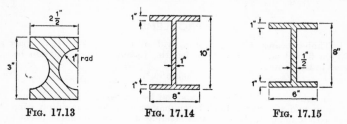

FIG. 17.13   FIG. 17.14   FIG. 17.15

of area of the section about its axis of bending and find the maximum bending stress in the material.

($I = 368$ in.⁴; $1\cdot305$ tons/in.²)

9. The steel joist shown in section in Fig. 17.15 is simply supported over a span of 8 ft. Calculate the maximum bending stress in the joist and the stress at the inside face of each flange due to a load of 10 tons mid-way between the supports.

($I = 157$ in.⁴; $6\cdot12$ tons/in.²; $4\cdot58$ tons/in.², one tensile, other compressive)

10. A cantilever consists of a standard symmetrical I-beam having cross-sectional area $10\cdot3$ in.² and a second moment of area about its centroid of $283\cdot3$ in.⁴ The total depth, with its web vertical, is 13 in. Calculate (a) the load per foot run due to its own weight, (b) the maximum length allowed for the cantilever if the maximum bending stress is not to exceed 6,000 lb/in.² Steel weighs $0\cdot27$ lb/in.³

($33\cdot4$ lb/ft; $36\cdot1$ ft)

11. A cast-iron pipe is carried over a span of 20 ft and may be considered as simply supported at each end. The pipe is 7 in. bore, $\frac{1}{2}$ in. thick and full of water. Calculate the maximum bending stress in the pipe. Density of water = $62\cdot4$ lb/ft.³ Density of cast iron = $0\cdot28$ lb/in.³

(1,622 lb/in.²)

17.6. Strength of a Beam in Bending

For a given maximum stress f the greatest moment which may be applied to a beam is given by

$$M_{\max} = \frac{f}{y_{\max}} \times I$$

i.e. M_{max} is proportional to I and inversely proportional to y_{max}, the distance of the extreme fibres from the neutral axis. For a rectangular section

$$I = \frac{bd^3}{12}, \text{ and } y_{max} = \tfrac{1}{2} d$$

Hence
$$M_{max} = \frac{f \times bd^3/12}{\tfrac{1}{2} d}$$
$$= \frac{f}{6} \times bd^2$$

which is proportional to the square of the depth of the beam.

For the same area of section (or weight per unit length) the I-value for various beams varies widely with the *shape* of section. Thus Fig. 17.16 shows four typical sections, each having an area of

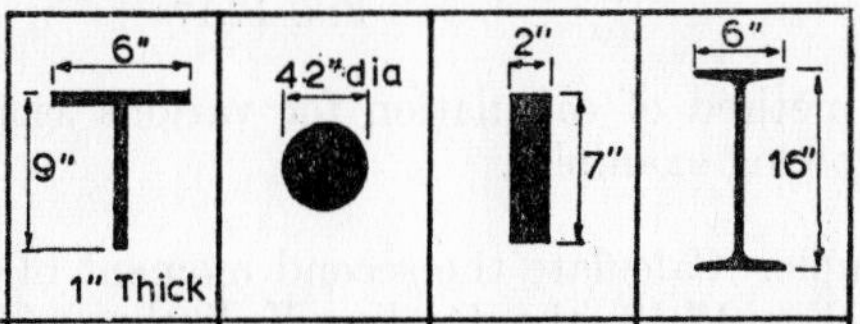

I (in.^{4})	112·7	15·5	57·1	618
M_{max} (ton-in)	94·3	36·9	81·3	386·5

FIG. 17.16

about 14 in.^{2} The table indicates the corresponding I and maximum moment which can be carried for the same maximum bending stress of 5 tons/in.^{2}

Comparison of these figures shows that the standard rolled steel joist is by far the strongest in bending. Evidently in building up a beam section it is advantageous to place the greatest area at the largest possible distance from the centroid.

For steel having the same strength in tension as in compression a symmetrical section is usually adequate. For cast iron, however, which has a lower strength in tension than in compression, the centroid of the cross-section should lie nearer to the tension flange so that the greatest stress occurs at the compression flange.

17.7. Calculation of I for Complex Sections

In dealing with complex and unsymmetrical sections the previous method of calculating I is insufficient. Also the position of the centroid and thus the neutral axis may be unknown. It is necessary therefore first to locate the centroid and then obtain the second moment of area about the neutral axis. The calculation of the second moment requires the theorem of parallel axes. The *theorem of parallel axes* states that if I_G is the second moment of area of a section about an axis G–G through the centroid and I_X is the second moment about an axis X–X parallel to G–G, then

$$I_X = I_G + Ah^2$$

where A is the area of the section and h the perpendicular distance between the axes G–G and X–X, Fig. 17.17.

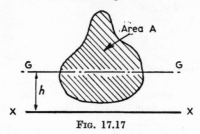

FIG. 17.17

The method of calculation for various sections is illustrated in the following examples.

Example. Calculate the second moment of area of the **T**-section shown, Fig. 17.18, about a line X–X through the centroid parallel to the flange face.

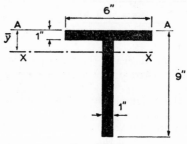

FIG. 17.18

Solution

TO FIND POSITION OF CENTROID

Area of section $= 14$ in.^{2}

moment of flange area about edge A–A $= 6 \times \frac{1}{2} = 3$ in.^{3}

moment of web area about A–A $= 8 \times 5 = 40$ in.^{3}

total moment $= 43$ in.^{3}

Let distance of centroid from A–A be $\bar{y}$, then

(total area) $\times \bar{y} = 43$

i.e. $14 \times \bar{y} = 43$

thus $\bar{y} = 3{\cdot}07$ in.

CALCULATION OF I_{X-X}

Flange: second moment of flange about its own centroid—

$$I_G = \frac{bd^3}{12}$$

$$= \frac{6 \times 1^3}{12}$$

$$= 0{\cdot}5 \text{ in.}^4$$

Distance of centroid of flange from axis X–X through centroid of section is

$$3{\cdot}07 - 0{\cdot}5$$

$$= 2{\cdot}57 \text{ in.}$$

Second moment of flange about axis X–X is

$$I_{\text{flange}} = I_G + Ah^2$$
$$= 0{\cdot}5 + 6 \times 2{\cdot}57^2$$
$$= 40{\cdot}1 \text{ in.}^4$$

Web: I for web about its own centroid is—

$$I_G = \frac{bd^3}{12} = \frac{1 \times 8^3}{12} = 42{\cdot}7 \text{ in.}^4$$

Distance of web centroid from axis X–X is

$$5 - 3{\cdot}07 = 1{\cdot}93 \text{ in.}$$

$$I_{\text{web}} \text{ about X–X} = I_G + Ah^2$$
$$= 42{\cdot}7 + 8 \times 1{\cdot}93^2$$
$$= 72{\cdot}5 \text{ in.}^4$$

Therefore, total I of section about X–X $= I_{\text{flange}} + I_{\text{web}}$
$$= 40{\cdot}1 + 72{\cdot}5$$
$$= \mathbf{112{\cdot}6 \text{ in.}^4}$$

The solution can be conveniently set out in tabular form; thus, in inch units—

Part	b	d	A	I about own centroid $bd^3/12$	h	Ah^2	I about X–X
Flange	6	1	6	$\frac{6 \times 1^3}{12} = 0{\cdot}5$	2·57	39·6	$0{\cdot}5 + 39{\cdot}6 = 40{\cdot}1$
Web	1	8	8	$\frac{1 \times 8^3}{12} = 42{\cdot}7$	1·93	29·8	$42{\cdot}7 + 29{\cdot}8 = 72{\cdot}5$
							Total I_X 112·6 in.⁴

Example. Calculate the second moment of area of the beam section shown, Fig. 17.19, about axis X–X through its centroid. The centroid is 5·58 in. from the face of the bottom flange.

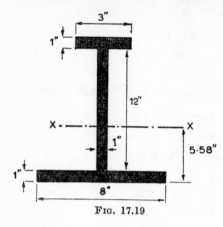

FIG. 17.19

Solution

For each sectional area let

b = breadth;

d = depth;

A = area, bd;

h = distance of its centroid from centroidal axis X–X;

I_G = second moment of area about its own centroid ($bd^3/12$).

Then, for each section, the second moment of area about axis X–X is given by—

$$I_X = I_G + Ah^2$$

The calculation of the total I for the section is set out in the following table (all quantities in inch units).

Part	b	d	A	h	$bd^3/12$	Ah^2	$I_X = I_G + Ah^2$
Top flange	3	1	3	7·92	0·25	188·2	188·45
Web	1	12	12	1·42	144·0	24·2	168·2
Bottom flange	8	1	8	5·08	0·667	206·3	206·97
						Total I_X	563·6 in.⁴

The total I_X is found by summing the values given in the last column.

PROBLEMS

Calculate the second moment of area of each of the sections shown in Fig. 17.20 about an axis X–X through the centroid.

Answers—
(a) 86·2 in.⁴
(b) Centroid 6 in. from top flange face; I = 508 in.⁴
(c) Centroid 5·86 in. from top edge; I = 547 in.⁴
(d) Centroid 3·75 in. from top flange face; I = 23·04 in.⁴
(e) Centroid 3·15 in. from top edge; I = 67·6 in.⁴
(f) Centroid 1·93 in. from top edge; I = 33·85 in.⁴
(g) Centroid 0·125 in. from centre of 6 in. circle; I = 59·6 in.⁴
(h) Centroid 2·29 in. from base; I = 86·8 in.⁴

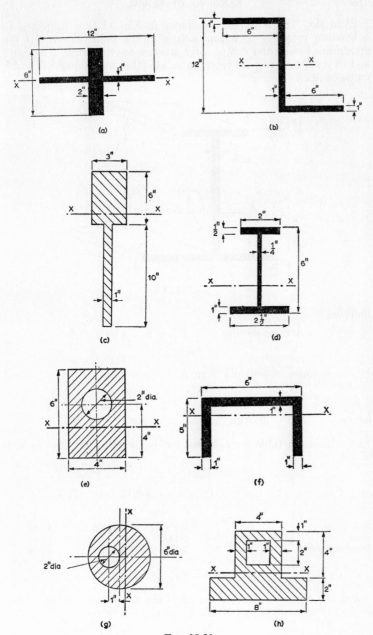

Fig. 17.20

Example. The beam section shown in Fig. 17.21 is subjected to a bending moment M ton-in. acting in the sense shown. If the maximum tensile and compressive stresses are limited to 2 tons/in.^{2} and 3 tons/in.^{2}, respectively, calculate the maximum allowable value of M.

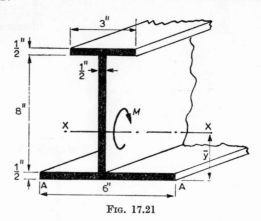

Fig. 17.21

Solution

$$\text{Area of section} = 3 \times \tfrac{1}{2} + 8 \times \tfrac{1}{2} + 6 \times \tfrac{1}{2}$$
$$= 8 \cdot 5 \text{ in.}^2$$

If $\bar{y}$ is distance of centroid from A–A, then taking moments about A–A—

$$8 \cdot 5 \times \bar{y} = 6 \times \tfrac{1}{2} \times \tfrac{1}{4} + 8 \times \tfrac{1}{2} \times 4\tfrac{1}{2} + 3 \times \tfrac{1}{2} \times 8\tfrac{3}{4}$$

hence $\bar{y} = 3 \cdot 75$ in.

The calculation table for I_X is set out below (all quantities in inch units).

Part	b	d	A	h	$bd^3/12$	Ah^2	$I_X = I_G + Ah^2$
Top flange	3	0·5	1·5	5·0	0·031	37·5	37·53
Web	0·5	8	4·0	0·75	21·35	2·25	23·6
Bottom flange	6	0·5	3·0	3·5	0·063	36·7	36·76
							$I_X = 97·9$ in.^{4}

h is the distance of the centroid of the particular portion of the section from neutral axis X–X. Using the formula—

$$M = \frac{f}{y} I$$

In tension, $y_{max} = 3.75$ in. and $f_{max} = 2$ ton/in.²

therefore $M = \dfrac{2 \times 97.9}{3.75} = 52.2$ ton-in.

In compression, $y_{max} = 5.25$ in. and $f_{max} = 3$ ton/in.²

therefore $M = \dfrac{3 \times 97.9}{5.25} = 55.9$ ton-in.

The maximum allowable bending moment must be the smaller of the two values found, i.e. **52·2 ton-in.**

PROBLEMS

1. Fig. 17.22 shows the section of a cantilever beam 10 ft long, which is

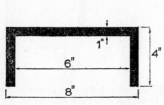
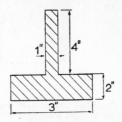

FIG. 17.22   FIG. 17.23

to carry a concentrated load of 10 cwt at its free end. Calculate the maximum tensile stress in the beam if the flange of the channel is uppermost.

(Centroid 1·36 in. from top face; $I = 18.9$ in.⁴; stress 9,670 lb/in.²)

2. Calculate the maximum bending moment which can be carried by a cast-iron bracket having the **T**-section shown in Fig. 17.23, if the maximum bending stress permitted is 2,000 lb/in.²

(Centroid 2·2 in. from bottom face; $I = 28.95$ in.⁴; moment 1,270 lb-ft)

3. A cantilever 20 ft long has the section shown in Fig. 17.24. The short flange is uppermost and the beam carries a uniformly distributed load of

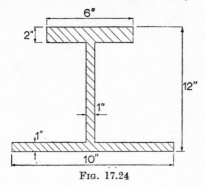

FIG. 17.24

10 cwt/ft run. Calculate the stresses at the two faces of the short flange at the section where the beam is fixed, stating whether they are tensile or compressive.

(Centroid 6·02 in. from bottom face; $I = 665·3$ in.⁴; stresses, 24,150 and 16,100 lb/in.² tensile)

4. A light bridge is to be supported by a number of beams of the section shown in Fig. 17.25 in which the top flange is uppermost. The beams are

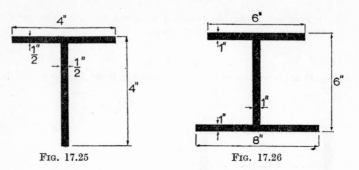

FIG. 17.25   FIG. 17.26

simply supported on a span of 30 ft and carry a load of 2 tons at the mid-point. The maximum allowable stress in the beam material is 5 tons/in.² Calculate the minimum number of beams required.

(Centroid 2·82 in. from bottom face; $I = 5·35$ in.⁴; number of beams, nineteen)

5. Calculate the maximum tensile stress in a steel beam due to its own weight if it is of the section shown in Fig. 17.26 and simply supported over a span of 15 ft. Weight of steel $= 0·26$ lb/in.³

(Centroid 2·72 in. from bottom face; $I = 92·4$ in.⁴; stress 672 lb/in.²)

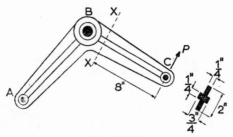

FIG. 17.27

6. In the cast-iron bracket lever shown in Fig. 17.27 the pull P is perpendicular to the bracket arm. Considering section X–X find the maximum allowable value of P if the stress due to bending is not to exceed 1 ton/in.²

(46·7 lb)

7. A car front axle is loaded as in Fig. 17.28. The axle consists of a symmetrical I-section beam 8 in. deep, 4 in. wide, with a uniform flange and

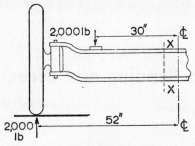

Fig. 17.28

web thickness of $\frac{1}{2}$ in. Calculate the tensile stress at section X–X due to bending.

$$(2,500 \text{ lb/in.}^2)$$

8. A compound girder is built up of an I-section rolled steel joist 10 in. deep, area of section 7·35 in.²; $I = 122 \cdot 3$ in.⁴; together with a pair of plates, section 9 in. by 1 in. One plate is fixed to each flange. Calculate I for the whole section about its centroid and hence find the maximum allowable central point load for a maximum stress of 5 tons/in.² The span of the beam is 20 ft.

$$(I = 668 \cdot 3 \text{ in.}^4; \ 9 \cdot 28 \text{ tons})$$

Combined Bending and Direct Stress

18.1. Principle of Superposition

THE stress at any point of a structure, beam or strut carrying several loads may be found by considering each load separately *as if it acted alone.* The total stress is then the algebraic sum of the stresses due to each separate load. This is the *method of superposition.*

A particular case is that of combined bending and direct stress due to a single load. The cantilever shown in Fig. 18.1 (*a*) is subject

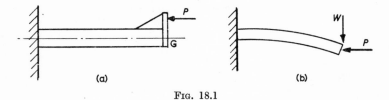

FIG. 18.1

to the axial load P offset from the centroid of cross-section G. This produces two effects: (*a*) a simple compression; (*b*) a bending moment about an axis through G. The stress due to each effect may be calculated separately and added to give the total stress. The method of superposition does not apply if one load alters the *character* or effect of another. For example, the cantilever, Fig. 18.1 (*b*), subject to an axial load P and a transverse load W may deflect sufficiently under the transverse load so as to increase the moment due to P. Only when this deflexion is negligible does the principle of superposition apply.

18.2. Combined Bending and Direct Stress of a Loaded Column

A short concrete column is loaded in compression by a concentrated load W at point A on the axis of symmetry, distant e from the

322

centroid G of the cross-section, Fig. 18.2. It is required to find the maximum eccentricity of the load if there is to be no tensile stress in the concrete and to obtain the value for a rectangular section.

The moment applied to the column is the moment of the load about an axis through the centroid. Thus the eccentric load W

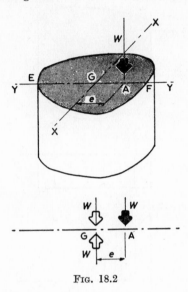

FIG. 18.2

may be replaced by: (*a*) a compressive load W at the centroid G; (*b*) a couple or bending moment $M = W \times e$ about the axis X–X through the centroid G.

Let A be the area of section, I the second moment of area about X–X, y the distance of any point in the plane of the section from X–X—

$$\text{direct compressive stress} = -\frac{W}{A}$$

$$\text{bending stress} = +\frac{M}{I}\, y, \text{ tensile in EG when } y \text{ is positive,}$$

compressive in GF, when y is negative

$$\begin{array}{l}\text{total stress at any point}\\ \text{distant } y \text{ from X–X}\end{array} = -\frac{W}{A} + \frac{M}{I}\, y$$

Fig. 18.3 shows the variation of direct, bending and total stress across the section. The effect of the eccentricity of loading is that the line of zero stress (neutral axis) is shifted to the left of the centroid. The form of the total stress diagram depends on the magnitudes of the direct and bending stresses.

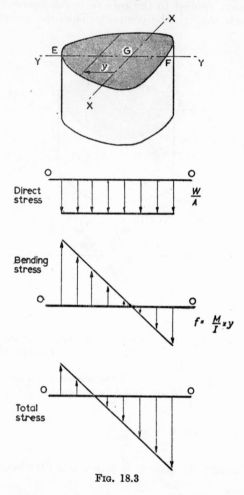

Direct stress

$\dfrac{W}{A}$

Bending stress

$f = \dfrac{M}{I} \times y$

Total stress

FIG. 18.3

The maximum tensile stress is at E. For no tension at any point the stress at E must be just zero. Now $M = W \times e$ and at E, $y = y_1$; therefore

$$\text{stress at E} = -\frac{W}{A} + \frac{W \times e}{I} y_1$$

$$= 0, \text{ for no tensile stress}$$

hence
$$\frac{We y_1}{I} = \frac{W}{A}$$

or
$$e = \frac{I}{Ay_1}$$

For a rectangular section, breadth b, depth d, $A = bd$, $I = bd^3/12$, $y_1 = \frac{1}{2} d$. Therefore

$$e = \frac{bd^3/12}{bd \times \frac{1}{2} d}$$

$$= \frac{d}{6}$$

Thus for no tension in a rectangular section the load must act on or within the distance $d/6$ from the centroid. This is known as the *middle-third rule*.

Example. A short hollow cast-iron column (Fig. 18.4) is to support a vertical load of 100 tons. The external diameter of the

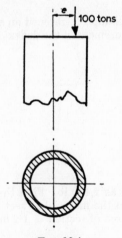

Fig. 18.4

column is 10 in. and the thickness 1 in. Find the maximum allowable eccentricity of this load if the maximum tensile stress is not to exceed 2 tons/in.² What is then the value of the maximum compressive stress?

Solution

$$A = \frac{\pi}{4} (10^2 - 8^2) = 28 \cdot 3 \text{ in.}^2$$

$$I = \frac{\pi}{64}(10^4 - 8^4) = 290 \text{ in.}^4$$

$$\text{direct stress} = -\frac{100}{28\cdot3} = -3\cdot54 \text{ tons/in.}^2 \text{ (compressive)}$$

bending moment $= 100\,e$, where e is the eccentricity of the load from the centroid.

$$\text{maximum bending stress} = \frac{My}{I} = \pm\frac{100 \times e \times 5}{290}$$

$$= \pm 1\cdot725\,e \text{ tons/in.}^2$$

$$\text{maximum tensile stress} = 1\cdot725\,e - 3\cdot54 = 2 \text{ tons/in.}^2$$

therefore $\qquad\qquad e = \textbf{3·21 in.}$

$$\text{Maximum compressive stress} = -1\cdot725\,e - 3\cdot54$$
$$= -1\cdot725 \times 3\cdot21 - 3\cdot54$$
$$= -\textbf{9·08 tons/in.}^2$$

Example. A screw clamp is tightened on a proving ring as shown, Fig. 18.5. From measurement of the deflexion of the ring the clamp-

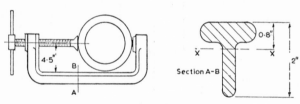

Fᵢɢ. 18.5

ing force is estimated as 2,400 lb. Find the maximum tensile and compressive stresses in the material at section A–B due to bending and direct loading. Area of section $= 1\cdot2$ in.^{2}, $I_{XX} = 0\cdot4$ in.^{4}

Solution

The resisting force exerted by the ring puts section A–B of the clamp under a direct tensile load of 2,400 lb and a bending moment $= 2,400\,(4\cdot5 + 0\cdot8) = 12,720$ lb-in. about the axis X–X, through the centroid of section. Since the effect of the resisting force exerted by the ring is to tend to open out the clamp the top portion of the section is in tension and the bottom in compression.

$$\text{Direct stress} = \frac{2,400}{1\cdot2} = 2,000 \text{ lb/in.}^2 \text{ tension}$$

$$\text{bending stress at top face} = \frac{M}{I} y = \frac{12,720}{0\cdot4} \times 0\cdot8$$

$$= 25,440 \text{ lb/in.}^2 \text{ (tension)}$$

$$\text{bending stress at bottom face} = -\frac{12,720}{0\cdot4} \times 1\cdot2$$

$$= -38,160 \text{ lb/in.}^2 \text{ (compression)}$$

$$\text{at top face, maximum stress} = 2,000 + 25,440$$

$$= \textbf{27,440 lb/in.}^2 \text{ (tension)}$$

$$\text{at bottom face, maximum stress} = 2,000 - 38,160$$

$$= -\textbf{36,160 lb/in.}^2 \text{ (compression)}$$

Example. A uniform masonry chimney of outside diameter 9 ft, inside diameter 7 ft is subjected to a horizontal wind load of 120 lb/ft of height. The weight of masonry is 110 lb/ft³. Calculate the maximum chimney height to avoid tensile stress at the base section.

Solution

Total wind load on height h ft (Fig. 18.6) $= 120\,h$ lb

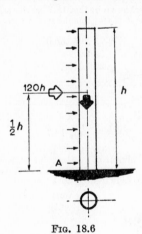

FIG. 18.6

bending moment at base section due to this load $= 120\,h \times \tfrac{1}{2}\,h$

$$= 60\,h^2 \text{ lb-ft}$$

$$I \text{ of section} = \frac{\pi}{64}\,(9^4 - 7^4) = 204 \text{ ft}^4$$

$$y_{\text{max}} = 4\cdot5 \text{ ft}$$

maximum tensile stress at base $= \dfrac{My}{I} = \dfrac{60\,h^2 \times 4.5}{204}$

$= 1.325\,h^2$ lb/ft² at point A

total weight of chimney

$= $ volume $\times$ specific weight

$= $ area of section $\times$ height $\times$ specific weight

$= Ah \times 110$

compressive stress at base due to dead load $= \dfrac{Ah \times 110}{A}$

$= 110\,h$ lb/ft²

For no tensile stress at base, total stress at A $= 0$. Therefore

$$1.325\,h^2 - 110\,h = 0 \quad \text{or} \quad h = \textbf{83·1 ft}$$

PROBLEMS

1. A 2 in. diameter tie bar carries a pull of 8 tons offset a distance of $\frac{1}{8}$ in. from the axis of the bar. Calculate the maximum and minimum tensile stresses in the bar.

(1·275, 3·82 tons/in.²)

2. The cranked tie bar shown in Fig. 18.7 carries a load of P tons. Calculate the maximum value of P if the tensile stress in section X–X is limited to 5 tons/in.²

(9·6 tons)

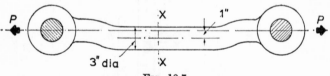

FIG. 18.7

3. A short cast-iron column of rectangular section 2 in. $\times$ 1·25 in. carries a load of P ton as shown in Fig. 18.8. Calculate the greatest value of P if the maximum tensile stress is limited to 1 ton/in.²

($\frac{1}{4}$ ton)

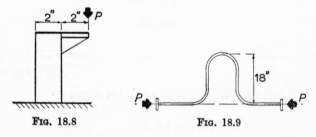

FIG. 18.8   FIG. 18.9

4. Fig. 18.9 shows an expansion loop in a steam pipe. The pipe has an external diameter of 4 in. and internal diameter of $3\frac{1}{2}$ in. If the end load P is 1,000 lb calculate the maximum tensile stress in the pipe.

$$(6,600 \text{ lb/in.}^2)$$

5. The aircraft undercarriage shown in Fig. 18.10 is constructed of alloy tube. Calculate the maximum tensile and compressive stresses in the tube A if it is $2\frac{1}{2}$ in. outside diameter and $\frac{1}{2}$ in. thick.

$$(41,700 \text{ lb/in.}^2 \text{ tensile, } 48,000 \text{ lb/in.}^2 \text{ compressive})$$

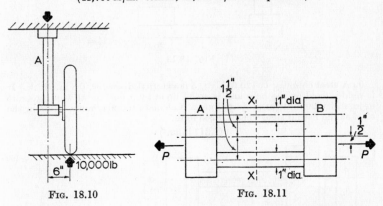

FIG. 18.10   FIG. 18.11

6. Two blocks A and B are connected by two short 1 in. diameter bars as shown, Fig. 18.11. Calculate the maximum pull P at a distance of $\frac{1}{2}$ in. from the axis of symmetry which may be exerted if the tensile stress at the section X–X is limited to 6 tons/in.^{2}

$$(6\cdot58 \text{ tons})$$

7. Calculate the maximum force P which can be exerted in the press frame shown (Fig. 18.12), if the tensile stress is limited to 4 tons/in.^{2} What is then the maximum compressive stress?

$$(130 \text{ tons; } 2 \text{ tons/in.}^2)$$

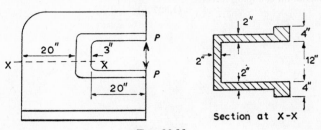

Section at X-X

FIG. 18.12

8. The pillar of the radial drill shown, Fig. 18.13, is made of a hollow steel tube of 8 in. outside diameter and 6 in. inside diameter. Calculate the maximum tensile stress in the pillar.

$$(1,790 \text{ lb/in.}^2)$$

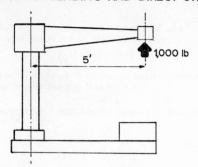

FIG. 18.13

9. A steel chimney is 120 ft high, 5 ft external diameter, 0·8 in. thick. It is rigidly fixed at the base and is acted upon by a horizontal wind pressure of intensity 20 lb/ft² of projected area. Calculate the maximum stress in the steel at the base if steel weighs 0·283 lb/in.³

(2,317 lb/in.²)

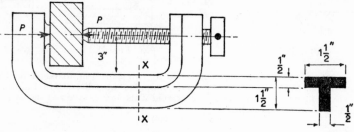

FIG. 18.14

10. The clamp shown, Fig. 18.14, exerts a force of P lb on the workpiece. If the section X–X is to carry a maximum tensile stress of 6,000 lb/in.² find the maximum clamping force.

(1,527 lb)

Fluid at Rest

19.1. Fluid

A FLUID may be a *liquid* or a *gas*; it offers negligible resistance to a change of shape and is capable of flowing. Liquid and gas are distinguished as follows—

1. A gas completely fills the space in which it is contained; a liquid usually has a free surface, Fig. 19.1.

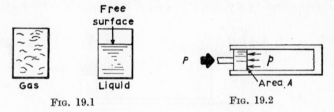

FIG. 19.1   FIG. 19.2

2. A gas is a fluid which can be compressed relatively easily; a liquid can be compressed only with difficulty.

The statics of a fluid, or *hydrostatics*, is the study of force and pressure in a fluid at rest.

19.2. Pressure

A fluid in a closed cylinder (Fig. 19.2) may be put into a state of pressure by applying a force P to the piston shown. Neglecting the weight of the fluid, the pressure p in the fluid is the ratio—

$$\frac{\text{force } P \text{ on piston}}{\text{area } A \text{ of piston}}$$

or
$$p = \frac{P}{A}$$

The units of pressure are pounds per square foot (lb/ft²) or pounds per square inch (lb/in.²).

Pressure in a fluid has the following important features—

1. The pressure at a point is the same in all directions.

2. The pressure exerted at a point on any surface is normal to the surface.

Fig. 19.3 shows equal pressures acting on all surfaces of a very small body immersed in a fluid. The pressure is everywhere normal

FIG. 19.3

to the surface. Similarly the pressure exerted by a fluid on its container is everywhere normal to the vessel wall, Fig. 19.3.

19.3. Transmission of Fluid Pressure

A simple hydraulic press is shown in Fig. 19.4. A load of weight W is supported by a piston C of area A in the cylinder D. Cylinder

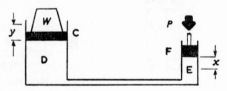

FIG. 19.4

D is connected by a pipe to another cylinder E which, in turn, contains a piston F of area a. The cylinders are filled with a liquid which is assumed incompressible. It is required to find the force P on the piston F in order to hold the load W in equilibrium. To do this we make use of the *principle of work*.

Let piston F move down a distance x causing piston C to rise a distance y, then

$$\text{volume of liquid leaving E } = a \times x$$

$$\text{volume of liquid entering D} = A \times y$$

Since the liquid is incompressible

$$Ay = ax$$

or

$$y = \frac{ax}{A}$$

work done by force $P = P \times x$

work done on load $W = W \times y$

Neglecting friction, the work done by P must be equal to the work done on W, therefore

$$Px = Wy$$
$$= W \times \frac{ax}{A}$$

or
$$\frac{P}{a} = \frac{W}{A}$$

But P/a is the pressure in cylinder E, and W/A is the pressure in cylinder D. Hence these two pressures are equal.

This is a demonstration of the *principle of transmission of pressure*, which states that the pressure intensity at any point of a fluid at rest is transmitted without loss to all other points of the fluid. The principle does not depend on frictionless pistons. The effect of friction is merely to increase the effort P, required to hold the load W, above the theoretical value $W \times a/A$. This effect is true of machines in general.

Similarly, the principle of transmission of pressure does not depend on the fluid being incompressible. It applies to gases provided the forces are applied sufficiently slowly. (Owing to the compression of gas the work principle does not apply in a simple form.)

19.4. Density; Specific Gravity; Specific Weight

The *density* of a substance is the mass per unit volume. For water it is about $62 \cdot 4$ lb-mass/ft^3.

The *specific weight w* of a substance is the weight per unit volume. Since 1 lb-mass weighs 1 lb-wt, density and specific weight are numerically equal for a given substance. Thus the specific weight of water is

$$w_{\text{water}} = 62 \cdot 4 \text{ lb/ft}^3$$

The *specific gravity s* of a substance is the ratio—

$$\frac{\text{weight of substance}}{\text{weight of equal volume of pure water}}$$

It may also be expressed as the ratio of the masses. It is a pure number and has no units. For example, the statement that mercury has a specific gravity of $13 \cdot 59$ means that it has a weight or mass $13 \cdot 59$ times as great as an equal volume of water.

In general, the specific weight w of a substance is given in terms of its specific gravity s, and the specific weight of water, by the expression

$$w = s \times w_{\text{water}}$$

Thus, if the specific gravity of petrol is $0 \cdot 8$ its specific weight is $0 \cdot 8 \times 62 \cdot 4$, or $49 \cdot 9$ lb/ft^3.

19.5. Pressure in a Fluid due to its own Weight

Consider a vertical tube of fluid, Fig. 19.5, of height h, uniform cross-sectional area A and specific weight w.

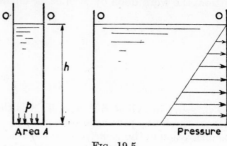

Fɪɢ. 19.5

Total weight of fluid column = specific weight × volume

$$= w \times Ah$$

$$\text{pressure } p \text{ at depth } h = \frac{\text{weight of column}}{\text{area of base}}$$

$$= \frac{wAh}{A}$$

or
$$p = wh$$

It follows, therefore, that the pressure in a fluid due to its own weight is proportional to the depth h below the free surface O–O. Fig. 19.5 shows the vertical variation with depth of the pressure in

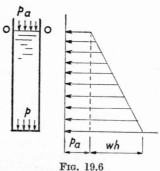

Fɪɢ. 19.6

an open tank of liquid. If the *atmospheric pressure* on the free surface of the liquid is p_a (Fig. 19.6) the total pressure p at depth h in the liquid is

$$p = p_a + wh$$

The pressure of the atmosphere is usually about 14·7 lb/in.²

19.6. Measurement of Pressure

A container at zero *absolute pressure* is one which is completely empty. The absolute pressure of a fluid is measured above this zero. The absolute pressure of the atmosphere is measured by a *barometer*, which consists of a tube sealed at the top and standing with its open end in a mercury bath open to the atmosphere, Fig. 19.7. Let the mercury rise to a height h above its free surface at

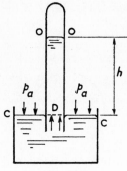

FIG. 19.7

C. By the principle of transmissibility of pressure, the upward pressure exerted by the mercury in the tube at D is equal to the downward pressure p_a exerted by the atmosphere on the free surface C. But

$$\text{pressure at D} = wh$$

where w is specific weight of mercury. Hence at D

$$p_a = wh$$

or   atmospheric pressure = specific weight of barometer fluid
$\times$ "height" h of barometer

For example, the height of a mercury barometer corresponding to an atmospheric pressure of 14·7 lb/in.² is given by—

$$h = \frac{p_a}{w}$$

$$= \frac{p_a}{s \times w_{\text{water}}}$$

$$= \frac{14 \cdot 7 \times 144}{13 \cdot 59 \times 62 \cdot 4}$$

$$= 2 \cdot 5 \text{ ft} \quad \text{or} \quad 30 \text{ in.} \quad \text{or} \quad 76 \text{ cm}$$

19.7. Measurement of Gauge Pressure

Gauge pressure is pressure measured above that of the atmosphere by a *manometer* or pressure gauge. Hence the absolute pressure is the sum of the gauge and atmospheric pressures,* thus—

absolute pressure = gauge pressure + atmospheric pressure

The simplest type of manometer is the *piezometer tube*, which is an open tube fitted into the top of the vessel containing liquid, whose pressure is to be measured, Fig. 19.8. If the vessel contains liquid

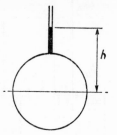

FIG. 19.8. PIEZOMETER TUBE

under pressure, the free surface of the liquid in the open tube will rise to a height h above the centre line of the vessel. The gauge pressure is—

$$p = wh$$

The height h is known as the *pressure head* and is often expressed in feet or inches of water. For example, a head of 1 in. of water corresponds to a pressure—

$$p = wh$$
$$= 62.4 \times \tfrac{1}{12}$$
$$= 5.2 \text{ lb/ft}^2$$
$$= 0.0361 \text{ lb/in.}^2$$

A pressure is often expressed as an equivalent *head of water*. Thus a head of 2 ft of oil of specific gravity 0·8 is equivalent to a head of $2 \times 0.8 = 1.6$ ft of water.

19.8. Measurement of Pressure Differences

The pressure difference between two points of a pipe containing liquid may be measured by an inverted U-tube, formed by two piezometer tubes combined, Fig. 19.9. The pressure difference is measured by the distance h between the two liquid levels. For

---

* All pressures stated in this book denote absolute pressures unless otherwise stated.

example, if the pipe and tube contain oil of specific gravity 0·8, a difference in head h of 1 in. corresponds to a pressure difference of

$$\frac{62 \cdot 4}{12^3} \times 0 \cdot 8$$

$$= 0 \cdot 0289 \ \text{lb/in.}^2$$

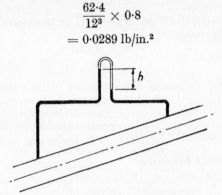

FIG. 19.9. INVERTED U-TUBE

19.9. Total Thrust on a Vertical Plane Surface

Consider a plane surface of area A immersed vertically in a liquid of specific weight w. The pressure on one side of the surface is

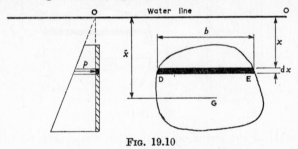

FIG. 19.10

normal to the surface and gives rise to a resultant force or *thrust* on that side, Fig. 19.10.

Pressure p on one side of thin strip DE at depth $x = wx$

$$\text{area of strip of breadth } b, \text{ thickness } \mathrm{d}x = b \times \mathrm{d}x$$

$$\text{force on strip} = p \times b \ \mathrm{d}x$$

$$= wx \times b \ \mathrm{d}x$$

$$= wbx \ \mathrm{d}x$$

$$\text{total force } P \text{ on area } A = \int wbx \ \mathrm{d}x$$

$$= w \int bx \ \mathrm{d}x$$

But $\int bx\,dx$ is the total moment of area A about an axis through O in the water surface—

$$= A \times \bar{x}$$

where $\bar{x}$ is the depth of the centroid G of the plane surface below the water line. Hence

$$P = w \times A\bar{x}$$
$$= wA\bar{x}$$

Thus the total thrust on an immersed plane vertical surface is proportional to the depth of the centroid of the wetted area below the free surface. Note, however, that the line of action of the total thrust does not pass through the centroid but through a point called the *centre of pressure*, which has yet to be found.

19.10. Centre of Pressure

The centre of pressure is the point of application of the resultant force due to fluid pressure on one face of an immersed surface. To determine the depth $\bar{y}$ of the centre of pressure we use the *principle of moments*. The sum of the moments about the water surface O–O

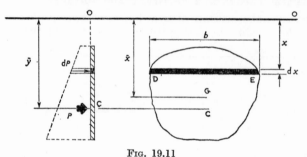

Fig. 19.11

(Fig. 19.11) of the forces on all the thin strips such as DE must equal the moment $P \times \bar{y}$ of the resultant thrust P about O–O.

Force on strip DE = pressure × area of strip

or
$$dP = p \times b\,dx$$
$$= wx \times b\,dx, \text{ since } p = wx$$

Moment of this force about O–O is—

$$dP \times x$$
$$= wxb\,dx \times x$$
$$= wx^2b\,dx$$

total moment about O–O $= \displaystyle\int wx^2b\,dx$

and this is equal to the moment $P \times \bar{y}$ of the resultant force P about O–O. Hence

$$P \times \bar{y} = w \int x^2 b \, \mathrm{d}x, \text{ since } w \text{ is a constant}$$

But $\int x^2 b \, \mathrm{d}x$ is the total second moment of area I_0 of the area A about O–O, thus

$$P \times \bar{y} = w \times I_0$$

Now $P = wA\bar{x}$, where $\bar{x}$ is the distance of the centroid G below O–O. Thus

$$\bar{y} = \frac{wI_0}{P}$$

$$= \frac{wI_0}{wA\bar{x}}$$

$$= \frac{I_0}{A\bar{x}}$$

$$= \frac{\text{second moment of area about O–O}}{\text{first moment of area about O–O}}$$

Note that this refers to *wetted* area only. This last expression is conveniently re-written as follows—

Let I_G = second moment of area A about axis through G parallel to water surface O–O

$$= Ak^2$$

where k is the corresponding radius of gyration. Then the parallel axis theorem for second moments of area states—

$$I_0 = I_G + A\bar{x}^2$$

Hence $$\bar{y} = \frac{I_0}{A\bar{x}}$$

$$= \frac{I_G + A\bar{x}^2}{A\bar{x}}$$

$$= \frac{Ak^2 + A\bar{x}^2}{A\bar{x}}$$

$$= \frac{k^2 + \bar{x}^2}{\bar{x}}$$

$$= \frac{k^2}{\bar{x}} + \bar{x}$$

Thus the distance of the centre of pressure C below the centroid G is

$$GC = \bar{y} - \bar{x}$$

$$= \frac{k^2}{\bar{x}}$$

This expression tends to zero as the distance $\bar{x}$ becomes very large. Hence the centre of pressure is always below the centroid of the

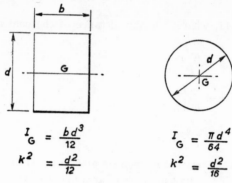

$$I_G = \frac{bd^3}{12}$$

$$k^2 = \frac{d^2}{12}$$

$$I_G = \frac{\pi d^4}{64}$$

$$k^2 = \frac{d^2}{16}$$

Fig. 19.12

wetted area, but tends to coincide with the centroid at very great depth.

The second moment of area I_G and the corresponding k^2 for rectangular and circular areas are shown in Fig. 19.12.

Example. A lock gate has sea-water to a depth of 12 ft on one side and 6 ft on the other. Find (*a*) the resultant thrust per foot

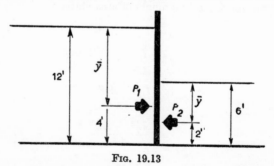

Fig. 19.13

width on the gate, (*b*) the resultant moment per foot width tending to overturn the gate at its base, Fig. 19.13. Specific weight of sea-water = 64 lb/ft³.

Solution

On left-hand side—

$$\text{depth of centroid, } \bar{x} = 6 \text{ ft}$$

total force P_1 from left to right $= wA\bar{x}$

$$= 64 \times 12 \times 1 \times 6$$

$$= 4{,}610 \text{ lb/ft width}$$

depth of centre of pressure, $\bar{y} = \bar{x} + \dfrac{k^2}{\bar{x}}$

where

$$k^2 = \frac{d^2}{12}$$

$$= \frac{12^2}{12} = 12 \text{ ft}^2$$

therefore

$$\bar{y} = 6 + \frac{12}{6}$$

$$= 8 \text{ ft}$$

Thus the total thrust on the left-hand side acts at 4 ft from the base. Moment of total force about the base is—

$$4{,}610 \times 4 = 18{,}440 \text{ lb-ft/ft width}$$

Similarly, on right-hand side—

$$\bar{x} = 3 \text{ ft}$$

$$P_2 = 64 \times 6 \times 1 \times 3 = 1{,}150 \text{ lb/ft width}$$

$$\bar{y} = 3 + \frac{6^2}{12} \times \frac{1}{3} = 4 \text{ ft}$$

moment of force P_2 about base $= 1{,}150 \times 2$

$$= 2{,}300 \text{ lb-ft/ft width}$$

resultant thrust (from left to right) $= P_1 - P_2$

$$= 4{,}610 - 1{,}150$$

$$= \mathbf{3{,}460 \text{ lb/ft width}}$$

net overturning moment $= 18{,}440 - 2{,}300$

$$= \mathbf{16{,}140 \text{ lb-ft/ft}} \text{ width, clockwise}$$

Example. A fuel tank contains oil of specific gravity 0·7. In one vertical side is cut a circular opening 6 ft diameter closed by a trap door hinged at the lower end B (Fig. 19.14) and held by a bolt at the upper edge A. If the fuel level is 6 ft above the top edge of the

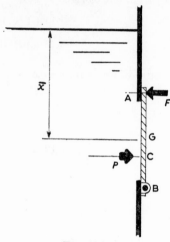

Fɪɢ. 19.14

opening, calculate (*a*) the total force on the door, (*b*) the force *F* in the bolt, (*c*) the force on the hinge. Specific weight of water = 62·4 lb/ft³.

Solution

   (*a*) Specific weight of fuel, $w = w_{\text{water}} \times s = 62\cdot4 \times 0\cdot7$

$$= 43\cdot7 \text{ lb/ft}^3$$

depth of centroid of door, $\bar{x} = 6 + 3 = 9$ ft

   total force *P* on door $= wA\bar{x}$

$$= 43\cdot7 \times \frac{\pi}{4} \times 6^2 \times 9 = \textbf{11,120 lb}$$

   (*b*) Depth of centre of pressure C below centroid G is—

$$\frac{k^2}{\bar{x}} = \frac{d^2}{16\,\bar{x}}$$

therefore $\qquad\qquad GC = \dfrac{6^2}{16 \times 9} = \dfrac{1}{4}$ ft

Moments about hinge B—

$$F \times AB = P \times CB$$

$$F \times 6 = 11,120 \times \left(3 - \frac{1}{4}\right)$$

$$F = \mathbf{5,100 \ lb}$$

(c) Resultant horizontal force on hinge

$$= \text{water thrust} - \text{bolt force}$$

$$= P - F$$

$$= 11,120 - 5,100$$

$$= \mathbf{6,020 \ lb}$$

PROBLEMS

1. A tank 4 ft high, 3 ft wide and 8 ft long is filled with water. Find the total force and the position at which it acts for (a) an end, (b) a side, (c) the base.

((a) 1,497 lb at 1·33 ft above base; (b) 3,990 lb at 1·33 ft above base; (c) 5,995 lb mid-point)

2. A lock gate is of rectangular section 24 ft wide. The depth of water on the lower side is 8 ft, the depth on the opposite side is h ft. The maximum allowable resultant thrust is 150 tons. Calculate the least value of h if this thrust is not to be exceeded.

(22·5 ft)

3. A sluice gate 3 ft wide, 6 ft deep, weighs 800 lb and works in vertical guides. The water surface on one side of the gate is 1 ft below the upper edge of the gate. If the coefficient of friction between the gate and the guides is 0·4 find the force required just to lift the gate. (Specific weight of water 62·4 lb/ft³.)

(1,736 lb)

4. A dock gate 60 ft wide has sea-water of specific weight 64 lb/ft³ to a depth of 20 ft on one side and 10 ft on the other. Find (a) the resultant thrust on the gate, (b) the resultant moment tending to overturn the gate about its lower edge.

(257 tons, 2,000 ton-ft)

5. A dock gate 20 ft high and 30 ft wide is pivoted at its base A and held vertical by a cable at the top of the gate, Fig. 19.15. There is a total depth of 10 ft of salt water weighing 64 lb/ft³ on one side of the gate. Find the tension in the cable.

(18,450 lb)

6. A tank of water has vertical sides and a rectangular opening in one end. The opening is covered by a door hinged along its top edge A (Fig. 19.16) and held by four bolts at the lower end B. The opening is 2 ft wide and 5 ft deep and the hinge at A is 4 ft below the water surface. Find (a) the depth at which the resultant water thrust acts on the door, (b) the load on each bolt, (c) the load on the hinge at A.

(6·82 ft; 572 lb; 1,772 lb)

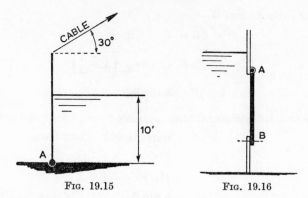

FIG. 19.15   FIG. 19.16

7. A tank with vertical sides contains oil of specific gravity 0·8 to a total depth of 6 ft. A hole 2 ft diameter is covered by a trap door, the lowest point of which is level with the base of the tank. Find (*a*) the total thrust on the door, (*b*) the depth below the surface of the line of action of this thrust.

(785 lb; 5·05 ft)

8. A vertical dock gate of rectangular section 8 ft deep and 4 ft wide pivots about a hinge at its lower edge. It is held in position by four $\frac{1}{2}$ in. diameter cables attached to its upper edge. The cables are at 45° to the horizontal. If sea-water weighs 64 lb/ft³ calculate (*a*) the maximum thrust on the dock gate, (*b*) the stress in the cables, (*c*) the vertical and horizontal forces on the hinge.

(8,190 lb; 4,920 lb/in.²; 2,730 lb; 5,460 lb)

9. A concrete reservoir dam has a vertical face on the water side and dimensions as shown, Fig. 19.17. The top water level reaches 8 ft below the

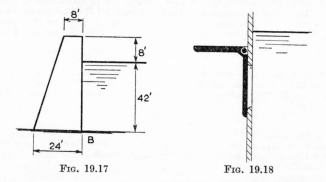

FIG. 19.17   FIG. 19.18

crest of the dam. Find the magnitude of the resultant thrust per foot width on the base (*a*) when the reservoir is empty, (*b*) when the reservoir is full. State in each case where the line of action of the resultant thrust cuts the base. Water weighs 62·4 lb/ft³, concrete weighs 150 lb/ft³.

(120,000 lb, 8 ft 8 in. from B; 132,000 lb, 15·1 ft from B)

10. Fig. 19.18 shows a pivoted sluice gate weighing 3,200 lb covering a rectangular opening 3 ft by 3 ft. The pivot of the gate is 4 ft above the base

of the opening. The gate is just about to open when the head of water is 4·5 ft above the base of the opening. Find the distance of the centre of gravity of the gate from the pivot. Specific weight of water, 62·4 lb/ft³.

(17·35 in.)

19.11. Inclined Surface

The method of finding the total force on an inclined surface, and the depth of the centre of pressure, is similar to that for the vertical surface. The variable distance x is now measured along the plane of the incline however, Fig. 19.19.

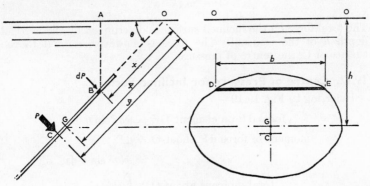

FIG. 19.19

Consider element DE of the inclined plane, distant x from the water line O–O, x being measured along the incline. The pressure p on the element at vertical depth AB is given by—

$$p = w \times \text{AB}$$
$$= w \times x \sin \theta$$

where θ is the acute angle made by the plane with the water surface.

$$\text{Force } \mathrm{d}P \text{ on the element} = p \times \text{area of element}$$
$$= wx \sin \theta \times b \, \mathrm{d}x$$
$$= wbx \sin \theta \, \mathrm{d}x$$

where b is width of element and $\mathrm{d}x = $ thickness of element.

$$\text{Total force } P \text{ on surface} = \int \mathrm{d}P$$

$$= \int wbx \sin \theta \, \mathrm{d}x$$

$$= w \sin \theta \int bx \, \mathrm{d}x$$

But $$\int bx \, \mathrm{d}x = \text{total moment of area } A \text{ about O–O}$$
$$= A \times \bar{x}$$

where $\bar{x}$ is the distance OG of centroid G from O–O. Therefore

$$P = wA\bar{x} \sin \theta$$

Now $\bar{x} \sin \theta$ is the *vertical* depth h of centroid G below O–O. Thus

$$P = wAh$$

The total force on the inclined surface is determined by the vertical depth h of the centroid. The force is, however, normal to the surface at C, the centre of pressure.

19.12. Centre of Pressure for Inclined Surface

Referring to Fig. 19.19—

$$\text{force } \mathrm{d}P \text{ on element DE} = wbx \sin \theta \, \mathrm{d}x$$
$$\text{moment of force } \mathrm{d}P \text{ about O} = \mathrm{d}P \times x$$
$$= wbx^2 \sin \theta \, \mathrm{d}x$$
$$\text{total moment about O} = \int wbx^2 \sin \theta \, \mathrm{d}x$$
$$= w \sin \theta \int bx^2 \, \mathrm{d}x$$
$$= w \sin \theta \times I_0$$

where $I_0 = \int bx^2 \, \mathrm{d}x = $ total second moment of area A about water line O–O. The total moment exerted by the elementary forces is equal to the moment of the resultant force P about O, i.e.

$$wI_0 \sin \theta = P \times \bar{y}$$

where $\bar{y}$ is the distance OC of centre of pressure C from O, measured along the inclined surface. But

$$P = wA\bar{x} \sin \theta$$

hence $$wI_0 \sin \theta = wA\bar{x} \sin \theta \times \bar{y}$$

thus $$\bar{y} = \frac{I_0}{A\bar{x}}$$

From the parallel axis theorem

$$I_0 = I_G + A\bar{x}^2 = A(k^2 + \bar{x}^2)$$

where I_G is the second moment of area about the centroid G, and k the radius of gyration about G. Therefore

$$\bar{y} = \frac{A(k^2 + \bar{x}^2)}{A\bar{x}}$$

or

$$\bar{y} = \bar{x} + \frac{k^2}{\bar{x}}$$

which is the same as for a vertical surface. Note, however, that $\bar{x}$ and $\bar{y}$ are now measured *along the inclined surface*. It follows that the distance GC of the centre of pressure from the centroid of area is given by

$$\mathrm{GC} = \frac{k^2}{\bar{x}}$$

Example. In Fig. 19.20 QR represents a trap-door, 10 ft wide and 8 ft deep, in the side of a water tank. It is pivoted at Q and

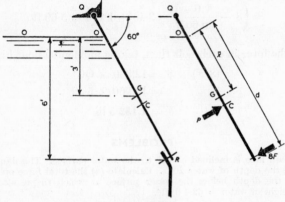

FIG. 19.20

held against water pressure by eight bolts at R. Calculate the force in each bolt. The water level is 6 ft vertically above R.

Solution

The vertical depth of centroid G of *wetted* surface OR is 3 ft and the area of wetted surface is

$$A = \frac{6}{\sin 60°} \times 10 = 69 \cdot 2 \text{ ft}^2$$

total force P on surface OR $= wAh$
$$= 62 \cdot 4 \times 69 \cdot 2 \times 3$$
$$= 12{,}960 \text{ lb}$$

The distance $\bar{x}$ of centroid G of *wetted* surface from water level O–O is

$$\frac{3}{\sin 60°} = 3 \cdot 46 \text{ ft}$$

For wetted area $\qquad k^2 = \dfrac{d^2}{12}$

$$= \frac{1}{12}\left(\frac{6}{\sin 60°}\right)^2$$

$$= 4 \text{ ft}^2$$

Distance GC of centre of pressure C from centroid G is

$$\frac{k^2}{\bar{x}} = \frac{4}{3 \cdot 46} = 1 \cdot 156 \text{ ft}$$

$$QC = QO + OG + GC$$

$$= \left(8 - \frac{6}{\sin 60°}\right) + 3 \cdot 46 + 1 \cdot 156 = 5 \cdot 69 \text{ ft}$$

If F is the force in each bolt then, taking moments about hinge Q—

$$(8\,F) \times 8 = 12{,}960 \times QC$$

$$= 12{,}960 \times 5 \cdot 69$$

hence $\qquad\qquad F = \mathbf{1{,}152 \cdot 5\ lb}$

PROBLEMS

1. A dam face is inclined at 50° to the water surface. The dam is 60 ft wide and the depth of water 20 ft. Calculate (a) the total force on the dam face, (b) the depth below the water surface at which the resultant force acts. Weight of water = 62·4 lb/ft³.

(978,000 lb; 13·33 ft vertically)

2. The side of a tank makes 45° with the water surface. A trap-door 1 ft diameter is hinged at a point 3 ft below the water surface and bolted against the water pressure at the lowest point of the door. Calculate (a) the force in the bolt, (b) the load on the hinge.

(86·5 lb; 77·8 lb)

3. A tank of oil of specific gravity 0·8 contains a rectangular trap-door 10 ft wide and 8 ft deep. The door makes an angle of 110° with the line of the water surface and is hinged at a point 2 ft vertically below the surface. If the door is held against oil pressure by four bolts along its lower edge find the force in each bolt.

(3,500 lb)

20

Fluid in Motion

THE science of a fluid in motion is most conveniently studied using energy methods. It will be found that, in addition to potential and kinetic energy, a fluid may possess *pressure energy* by virtue of the work done in introducing it into a container under pressure. The fluid will be assumed to be an incompressible liquid; the flow of a compressible gas is not considered.

20.1. Pressure Energy

Consider a tank of liquid with free surface at B, Fig. 20.1. We calculate the work done in introducing an additional volume of

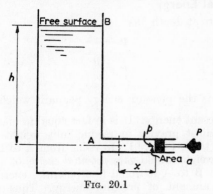

FIG. 20.1

liquid at level A into the tank against the pressure p at A. The liquid is to be forced into the tank by means of a small piston of area a; the head h of liquid (and thus pressure p) is assumed constant while this is done. The area a is assumed small enough for pressure p to be considered uniform across the face of the piston. Friction between the piston and cylinder is neglected. The force on the piston is—

$$P = p \times a$$

349

The work done in a small slow displacement x is—

$$P \times x = pa \times x$$

Since, if the piston is released, both fluid and piston would be forced out by the fluid pressure this work is not lost but is recoverable. It therefore represents energy possessed by the fluid forced into the tank, i.e. pressure energy.

Volume of liquid entering tank = area of cylinder × length

$$= a \times x$$

Weight of liquid entering tank = specific weight × volume

$$= w \times ax$$

Hence, energy possessed by *unit weight* of liquid is—

$$\frac{\text{work done on liquid}}{\text{weight of liquid}} = \frac{pax}{wax}$$

$$= \frac{p}{w}$$

This is the pressure energy of unit weight of liquid and is termed the *pressure head*. Since p is in pounds per square foot (lb/ft²), w in pounds per cubic foot (lb/ft³), the units of pressure energy are foot-pounds per pound (ft-lb/lb) or feet (ft).

20.2. Potential Energy

Since pressure at depth h is

$$p = wh$$

therefore

$$h = \frac{p}{w}$$

Now, since $\frac{p}{w}$ is the pressure energy per unit weight, the head h must also represent energy. It is in fact equal in magnitude to the work done against gravity in raising unit weight of the liquid slowly from A to B, Fig. 20.1. In rising from A to B a particle of liquid of unit weight would gain *potential energy* of amount $1 \times h$. In falling from B to A it would lose potential energy and gain a corresponding amount of pressure energy. Thus potential and pressure energy may be converted one into the other, i.e. *in a liquid at rest*—

potential energy + pressure energy = constant

or

$$h + \frac{p}{w} = \text{constant}$$

In any change, a gain in one term will be balanced by a corresponding loss in the other, to keep the sum of the two constant.

The units of potential energy are the same as those of pressure energy, i.e. foot-pounds per pound (ft-lb/lb) or feet (ft).

20.3. Kinetic Energy

Now let the piston of Fig. 20.1 be removed so that liquid may flow freely from the opening (orifice) at A. Consider a particle of unit weight falling freely from the free surface at B to level A and then escaping with velocity v. The potential energy lost by the particle in falling is balanced by the kinetic energy gained in attaining a velocity v just outside the tank at A.

potential energy lost per unit weight $= h$

kinetic energy gained per unit weight $= \dfrac{1}{2g} v^2$

potential energy lost $=$ kinetic energy gained

or
$$h = \frac{v^2}{2g}$$

Hence there is now an interchange of potential and kinetic energy; $v^2/2g$, the kinetic energy per unit weight is termed the *velocity head*. The units are foot-pounds per pound (ft-lb/lb) or feet (ft).

20.4. Interchange of Pressure and Kinetic Energy

It is not necessary for any particle to have actually fallen from B to A before flowing from the orifice. If already at the level A it will possess pressure energy $\dfrac{p}{w}$ and this in turn may be converted into kinetic energy on escaping. Thus we may write—

pressure energy lost $=$ kinetic energy gained

or
$$\frac{p}{w} = \frac{v^2}{2g}$$

This assumes that p is the pressure measured above that of the atmosphere outside the jet of fluid at A, i.e. the gauge pressure. This is usually the case.

20.5. Bernoulli's Equation (Conservation of Energy)

We have seen that, for an incompressible liquid in motion, there are three forms of energy to be considered—

(a) pressure energy, $\dfrac{p}{w}$;

(b) kinetic energy, $\dfrac{v^2}{2g}$;

(c) potential energy, H;

and there may be an interchange between any of these forms of energy. This is expressed by *Bernoulli's equation* which states that, for a liquid in motion—

pressure energy + kinetic energy + potential energy = constant

or, for unit weight of liquid

$$\frac{p}{w} + \frac{v^2}{2g} + H = constant$$

where the potential energy H is measured above an arbitrary datum level. The symbol H is now used for potential energy to prevent confusion with the *pressure head h.*

Bernoulli's equation shows that a "loss" or reduction in one term is always balanced by an increase in one or both of the other energy terms. Thus a drop in pressure p may accompany a corresponding increase in height H, or in velocity v. The equation holds in the above form provided—

(a) there is no loss of energy by friction or leakage;
(b) the motion is not turbulent or fluctuating.

Bernoulli's equation is a statement of the *principle of conservation of energy* for the particular case of a liquid in steady motion.

20.6. Pipe Flow: Equation of Continuity

If suffices 1, 2 denote two points A, B, respectively, in a pipe, Fig. 20.2, then for a liquid flowing in the pipe from A to B, Bernoulli's equation is

$$\frac{p_1}{w} + \frac{v_1^2}{2g} + H_1 = \frac{p_2}{w} + \frac{v_2^2}{2g} + H_2 = constant$$

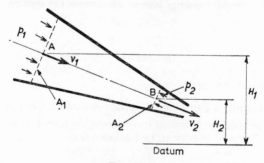

Fig. 20.2

This equation alone is usually insufficient to solve problems on pipe flow. We must find a second equation using the assumption that the liquid is incompressible.

If the liquid is incompressible the volume of liquid passing A per second must be the same as the volume passing B per second. Denoting the cross-sectional areas of the pipe by A_1 and A_2—

volume passing A per second = area of pipe × velocity of liquid

$$= A_1 \times v_1$$

volume passing B per second = $A_2 \times v_2$

Equating—

$$A_1 \times v_1 = A_2 \times v_2$$

or

$$\frac{v_1}{v_2} = \frac{A_2}{A_1}$$

This is known as the *equation of continuity* and, when the pipe dimensions are known, gives the ratio of the velocities at any two points in the pipe. The equation states that the velocity of flow is inversely proportional to the area of pipe section.

20.7. Flow-Rate

The flow-rate Q is the quantity of liquid flowing per second. Thus

$$Q = \text{volume per second}$$

$$= Av$$

If A is in square feet (ft²), v in feet per second (ft/sec) the flow rate Q is in cubic feet per second (ft³/sec) or *cusecs*.

The corresponding weight of liquid flowing per second is

$$w \times Q = wAv$$

20.8. Variation in Pressure Head along a Pipe

Fig. 20.3 shows the pressure head at two points A and B of an inclined pipe connected to an open tank and containing fluid *at rest*.

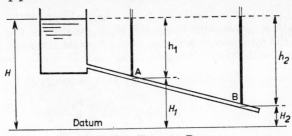

FIG. 20.3. FLUID AT REST

The pressure head of the liquid is measured by the head h in the piezometer tubes, since

$$h = \frac{p}{w}$$

The potential energy of the fluid at the free surface in the tank is H, and at point A the potential energy is H_1. Since the fluid is at rest the difference $H - H_1$ corresponds to the pressure head, i.e.

$$H - H_1 = h_1 = \frac{p_1}{w}$$

Similarly for point B, we have

$$H - H_2 = h_2 = \frac{p_2}{w}$$

hence

$$H = H_1 + h_1 = H_1 + \frac{p_1}{w}$$

$$= H_2 + h_2 = H_2 + \frac{p_2}{w}$$

Fig. 20.4 shows the corresponding piezometer head levels for a *flowing* liquid in a pipe of uniform section. Since the pipe has

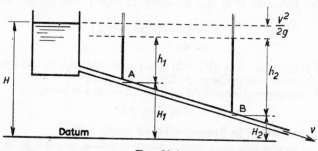

FIG. 20.4

constant area of section the velocity v and, therefore, the velocity head $v^2/2\,g$, is constant along the pipe. Neglecting friction and losses, the total energy is the same at all points along the pipe. If the liquid in the tank is assumed at rest, then Bernoulli's equation is

energy at free surface = energy at A = energy at B

i.e.

$$H = H_1 + \frac{p_1}{w} + \frac{v^2}{2\,g} = H_2 + \frac{p_2}{w} + \frac{v^2}{2\,g}$$

Fig. 20.5 shows the variation in head along a horizontal diverging pipe connected to a cylinder of liquid at constant pressure p. Since the area at B is greater than that at A, the velocity head $v^2/2\,g$ decreases between A and B and the pressure head h shows a corresponding increase. As before, the total energy remains constant along the pipe.

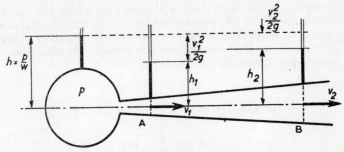

Fig. 20.5

Example. Water flows along a horizontal pipe which varies uniformly in section from 4 in. diameter at A to 6 in. diameter at B. At A the pressure is 18 lb/in.² and at B 20 lb/in.² Find the flow rate in cubic feet per second (cusecs).

Solution

$$\text{Area of section at A} = \frac{\pi}{4} \times 4^2 = 12 \cdot 56 \text{ in.}^2$$

$$\text{area of section at B} = \frac{\pi}{4} \times 6^2 = 28 \cdot 3 \text{ in.}^2$$

From equation of continuity—

$$\frac{v_1}{v_2} = \frac{A_2}{A_1}$$

therefore

$$v_1 = \frac{28 \cdot 3}{12 \cdot 56} \times v_2 = 2 \cdot 25 \, v_2$$

Applying Bernoulli's theorem to points A and B—

$$\frac{p_1}{w} + \frac{v_1^2}{2g} = \frac{p_2}{w} + \frac{v_2^2}{2g}$$

i.e.

$$\frac{18 \times 144}{62 \cdot 4} + \frac{v_1^2}{2 \times 32 \cdot 2} = \frac{20 \times 144}{62 \cdot 4} + \frac{v_2^2}{2 \times 32 \cdot 2}$$

thus

$$v_1^2 - v_2^2 = 297$$

Substituting for v_1 in terms of v_2—

$$(2 \cdot 25 \, v_2)^2 - v_2^2 = 297$$

hence

$$v_2 = 8 \cdot 55 \text{ ft/sec}$$

therefore

$$Q = A_2 v_2$$

$$= \frac{28 \cdot 3}{144} \times 8 \cdot 55$$

$$= \mathbf{1 \cdot 68 \ cusecs}$$

Example. Water flows down a sloping pipe which has one end 5 ft above the other. The pipe section tapers from 3 ft diameter at the top end A to 1·5 ft diameter at the lower end B. The flow of water is 2,000 gal/min. Find the difference in pressure between A and B in pounds per square inch.

Solution

$$\text{Area of pipe at A} = \frac{\pi}{4} \times 3^2 = 7\cdot07 \text{ ft}^2$$

$$\text{area of pipe at B} = \frac{\pi}{4} \times 1\cdot5^2 = 1\cdot77 \text{ ft}^2$$

$$Q = 2,000 \text{ gal/min}$$

$$= 2,000 \times 10 \text{ lb/min}$$

$$= \frac{2,000 \times 10}{62\cdot4 \times 60} \text{ cusecs}$$

$$= 5\cdot34 \text{ cusecs}$$

From equation of continuity—

$$Q = A_1 v_1 = A_2 v_2$$

therefore

$$5\cdot34 = 7\cdot07\, v_1 = 1\cdot77\, v_2$$

and

$$v_1 = 0\cdot754 \text{ ft/sec}$$

$$v_2 = 3\cdot02 \text{ ft/sec}$$

Applying Bernoulli's equation—

$$H_1 + \frac{p_1}{W} + \frac{v_1^2}{2g} = H_2 + \frac{p_2}{w} + \frac{v_2^2}{2g}$$

thus

$$5 + \frac{p_1}{62\cdot4} + \frac{0\cdot754^2}{64\cdot4} = 0 + \frac{p_2}{62\cdot4} + \frac{3\cdot02^2}{64\cdot4}$$

and

$$p_2 - p_1 = 62\cdot4 \left\{ \frac{0\cdot754^2 - 3\cdot02^2}{64\cdot4} + 5 \right\}$$

$$= 62\cdot4\,(-0\cdot133 + 5)$$

$$= 303 \text{ lb/ft}^2$$

$$= \mathbf{2\cdot11 \text{ lb/in.}^2}$$

PROBLEMS

1. A tank contains oil of specific gravity 0·85 to a depth of 8 ft. It discharges through a 1 in. diameter straight pipe at a point 20 ft below the bottom of the tank. Calculate the discharge in gallons per minute and the oil pressure at a point half-way along the pipe.

(87 gal/min; −3·68 lb/in.² gauge or 11·02 lb/in.²)

2. The diameter of a pipe tapers gradually in the direction of water flow as the level drops 30 ft from point A to point B. At A the pressure is 30 lb/in.² and the pipe diameter 8 in.; at B the diameter is 4 in. What is the pressure at B when the flow rate is 1,000 gal/min?

(37 lb/in.²)

3. A horizontal pipe tapers gradually from 6 in. to 12 in. diameter in the direction of flow. At the narrow section a pressure gauge reads 20 lb/in.² At the wide section the pressure is 40 lb/in.² Neglecting losses calculate the flow rate of water in cubic feet per second (cusecs).

(5·7 cusecs)

4. Oil of specific weight 56 lb/ft³ flows through a horizontal pipe which reduces smoothly from 3 in. to 2 in. diameter. If the pressure at these points is 10 lb/in.² and 7 lb/in.², respectively, find the velocity at the larger diameter and the flow rate in gallons per minute.

(11·06 ft/sec; 204 gal/min)

5. Oil of specific gravity 0·8 flows at the rate of 8 cusecs through a falling pipe which tapers gradually in the direction of flow. The diameter at a point A is 2 ft and at a point B, 12 ft vertically below A, it is 1 ft. The pressure at A is 12 lb/in.² Calculate the pressure at B.

(15·6 lb/in.²)

20.9. The Flow of Real Fluids

So far we have assumed the fluid to be perfectly frictionless and the pipe walls to be perfectly smooth. A frictionless fluid would flow as in Fig. 20.6, each layer travelling in a smooth path without

Fig. 20.6. Streamline or Laminar Flow

interference from adjacent layers. Such a smooth regular flow is called *laminar* or *streamline*. In practice we have to consider the effects of both *fluid friction* and pipe wall friction.

20.10. Viscosity

The *viscosity* of a fluid is the internal resistance to a change of shape. Typically viscous fluids are treacle, glycerine and thick oils; all fluids are viscous in some degree.

20.11. Flow at Low Velocities

Consider now a viscous fluid entering smoothly and slowly into a pipe. Owing to wall friction fluid sticks to the wall surface, forming a *boundary layer* which is at rest relative to the pipe,

Fig. 20.7. Owing to the viscosity of the fluid a drag force or shear stress is exerted on the remainder of the moving fluid by the boundary layer. The velocity of the fluid outside the boundary layer is, however, roughly uniform across the pipe, decreasing within the boundary layer to zero at the pipe wall.

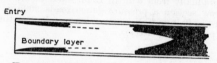

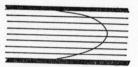

FIG. 20.7. FULLY-DEVELOPED VISCOUS
FLOW

FIG. 20.8. VELOCITY DIS-
TRIBUTION IN VISCOUS
LAMINAR FLOW

As the fluid continues down the pipe the boundary layer thickens until it completely fills the pipe. The flow is now said to be fully developed; this occurs at a distance equal to a few pipe diameters from the entry. The distribution of velocity across the pipe is now parabolic in form, Fig. 20.8. Note, however, that viscous flow is still regular, i.e. streamline or laminar. The viscous drag forces in the fluid involve a loss of pressure and thus a drop in pressure head along the pipe. This drop in pressure—

(*a*) is proportional to the mean flow velocity;
(*b*) is proportional to the length of pipe;
(*c*) increases inversely as the square of the pipe diameter;
(*d*) is greater with more viscous fluids;
(*e*) is independent of pipe roughness.

Viscous flow of this nature occurs with very viscous oils at low speeds and with ordinary fluids such as water when the pipe diameter is very small indeed.

20.12. Onset of Turbulence

At high velocities the fluid flow loses its regular streamline form and takes on an irregular motion. Fig. 20.9 shows the effect of flow

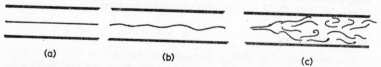

(a)   (b)   (c)

FIG. 20.9. (*a*) LAMINAR FLOW. (*b*) TRANSITION. (*c*) TURBULENT FLOW

velocity on the motion of a thin stream of dye injected into water flowing in a pipe. In Fig. 20.9 (*a*) the velocity is low, the flow laminar, and the dye flows as a thin thread. At a higher velocity the fluid takes on a sinuous wavy motion as shown by the dye, Fig. 20.9 (*b*). Finally, at sufficiently high velocities the dye thread breaks up and takes on the irregular motion of the main flow. This irregular motion is called *turbulence*, Fig. 20.9 (c). For a given fluid and pipe diameter there is a *critical velocity* above which turbulence sets in. This critical velocity increases with the viscosity and density of the fluid and decreases with the pipe diameter. That is, turbulence is more likely with fluids of low viscosity in large diameter pipes. For water this critical velocity would be about $\frac{1}{2}$ ft/sec in a 1 in. diameter pipe.

Turbulence arises from the initial presence of a boundary layer; fluid near the boundary tends to drag behind the main stream to disturb a uniform flow. Once turbulence has set in the viscosity of the fluid is no longer of great importance. Layers of fluid near the pipe wall still adhere to it however, even though the fluid is turbulent; a laminar boundary layer remains but is thinner than in viscous flow. When the pipe surface roughness is such that the irregularities are larger than the boundary layer thickness then pipe roughness becomes important.

20.13. Pressure Loss in Turbulent Flow

The drop in pressure head due to turbulence does not obey the same laws as in viscous laminar flow. The loss is now—

(a) proportional to the *square* of the mean velocity;
(b) proportional to the length of pipe, as before;
(c) inversely proportional to the pipe diameter;
(d) nearly independent of fluid viscosity, but may depend on pipe roughness.

In most practical pipeline applications turbulence may usually be assumed to occur. This is almost always the case for water flow. Note that the pressure loss in turbulent flow is much greater than that for viscous laminar flow.

20.14. Eddy Formation

The retarded boundary layer formed at the pipe wall as a result of pipe friction and fluid viscosity can—under certain conditions— give rise to the formation of *eddies* or *vortices*. Eddies occur at a discontinuity in the pipe surface, such as a sudden enlargement or contraction, rapid increases in pipe diameter, sharp bends and valves. At a discontinuity of section or obstruction the boundary layer breaks away from the pipe surface to form the eddy, with a consequent further loss of pressure at the obstruction, Fig. 20.10. The reader may compare this effect with his experience of a wind gust behind a rapidly moving vehicle.

Although eddies may be formed whether the flow is initially laminar or turbulent, turbulence of any sort in the oncoming fluid tends to promote the onset of eddies. The latter may perhaps be thought of as a turbulence on a larger scale, but localized near the obstruction. The formation of eddies involves a further source of pressure loss which is proportional to the square of the mean fluid velocity. Eddy formation at an enlargement in a pipe is prevented by allowing the pipe to open out only very gradually. Similarly the

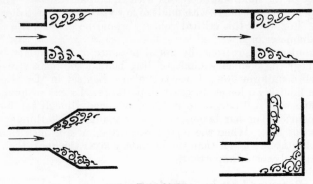

Fig. 20.10

provision of smooth changes of section (streamlining) at the *down-stream* side of an obstruction helps to reduce eddies and the loss of pressure.

20.15. Energy of a Fluid and Pressure Loss

Fig. 20.11 shows the effect of pressure loss due to friction on the pressure head, for liquid flow through a uniform horizontal pipe

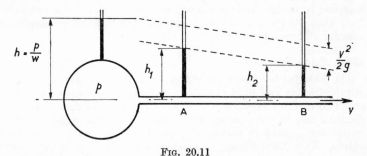

Fig. 20.11

connected to a reservoir at constant pressure p. Note that, since the area is uniform, the velocity head $v^2/2g$ is uniform along the pipe. The head h_f lost in friction is given by—

$$h_f = h_1 - h_2$$

or

$$h_1 - h_f = h_2$$

More generally we can say that—

$$[\text{total energy at A}] - \begin{bmatrix}\text{energy lost in friction} \\ \text{between A and B}\end{bmatrix} = \text{total energy at B}$$

i.e.
$$H_1 + \frac{p_1}{w} + \frac{v_1^{\,2}}{2\,g} - h_f = H_2 + \frac{p_2}{w} + \frac{v_2^{\,2}}{2\,g}$$

or
$$H_2 + h_1 + \frac{v_1^{\,2}}{2\,g} - h_f = H_2 + h_2 + \frac{v_2^{\,2}}{2\,g}$$

This is Bernoulli's equation modified to allow for friction loss in the pipe-line. The mechanical energy "lost" reappears, of course, as heat.

Example. A 2 in. diameter pipe-line falls a vertical distance of 100 ft from an open oil reservoir and discharges into an open tank. The head of oil above the pipe entrance is 20 ft and the loss of head

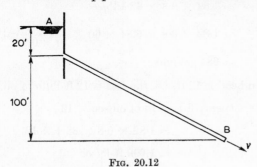

Fig. 20.12

due to pipe friction is 12 ft. Calculate the discharge in gallons per minute. Specific gravity of oil is 0·8.

What is the loss of energy due to friction, in foot-pounds per second (ft-lb/sec)?

Solution

Total head available, measured above pipe exit B—

$$= \text{head at entry} + \text{fall of pipe} - \text{friction head}$$
$$= 20 + 100 - 12$$
$$= 108 \text{ ft}$$

$$\text{velocity head at exit} = \frac{v^2}{2\,g}$$

The pressure at exit and at the free surface of the reservoir is atmospheric. Therefore there is no change in pressure energy between A and B. Thus

$$\text{kinetic energy at B} = \text{potential energy at A}$$

and
$$\frac{v^2}{2g} = 108$$

i.e.
$$v = \sqrt{2 \times 32 \cdot 2 \times 108}$$
$$= 83 \cdot 4 \text{ ft/sec}$$

(This result may be arrived at directly by applying Bernoulli's equation.)

The flow-rate is given by—

$$Q = Av$$
$$= \frac{\pi/4 \times 2^2}{144} \times 83 \cdot 3$$
$$= 1 \cdot 82 \text{ cusecs}$$
$$= 1 \cdot 82 \times 0 \cdot 8 \times 62 \cdot 4 \text{ lb/sec}$$
$$= 1 \cdot 82 \times 0 \cdot 8 \times 62 \cdot 4 \times 60 \times \frac{1}{10 \times 0 \cdot 8} \text{ gal/min}$$
$$= \textbf{681 gal/min}$$

The friction head is 12 ft, i.e. the loss is 12 ft-lb/lb of oil. Thus

$$\text{energy loss} = \text{lb of oil/sec} \times 12$$
$$= 1 \cdot 82 \times 0 \cdot 8 \times 62 \cdot 4 \times 12$$
$$= \textbf{1,090 ft-lb/sec}$$

(This corresponds to a loss of power of $1,090/550$, i.e. approx. 2 h.p.)

PROBLEMS

1. A horizontal pipe of 2 in. diameter connected to a cylinder of water at 30 lb/in.² gauge pressure discharges freely to the atmosphere. If the head lost in friction in the pipe is 14 ft calculate the discharge in gallons per minute.

(490)

2. Water is pumped up from a level A to level B through a vertical height of 36 ft, through a pipe tapered in diameter from 4 in. at A to 6 in. at B. The pressure head at A is 80 ft of water and at B, 45 ft. The friction loss of head between A and B is 5 ft. Find the discharge at B in cubic feet per second (cusecs) and the energy loss due to friction in foot-pounds per second (ft-lb/sec).

(1·915 cusecs; 5,800 ft-lb/sec)

20.16. Measurement of Pipe Flow-Rate: Venturi Meter

The flow-rate Q of liquid in a closed pipe is measured by a *Venturi meter*. This consists of a constriction in the pipe line, Fig. 20.13. The pipe converges in the direction of flow from the flange A to the

throat B, and then diverges gradually to the full pipe diameter at
C. Manometer tubes are inserted in the pipe at A and at the throat
B. The rate of flow of liquid in the pipe is then proportional to the

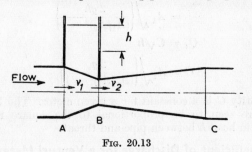

Fig. 20.13

square root of the difference in pressure or manometric head h
between the pipe and the throat. This is proved as follows—

Applying Bernoulli's equation to points A and B, assuming no
loss—

$$H_1 + \frac{p_1}{w} + \frac{v_1^2}{2g} = H_2 + \frac{p_2}{w} + \frac{v_2^2}{2g}$$

and, since for a horizontal pipe $H_1 = H_2$, then

$$\frac{v_2^2}{2g} - \frac{v_1^2}{2g} = \frac{p_1}{w} - \frac{p_2}{w}$$

But

$$\frac{p_1}{w} - \frac{p_2}{w} = h$$

the measured difference in pressure; hence

$$\frac{v_2^2}{2g} - \frac{v_1^2}{2g} = h \quad . \qquad . \qquad . \qquad . \quad (20.1)$$

The velocity v_2 at the throat B is obtained from the equation of
continuity—

$$v_2 A_2 = v_1 A_1$$

i.e.

$$v_2 = \frac{A_1}{A_2} v_1$$

Substituting for v_2 in equation (20.1)—

$$\frac{\{v_1(A_1/A_2)\}^2 - v_1^2}{2g} = h$$

or

$$v_1^2 \left(\frac{A_1^2}{A_2^2} - 1 \right) = 2gh$$

i.e.

$$v_1 = \sqrt{\left(\frac{2gh}{(A_1/A_2)^2 - 1} \right)}$$

The required theoretical flow-rate in the pipe is

$$Q_t = A_1 \times v_1$$

$$= A_1 \sqrt{\left\{ \frac{2gh}{(A_1/A_2)^2 - 1} \right\}}$$

or $$Q_t = C\sqrt{h}$$

where $$C = A_1 \sqrt{\left\{ \frac{2g}{(A_1/A_2)^2 - 1} \right\}}$$

This quantity C is a constant for a given meter. The flow-rate Q_t is therefore seen to be proportional to the square root of the difference in head h between pipe and throat.

20.17. Coefficient of Discharge for a Venturi Meter

In practice, owing to friction in the convergent portion, the discharge from the pipe is less than $C\sqrt{h}$. The *coefficient of discharge* C_d for the meter is defined as the ratio—

$$\frac{\text{actual discharge } Q}{\text{theoretical discharge } Q_t}$$

i.e. $$C_d = \frac{Q}{C\sqrt{h}}$$

and, actual discharge is

$$Q = C_d \times C\sqrt{h}$$

C_d is always less than unity and usually about 0·97; for very small meters it may be as low as 0·9. The discharge coefficient C_d for a meter may be found experimentally by weighing the actual discharge rate Q, and at the same time measuring the difference of

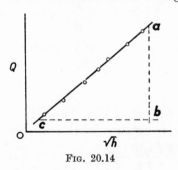

Fig. 20.14

head h. If Q is plotted against $\sqrt{h}$ a straight line graph is obtained, Fig. 20.14—

$$\text{slope } \frac{ab}{bc} = \frac{Q}{\sqrt{h}}$$

hence
$$C_d = \frac{Q}{C\sqrt{h}}$$

$$= \frac{1}{C} \times \frac{\mathbf{ab}}{\mathbf{bc}}$$

The constant C is determined from the dimensions of the meter.

Example. The flow in a 2 ft diameter horizontal water main is measured by means of a Venturi meter with a throat diameter of 1 ft. The difference in pressure between pipe and throat corresponds to 10 in. of mercury. Find the flow in cubic feet per second (cusecs) if the discharge coefficient for the meter is 0·99, and the specific gravity of mercury is 13·6.

Solution

$$\text{At pipe, } A_1 = \frac{\pi}{4} \times 2^2 = \pi \text{ ft}^2$$

$$\text{At throat, } A_2 = \frac{\pi}{4} \times 1^2 = \frac{\pi}{4} \text{ ft}^2$$

$$\text{Constant } C = A_1 \sqrt{\left\{ \frac{2\,g}{(A_1/A_2)^2 - 1} \right\}}$$

$$C = \pi \sqrt{\left\{ \frac{2 \times 32\cdot2}{(4^2 - 1)} \right\}}$$

$$= 6\cdot5 \text{ (ft and sec units)}$$

10 in. of mercury corresponds to $(10/12) \times 13\cdot6$ or 11·33 ft of water. Thus

$$Q = C_d \times C\sqrt{h}$$
$$= 0\cdot99 \times 6\cdot5 \times \sqrt{11\cdot33}$$
$$= \mathbf{21\cdot6 \text{ cusecs}}$$

PROBLEMS

1. A Venturi meter has an inlet diameter of 4 in. and a throat diameter of 2 in. What will be the difference of head in feet of water between inlet and throat if the flow rate is 200 gal/min of water? If the flow-rate is doubled what would then be the difference in head?

(8·78 ft, 35·12 ft)

2. A Venturi meter is to be designed to measure a maximum flow-rate of 4 cusecs in a 6 in. diameter pipe line, with a maximum difference of head between flange and throat of 12 ft. Calculate the corresponding throat diameter required, assuming no losses. If the throat diameter chosen is 4 in. what would be the flow-rate for a head of 12 ft?

(4·6 in.; 2·7 cusecs)

3. The measured discharge of water through a Venturi meter is 2,940 lb/min. The inlet and throat diameters are 4·8 in. and 2·2 in., respectively. The pressure drop between inlet and throat is 6 lb/in.[2] Find the discharge coefficient for the meter.

(0·97)

20.18. Discharge Through a Small Orifice

Liquid under a pressure head h is allowed to flow through an orifice, whose diameter is small compared with the head, Fig. 20.15.

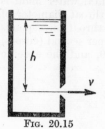

The velocity v of the issuing jet is then obtained by equating the pressure energy or head of the liquid in the tank to its kinetic energy or velocity head at the jet. Thus, neglecting energy losses the theoretical velocity of flow v is given by—

$$\frac{v^2}{2g} = h$$

Fig. 20.15   or $v = \sqrt{(2gh)}$

If A is the area of the orifice, the theoretical flow-rate Q_t, is given by

$$Q_t = A \times \sqrt{(2gh)}$$

20.19 Coefficient of Discharge for a Small Orifice

In practice this flow-rate is never achieved and we define a *coefficient of discharge* C_d by the ratio—

$$\frac{\text{actual discharge } Q}{\text{theoretical discharge } Q_t}$$

i.e. $$C_d = \frac{Q}{A\sqrt{(2gh)}}$$

Thus the actual flow-rate is

$$Q = C_d \times A\sqrt{(2gh)}$$

The value of C_d is about 0·6–0·7. The value depends slightly on the head h and on the shape and condition of the orifice. C_d is increased by the use of a sharp-edged orifice. Failure to attain the full theoretical discharge is due mainly to two reasons—

1. The theoretical velocity is not achieved due to losses.
2. The full area of the orifice is not utilized.

20.20. Coefficient of Velocity

Since the liquid is in motion near the inside of the orifice there will be a loss of head due to friction between liquid and tank wall. The velocity of the jet will therefore be slightly less than the theoretical value and the *coefficient of velocity* C_v is defined by the ratio—

$$\frac{\text{actual velocity of jet}}{\text{theoretical velocity of jet}}$$

i.e.
$$C_v = \frac{v}{\sqrt{(2\,gh)}}$$

20.21. Vena Contracta: Coefficient of Contraction

Fig. 20.16 shows a jet issuing from a sharp-edged orifice. The liquid in the tank streams into the orifice as shown, with the result

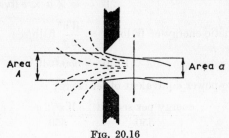

Area *A*   Area *a*

FIG. 20.16

that each particle of liquid has a component of velocity perpendicular to the jet axis at the opening. The effect is to cause the jet to contract just after leaving the orifice. The section of the jet where it first becomes parallel, and the area is least, is known as the *vena contracta*. The jet velocity therefore reaches its greatest value at the vena contracta. The ratio of the area of the vena contracta to the actual orifice is termed the *coefficient of contraction* C_c, i.e.

$$C_c = \frac{\text{area } a \text{ of jet at vena contracta}}{\text{area } A \text{ of orifice}}$$

$$= \frac{a}{A}$$

Hence the effective area of the jet is

$$a = C_c \times A$$

The coefficient of contraction for small sharp-edged circular orifices is usually about 0·63–0·65.

20.22. Relation Between the Coefficients

The actual velocity of the jet is $C_v\sqrt{(2\,gh)}$, hence the actual discharge is—

$$Q = \text{effective area} \times \text{actual jet velocity}$$

$$= a \times v$$

$$= C_c A \times C_v\sqrt{(2\,gh)}$$

$$= C_c C_v \times A\sqrt{(2\,gh)}$$

By comparison with the equation,

$$Q = C_d \times A\sqrt{(2\,gh)}$$

it is seen that

$$C_d = C_c \times C_v$$

20.23. Energy of a Jet

If a is the area of the jet (ft²), v its velocity (ft/sec), w the specific weight of the liquid (lb/ft³), and W the weight of liquid flowing per second, then

$$W = w \times a \times v \text{ lb/sec}$$

$$\text{Kinetic energy of } W \text{ lb/sec} = \frac{Wv^2}{2\,g} \text{ ft-lb/sec}$$

Since

$$1 \text{ h.p.} = 550 \text{ ft-lb/sec}$$

then the horse-power equivalent of jet energy is

$$\frac{\text{energy per second}}{550} = \frac{Wv^2/2\,g}{550}$$

Example. A hydraulic machine is driven by a jet from a nozzle of 1 in. diameter in a water main under a gauge pressure of 100 lb/in.² Neglecting any loss of energy find the horse-power supplied to the machine.

Solution

$$\text{Pressure head across machine, } h = \frac{100 \times 144}{62 \cdot 4} = 231 \text{ ft}$$

$$\text{velocity of jet, } v = \sqrt{(2\,gh)}$$

$$= \sqrt{(2 \times 32 \cdot 2 \times 231)}$$

$$= 122 \text{ ft/sec}$$

$$Q = Av$$

$$= \frac{\pi}{4} \times \frac{1^2}{144} \times 122$$

$$= 0 \cdot 666 \text{ cusecs}$$

$$\text{Weight of water per second, } W = 0 \cdot 666 \times 62 \cdot 4 = 41 \cdot 6 \text{ lb/sec}$$

$$\text{kinetic energy of jet} = \frac{Wv^2}{2\,g} \text{ ft-lb/sec} = \frac{41 \cdot 6 \times 122^2}{2 \times 32 \cdot 2}$$

$$= 9,600 \text{ ft-lb/sec}$$

$$\text{h.p. supplied} = \frac{9,600}{550} = \textbf{17·45 h.p.}$$

20.24. Experimental Determination of Orifice Coefficients

The most easily obtained coefficient is C_d, the coefficient of discharge. It is found directly by weighing the liquid discharged in a given time while the head h is kept constant. The coefficient of velocity C_v is found from the geometry of the jet.

Fig. 20.17 shows a jet issuing horizontally from an orifice. At a point distant y below the centre of the orifice the distance of the centre of the jet from the vena contracta is x. We may assume each particle of liquid to act as a projectile, travelling without interference from other particles.

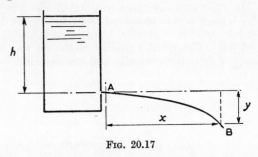

FIG. 20.17

If v is the actual horizontal velocity at the orifice, then the distance x is given by—

$$x = vt \quad \text{or} \quad v = \frac{x}{t}$$

where t is the time of flight from A to B. t is also the time taken for a particle to fall freely a distance y from rest, hence y is given by—

$$y = \tfrac{1}{2}gt^2 \quad \text{or} \quad t = \sqrt{\left(\frac{2y}{g}\right)}$$

hence

$$v = \frac{x}{t} = \frac{x}{\sqrt{(2y/g)}}$$

$$= x\sqrt{\left(\frac{g}{2y}\right)}$$

The theoretical velocity $= \sqrt{(2gh)}$

hence

$$C_v = \frac{\text{actual velocity}}{\text{theoretical velocity}}$$

$$= \frac{v}{\sqrt{(2gh)}} = \frac{x\sqrt{(g/2y)}}{\sqrt{(2gh)}}$$

$$= \frac{x}{2\sqrt{(yh)}}$$

Finally, the coefficient of contraction is obtained from the relation—

$$C_c = \frac{C_d}{C_v}$$

C_c may be obtained by direct measurement of the jet diameter at the vena contracta but this is neither an easy nor an accurate method.

Example. A tank of oil discharged through an orifice of 0·4 in. diameter. The measured discharge was 300 lb/min when the head of oil in the tank was 6 ft measured from the centre line of the orifice. The jet issued horizontally, falling a distance of 13·2 in. in a distance of 5 ft. The specific gravity of the oil was 0·76. Find the coefficients of discharge, velocity and contraction.

Solution

$$Q = 300 \text{ lb/min}$$

$$= \frac{300}{60 \times 0.76 \times 62.4} \text{ cusecs}$$

$$= 1.055 \text{ cusecs}$$

$$Q = C_d \times A\sqrt{(2\,gh)}$$

where h is head of oil in feet. Thus

$$1.055 = C_d \times \frac{\pi \times 0.4^2}{4 \times 144}\sqrt{(2 \times 32.2 \times 6)}$$

i.e. $\qquad C_d = \mathbf{0.616}$

$$C_v = \frac{x}{2\sqrt{(yh)}}$$

$$= \frac{60}{2\sqrt{(13.2 \times 72)}}$$

$$= \mathbf{0.975}$$

$$C_d = C_c \times C_v$$

therefore $\qquad C_c = \dfrac{0.616}{0.975}$

$$= \mathbf{0.631}$$

PROBLEMS

1. A tank of oil, of specific gravity 0·8, discharges through a $\frac{1}{2}$ in. diameter orifice. The head of oil above the centre line of the orifice is kept constant at 4 ft and the measured discharge rate is 4 gal/min. Calculate the coefficient of discharge for the orifice.

(0·61)

2. A large tank contains water to a depth of 3 ft. Water issues from a sharp-edged orifice of 1 in. diameter and is collected in a circular tank of 3 ft diameter. The water level in the cylinder rises 2 ft in 5 min. Calculate the discharge coefficient for the orifice.

(0·62)

3. A square section sharp-edged orifice is to discharge 200 lb of water per minute under a constant head of 2 ft 6 in. Assuming a coefficient of discharge of 0·63 find the length of the side of the orifice.

(0·98 in.)

4. A tank of water on level ground has a sharp-edged orifice in the side 16 in. from the bottom. The coefficient of velocity of the orifice is 0·98. Find how far from the orifice the jet will strike the ground when the head of water in the tank is 8 ft.

(70 in.)

5. In an experiment on an orifice the following results were obtained: orifice diameter, $\frac{1}{4}$ in.; discharge of water, 52 lb in 4 min; fall of jet, 1 ft in a horizontal distance of 3 ft 11 in.; head of water above centre line of orifice, 4 ft. Calculate the coefficients of discharge, velocity and contraction.

(0·637, 0·98, 0·65)

6. A jet issues horizontally from an orifice under a head of 5 ft. The ordinates of its path, measured from the vena contracta, are 4 ft horizontally and 21 in. vertically. Obtain, from first principles, the coefficient of velocity for the orifice.

(0·944)

7. A pressure vessel contains water at 300 lb/in.² gauge pressure. A jet issues from a nozzle of 2 in. diameter, having a coefficient of velocity 0·95 and coefficient of discharge 0·65. Find the horse-power of the jet.

(20·1)

8. Water flows from an orifice in the side of a tank. The head of water above the level of the orifice is 12 ft and the opening is 1 in. diameter. If the coefficient of discharge for the orifice is 0·64 calculate the h.p. equivalent of the energy of the jet.

(0·132)

21

Experimental Errors and the Adjustment of Data

21.1. Experiment

THE object of a student's experiment may be one or more of the following—

1. To verify a textbook theory.
2. To carry out a standard industrial test, such as a hardness or tensile test.
3. To determine the performance of a machine.
4. To determine a physical constant, such as the acceleration due to gravity, the discharge coefficient for an orifice, or the modulus of elasticity of a metal.

The object of the experienced investigator, however, might be to carry out an experiment when an adequate theory is not known, to verify or reject a new theory, or to provide data on which a theory may be based. Whether student or experienced investigator, however, the *scientific method* used is fundamentally the same, i.e.

1. To alter only one variable at a time.
2. To test the experimental method to show that it is valid, i.e. actually measures the effect it is designed to measure.
3. To test the reliability of the experiment, i.e. that the results are repeatable by any competent investigator and free from errors.

The scientist who subjects a theory to experimental test may often try to devise an experiment to show that his theory is false rather than to show it is correct. The engineer or the student will not usually go so far in expressing doubt. Nevertheless it is the *discrepancy* between theory and experiment that is often of greatest interest, and the *errors* that are of greatest importance in testing the reliability of the experiment. For example, a knowledge of the

372

errors and of their source will often show how the experiment may be improved.

21.2. Error and Discrepancy

We distinguish between error and discrepancy as follows—

Error is the difference between a measured quantity and the true value. Since the true value is often unknown the term "error" usually refers to the estimated uncertainty in the result. If Δx is the *absolute error* in measurement of a quantity of magnitude x, the *relative error* is defined as the ratio $\Delta x/x$. The percentage error is given by $\Delta x/x \times 100$ per cent.

Discrepancy is the difference between two measured values when errors have been minimized, corrected or taken into account. For example, an experimental determination of the ultimate tensile strength of a steel will often differ from that given in a handbook. Nevertheless, since the properties of a steel may vary from batch to batch, the experimental value may be the more reliable for the batch from which the specimen was taken. Similarly a discrepancy may exist between an experimental and a theoretical result. For example, the period of vibration of a spring-supported light mass may differ from that calculated. A suitable graphical procedure may show that a more advanced theory is required to take into account the mass of the spring.

Note, however, that we are not justified in suggesting a discrepancy between theory and experiment, unless the sources of error have been fully investigated.

21.3. Classification of Errors

Errors may be of three kinds, each of which requires different treatment; they are—

(*a*) mistakes;
(*b*) consistent or systematic errors;
(*c*) accidental or random errors.

(*a*) MISTAKES

Mistakes are usually avoidable and are due to inexperience, inattentiveness and faulty use of the apparatus. Doubtful results should be repeated immediately if possible. For this reason a graph of measured values should be plotted as the test proceeds; mistakes can then be seen immediately. Where a physical disturbance occurred or an obvious mistake was made the measurement should be rejected. If there is no evident reason why a doubtful result should occur this result should be *retained*, but repeated if possible. Sometimes it may be possible to repeat the measurement several times, then the doubtful value will have only a small effect on the average value. Mistakes in calculations should not be tolerated.

(b) Constant or Systematic Errors

Constant or systematic errors may be due to: (i) the instrument; (ii) the observer; (iii) the experimental conditions.

(i) The Instrument

An instrument may read consistently high or low; the error involved is constant and may be allowed for by calibration against a standard. This type of error is vividly illustrated by comparing the scales of a number of rules made of different materials. A difference of length over a few inches is often visible to the naked eye.

Constant errors are usually *determinate*, i.e. they may be allowed for, or a *correction* made. For example, a spring balance may read $\frac{1}{2}$ lb when unloaded. This *zero* error may be allowed for by subtracting $\frac{1}{2}$ lb from all readings. Note, however, that it is sometimes necessary to check whether an error is uniform along the scale or varies with the reading. A complete calibration of an instrument involves checking every major scale reading against an accurate standard.

We have to distinguish now between *accuracy* and *precision*. A precision instrument will give consistent readings, perhaps to several significant figures, but will be accurate only if calibrated. For example, a micrometer may be read more precisely, to "tenths of thousandths," by using a large rotating drum and a vernier scale. However, only if the screw is accurately made and the micrometer correctly calibrated can we regard it as accurate.

A similar term used in connexion with an instrument is its *sensitivity*, or change in reading for a given change in a measured quantity, e.g. number of scale divisions of a balance per pound weight. A spring balance having a large deflexion for each pound weight added is said to be very sensitive. It will measure deflexion very precisely if supplied with a vernier scale, but will be accurate only if the scale is carefully marked, calibrated and set.

When an instrument, e.g. a dial gauge, relies on gears or other mechanism having friction or back-lash, readings should all be taken on an increasing scale or all on a decreasing scale. A reversal of the mechanism should be avoided if possible. For example, when measuring the load on a specimen in a testing machine by a movable poise the latter should be moved continually in one direction and never reversed, at least up to the maximum load. If by chance the poise overshoots, the investigator should wait until the pull on the specimen has caught up with the measured load.

(ii) The Observer

Personal errors are due to the reaction or judgment of an observer. They are sometimes constant, at least over a short period of time. For example, two observers each operating an accurate stop-clock will usually obtain a different time reading on receiving the same signal. The delay in stopping the clock is personal to the observer and can be taken into account. However, in starting and stopping the clock to obtain two consecutive readings the delay errors, if the same, will cancel. It is usually advisable that a given set of readings be all taken by the same observer. Note, however, that the personal error may vary from day to day, or vary due to boredom and tiredness in a long experiment.

(iii) Experimental Conditions

Accurate calibration of an instrument often depends on experimental conditions such as the temperature and barometric pressure. For this reason very accurate measurements and the checking of standard gauges are usually made in a room designed to remain at a constant temperature. When the instrument is used under conditions different from that in which it was calibrated a correction can often be made. For example, the change in length of a metal scale is proportional to the change in temperature.

Finally, an experiment is said to be accurately performed if it has small systematic errors.

21.4. Random Errors

If a measurement is repeated under similar conditions the values do not usually agree exactly. There is a scatter in the results about a mean value due to accidental or random error. A random error has the following properties: (a) a small error occurs more frequently than a large error; (b) a result is just as likely to be too large as too small.

Random errors may occur due to the following—

1. By an error of judgment; as when reading to 0·0001 in. a micrometer scale divided at 0·001 in. intervals, without the aid of a vernier.

2. Unnoticed fluctuating conditions of temperature or pressure.

3. Small disturbances.

4. Lack of definition. For example the diameter of a rod of wood cannot be stated so precisely as that of a ground steel bar, even though the most accurate micrometer be used.

The effect of random errors on the result can be reduced by: (a) taking a mean value of a set of readings of the same measurement; (b) drawing a smooth curve through a set of points on a graph. Graphical methods are considered in paragraph 21.14.

An experiment which has small random errors is said to be performed precisely, but not necessarily accurately.

21.5. Errors of Calculation

Errors of calculation (but not mistakes) arise by virtue of the method of calculation, whether slide rule, logarithmic tables or calculating machine (in increasing order of accuracy). Consider the calculation of z from the formula

$$z = x^4 - y^4$$

where
$$x = 1\tfrac{1}{4} \ (1\cdot25000) \text{ in.}$$
$$y = 1\tfrac{1}{16} \ (1\cdot06250) \text{ in.}$$

(Note—Since we have written the decimal figure to five places this implies x and y to be accurate to that degree.) Carrying out the calculation using a slide rule we obtain

$$z = 2\cdot44 - 1\cdot275$$
$$= 1\cdot165 \text{ in.}^4$$

A more accurate method is to apply our knowledge of algebra to write

$$z = 1\cdot25^4 - 1\cdot0625^4$$
$$= (1\cdot25^2 - 1\cdot0625^2)(1\cdot25^2 + 1\cdot0625^2) \text{ difference of two squares}$$

and factorizing the first bracket again

$$z = (1 \cdot 25 - 1 \cdot 0625)(1 \cdot 25 + 1 \cdot 0625)(1 \cdot 25^2 + 1 \cdot 0625^2)$$
$$= 0 \cdot 1875 \times 2 \cdot 3125 \times 2 \cdot 691$$
$$= \textbf{1} \cdot \textbf{167 in.}^4, \text{ by slide rule}$$

Using six-figure logarithms we would obtain

$$z = \textbf{1} \cdot \textbf{16697 in.}^4$$

Calculation using a machine would show an error due to the use of six-figure tables of about $0 \cdot 0000069$ in.[4]

A comparison with the result using four-figure tables is left to the reader.

Note, however, that the longer the calculation the greater is the likelihood of error. A calculation involving say three or four steps may be sufficiently accurate using a slide rule; if, say, a dozen steps are required, four- or five-figure tables may be required to give the same accuracy in the final figure.

21.6. Justifiable Accuracy

In experimental work we must justify the accuracy of the results we give. Let Δx be a *small* error in the measurement of x in the example of the previous paragraph, then the corresponding error in z is given by

$$\Delta z \simeq \frac{dz}{dx} \times \Delta x$$

approximately, provided Δx is small compared with x. Since

$$z = x^4 - y^4$$

then $$\frac{dz}{dx} = 4 x^3, \text{ if } y \text{ is assumed constant}$$

hence $$\Delta z \simeq 4 x^3 \Delta x$$

If the error in x be $\dfrac{1}{1,000} = 0 \cdot 001$ in., the error in z would be

$$\Delta z \simeq 4 \times 1 \cdot 25^3 \times 0 \cdot 001$$
$$= 0 \cdot 0078$$
$$\text{or about } 0 \cdot 01 \text{ in.}^4$$

Hence for a measurement of x accurate to $0 \cdot 001$ in., we would be justified in giving an answer to two decimal places only, i.e.

$$z = 1 \cdot 17 \text{ in.}^4$$

On the other hand, if the error in x is $\frac{1}{64}$ in., then

$$\Delta z = 4 \times 1 \cdot 25^3 \times \tfrac{1}{64}$$
$$= 0 \cdot 12 \text{ in.}^4, \text{ approximately}$$

The error is now in the first decimal place and we would be justified in giving an answer to the first place only, i.e.

$$z = 1 \cdot 2 \text{ in.}[4]$$

Evidently, for most practical purposes the use of a slide rule gives answers of a sufficient accuracy (to two significant figures). However, if the measured data is accurate to, say, four significant figures, it is not sufficient to use a slide rule for calculations and then ascribe any discrepancy to "slide rule error." In this case tables should be used.

It should be remembered that four-figure tables are accurate to three figures only and may have an error of up to about $0 \cdot 0004$ in the last figure.

21.7. Possible Errors

It is necessary to make an estimate of the possible error involved in a particular measurement. For example, a stop-clock divided in 1 sec intervals usually involves a possible error of about $\frac{1}{2}$ sec; a stop-watch reading to $\frac{1}{5}$ sec may have an error of about $\frac{1}{5}$ sec. Similarly, a good micrometer having a scale divided into $0 \cdot 001$ in. intervals may have an error of $0 \cdot 0002$ in.; and a dial gauge, reading to $0 \cdot 0001$ in., may have an error of the same magnitude, possibly more, if not carefully calibrated. A useful exercise is to check a commercial dial gauge against an accurate set of gauge blocks.

21.8. Propagation of Error, or Derived Error

An experimental result is often calculated from two or more measured quantities. An error in each measured value results in an error in the derived (calculated) value. For example, suppose an average speed v to be derived from measurements of distance s and time t by the formula—

$$v = \frac{s}{t}$$

If the time taken to travel 100 ft is 20 sec the derived speed is $\frac{100}{20} = 5$ ft/sec. If, however, the possible error in the time is $\pm 0 \cdot 1$ sec, the derived speed would be $\frac{100}{20 \cdot 1} = 4 \cdot 975$ ft/sec, or $\frac{100}{19 \cdot 9} = 5 \cdot 025$ ft/sec, approximately.

Thus, if the time is $0 \cdot 1$ sec too great the speed will be recorded as $0 \cdot 025$ ft/sec too low; and if the time is $0 \cdot 1$ sec too short the speed will be recorded as $0 \cdot 025$ ft/sec too great.

21.9. Region of Uncertainty

In the above example of a derived error, the (random) error in time t could be either positive (high), or negative (low), i.e.

$$\Delta t = \pm 0 \cdot 1 \text{ sec}$$

Hence the error in velocity is more exactly expressed as—

$$\Delta v = \mp\ 0.025 \text{ ft/sec}$$

(assuming error in s negligible). The result of the experiment is therefore stated as—

$$v = 5 \pm 0.025 \text{ ft/sec}$$

Thus v lies between 5·025 and 4·975 ft/sec, i.e. v has some value in the *region of uncertainty* between these two values.

The magnitude of the term $\pm$ 0·025 indicates the reliability of the result.

21.10. Accepted Value

If the value, $v = 5$ ft/sec, is obtained by taking the average value of a number of tests it then represents the *best estimate* of the velocity and, subject therefore to the judgment and common sense of the experimenter, becomes the *accepted value* for that quantity.

21.11. Error Derived from the Sum of Two Quantities

Let a value z be derived from the sum of the measured quantities x and y. Thus

$$z = x + y \qquad . \qquad . \qquad . \qquad . \quad (21.3)$$

If Δx and Δy are errors in x and y the corresponding error Δz in z is given by—

$$z + \Delta z = (x + \Delta x) + (y + \Delta y) \qquad . \qquad . \quad (21.4)$$

Subtracting equation (21.3) from equation (21.4) gives—

$$\Delta z = \Delta x + \Delta y$$

Hence the (absolute) error in z is the sum of the errors in x and y.

Example. A gauge block of thickness 0·400 in. has an error of $\pm$ 0·0002 in. It is combined with a similar block of thickness 0·800 in., which has a possible error of 0·0003 in. Find the possible error in the thickness.

Solution

The total thickness of the combined gauge block is

$$(0.400 + 0.800) = 1.200 \text{ in.}$$

and the possible error in the thickness is therefore

$$\pm\ (0.0002 + 0.0003)$$
$$= \pm\ \mathbf{0.0005 \text{ in.}}$$

Note that the magnitudes of the errors have been added inside the bracket without regard to sign.

It is not so evident that if the values of two quantities are *subtracted* the error is still the *sum* of the errors (i.e. regions of uncertainty) of the two quantities. This is demonstrated in the following example.

Example. The initial temperature of a thermometer is $12 \pm 0.2°C$. The final temperature is $48 \pm 0.4°C$. What is the possible error in the rise of temperature ?

Solution

The initial temperature lies between 11.8 and $12.2°C$ and the final temperature lies between 47.6 and $48.4°C$, Fig. 21.1. Hence the rise in temperature lies between—

    (*a*) greatest final value and least initial value;
    (*b*) least final value and greatest initial value.

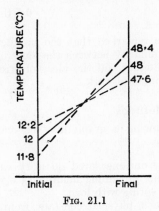

FIG. 21.1

Therefore rise in temperature lies between

$$48.4 - 11.8 = 36.6°C$$

and

$$47.6 - 12.2 = 35.4°C$$

Thus

$$\text{mean rise} = \frac{36.6 + 35.4}{2}$$

$$= 36°C$$

$$\text{region of uncertainty} = \pm \frac{36.6 - 35.4}{2}$$

$$= \pm 0.6°C$$

Thus

$$\text{rise in temperature} = \mathbf{36 \pm 0.6°C}$$

The region of uncertainty could have been obtained immediately by *adding* the magnitude of the two separate errors; thus—

$$\text{error of rise} = \pm\ (0\cdot2 + 0\cdot4)$$

$$= \pm\ 0\cdot6°C, \text{ as before}$$

Note, however, that if the errors in the temperatures had been each of one sign only (+ *or* −) the error in the difference or rise in temperature would be found by *subtracting* the errors (due regard being paid to sign). Thus if

$$\text{initial temperature} = 12 + 0\cdot2°C$$

and
$$\text{final temperature} = 48 - 0\cdot4°C$$

then
$$\text{error in rise of temperature} = -\ 0\cdot4 - (+\ 0\cdot2)$$

$$= -\ \mathbf{0\cdot6°C}$$

Finally it may be remarked that the production engineer will have recognized a similarity between the ideas of limits and tolerances in practical gauging and the ideas of errors and regions of uncertainty in experimental work.

21.12. Graphical Methods

The object of drawing a graph may be one or more of the following—

1. To show how one measured quantity varies with another (all other conditions remaining unaltered), e.g. the variation of the extension of a spring with load.
2. To determine a physical constant from the slope of the graph, e.g. stiffness of a spring.
3. To eliminate or reduce the effect of random errors on the result.
4. To derive a mathematical relationship between the measured quantities, and hence deduce a physical "law."

The types of graph which may be met with will be usually one of the following: (*a*) straight line graphs; (*b*) curves which may be reduced to a straight line graph by a suitable mathematical method; (*c*) empirical curves, whose shape is initially unknown but is determined by using the experimental results alone.

21.13. The Straight Line Graph

The construction and use of a simple straight line graph will be illustrated in the following example.

Table 21.1 gives the extension (x in.) of a spring for various values of the load (W lb). It is required to find a value for the stiffness of the spring.

TABLE 21.1

Load W (lb)	0	2	4	6	8	10	12	13	14	15	16
Extension x (in.)	0	0·11	0·19	0·30	0·39	0·515	0·63	0·75	0·9	1·15	1·32

In mathematics it is customary to plot the *independent variable* horizontally, along the base, and the *dependent* quantity is plotted

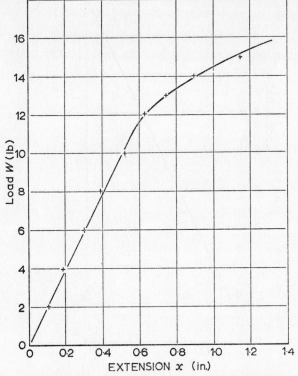

FIG. 21.2. LOAD–EXTENSION DIAGRAM FOR A SPRING

on the vertical ordinate. In this example the extension x obviously depends on the load W, which may have any independent value. Hence we should normally plot W along the base and x along the vertical axis. However, it is conventional for engineers to plot a load–extension diagram as in Fig. 21.2, i.e. with the extension plotted along the base. As will be seen this allows the spring stiffness to be obtained directly from the slope of the graph.

Through the points plotted in Fig. 21.2 is drawn the *best straight line* such that as many points lie on one side of the line as lie on the other. In this case, however, it can be seen that above a load of about 12 lb the points deviate in a regular manner from a straight

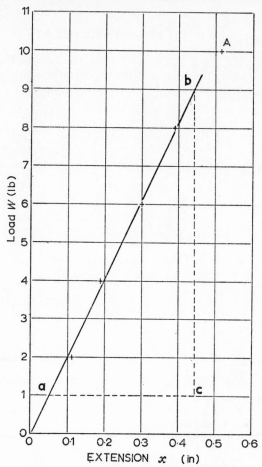

FIG. 21.3. LOAD–EXTENSION DIAGRAM

line. The spring has evidently been overloaded. If this curved portion is of interest a smooth curve is drawn through the experimental points so that any *scatter* occurs evenly about the curve. The stiffness S of a spring is defined for an elastic spring as the ratio

$$S = \frac{\text{load}}{\text{extension}} = \frac{W}{x}$$

This refers only to the portion of the load–extension graph which obeys Hooke's law, i.e. the straight-line portion.

Evidently each experimental point is in error by some amount (i.e. does not lie on the straight line), hence the stiffness calculated from the values for each point would be in error. The best result for the stiffness is therefore obtained from the gradient of the straight line, and it should be noted that the line need not pass through the origin.

To obtain the most accurate value of the gradient the results are re-plotted in Fig. 21.3 to a larger scale. The point A has been disregarded as it is doubtful whether it lies on the straight or curved portion of the graph. The points **a**, **b** are chosen such that they lie *on the straight line*. The right-angled triangle **abc** is completed and the stiffness calculated from the slope, thus

$$S = \frac{W}{x} = \frac{\mathbf{bc}}{\mathbf{ac}}$$

$$= \frac{8 \text{ (lb)}}{0 \cdot 395 \text{ (in.)}}$$

$$= \mathbf{20 \cdot 25 \ lb/in.}$$

Note that for accuracy points **a** and **b** should be *as far apart as possible*.

Since the plotted points lie close to, and fairly on either side of, the straight line, the error in the slope is probably small.

It may be remarked that if there had been appreciable scatter in the results it would have been insufficiently accurate to use only four or five points to determine the straight line.

21.14. Equation to a Straight Line

If for a set of values of a certain quantity x there corresponds a single set of values of another quantity y (such that when y is plotted against x a smooth curve is obtained), then y is said to be a *function* of x. That is, there is a functional relationship between y and x. If the graph of y against x is a straight line there is said to be a *linear* relationship between y and x.

It may be shown that the equation of a straight line is of the form

$$y = mx + c$$

where m is the gradient $\mathbf{bc/ac}$ of the line (Fig. 21.4), and c is the value of y at which the straight line cuts the vertical axis.

In the special case when $c = 0$, and the line passes through the origin, we have

$$y = mx$$

or $$\frac{y}{x} = m, \text{ a constant}$$

We now say that y *is proportional to* x, i.e. doubling the value of x will result in doubling the value of y. Note that this is only true when the straight line passes through the origin.

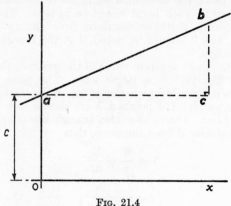

FIG. 21.4

21.15. Equations which may be Reduced to a Straight Line

If theory suggests a possible relationship between x and y such that

$$y = ax^n \qquad . \qquad . \qquad . \qquad . \quad (21.6)$$

where a and n are *unknown* constants, then this equation may be put into the form of a straight line as follows: Taking logs of both sides of equation (21.6), we obtain

$$\log y = n \log x + \log a \qquad . \qquad . \qquad . \quad (21.7)$$

or putting $Y = \log y$, $X = \log x$, and $C = \log a$, then

$$Y = nX + C$$

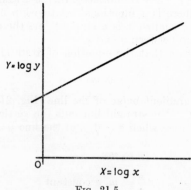

FIG. 21.5

This is the equation of a straight line. Hence we plot Y against X to obtain the straight line shown, Fig. 21.5. As before, the slope of the line is n and the intercept with the Y axis is C. Hence a and n may be calculated.

Again suppose
$$y = ae^{nx}$$
where
$$e = 2 \cdot 7128 \ldots$$

then taking logs to base 10
$$\log_{10} y = nx \log_{10} e + \log_{10} a$$
therefore
$$Y = 0 \cdot 4343 \, nx + C$$

where $Y = \log_{10} y$, and $C = \log_{10} a$. Hence a straight line is obtained by plotting $\log_{10} y$ against x, Fig. 21.6. The gradient is now $0 \cdot 4343 \, n$, and the intercept is $\log_{10} a$.

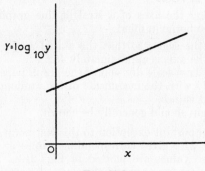

FIG. 21.6

Note that the above method does not apply to curves of the form
$$y = mx^n + c$$

In this case the value of the index n must usually be known or guessed beforehand. For example, if $n = \frac{1}{2}$, then
$$y = mx^{\frac{1}{2}} + c$$
$$= m\sqrt{x} + c$$
$$= mX + c$$

where $X = \sqrt{x}$. This is the equation of a straight line. Hence, if our choice $n = \frac{1}{2}$ is correct, a graph of y against $\sqrt{x}$ will be a straight line, Fig. 21.7.

Note that unless the equation connecting y and x is reduced to a straight line form by some algebraic device it is usually difficult to obtain the value of the constants m, n, a, etc.

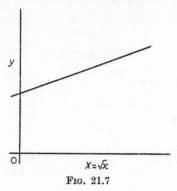

$$X = \sqrt{x}$$

Fig. 21.7

21.16. Choice of Axes

When choosing the axes of a straight line graph the following points should be borne in mind—

1. Choose the scales so that the actual angle which the line makes with the axis is approximately $45°$.

2. The smallest scale division of the graph paper should correspond roughly with the magnitude of the random error (scatter) of the plotted values.

3. The origin should generally be shown.

There is an important exception to this last point, however. For example, Table 21.2 gives corresponding values of two quantities x and y. These values are plotted in Fig. 21.8. As shown, the points are too close together and the slope of a straight line drawn through them cannot be determined accurately.

TABLE 21.2

x	6	6·5	7	7·5	8	8·5	9
y	4·10	4·25	4·38	4·54	4·66	4·80	4·96

The values are re-plotted correctly in Fig. 21.9. As a warning the words "false zero" are added at the intersection of the axes. This is often necessary since, when comparing two graphs from different sources, the shape and position of each curve is the first thing that strikes the eye and a misleading impression can be obtained.

To obtain the equation of the straight line from the graph of Fig. 21.9 the method is as follows: Choose the points **a**, **b** on the line and read off the corresponding values of x and y.

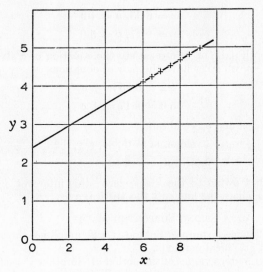

FIG. 21.8. INCORRECT GRAPH

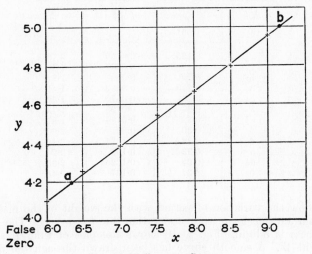

FIG. 21.9. CORRECT GRAPH

Thus

At a	$x = 6\cdot35, y = 4\cdot2$
At b	$x = 9\cdot17, y = 5\cdot0$

Since both pairs of values satisfy the equation of a straight line, $y = mx + c$, we must have the pair of equations—

$$4\cdot2 = 6\cdot35\,m + c$$
$$5\cdot0 = 9\cdot17\,m + c$$

Solving for m and c, we obtain

slope, $m = 0\cdot284$, say, $0\cdot28$

intercept, $c = 2\cdot40$

Note that owing to the "false zero" this intercept c is not the value of y where the line cuts the vertical axis.

VIBRATION OF A SPRING-SUPPORTED MASS

The following example illustrates and amplifies the above discussion of graphical methods.

Table 21.3 gives values of the period of vibration T sec (column 2) of a spring-supported mass of weight W lb (column 1). It is required

TABLE 21.3

(1) W (lb)	(2) T (sec)	(3) T^2	(4) $\sqrt{W}$
$\frac{1}{2}$	0·125	0·0156	0·707
1	0·17	0·0289	1·00
$1\frac{1}{2}$	0·20	0·040	1·22
2	0·235	0·0552	1·41
$2\frac{1}{2}$	0·24	0·0576	1·58
3	0·27	0·0729	1·73
$3\frac{1}{2}$	0·28	0·0784	1·87
4	0·30	0·09	2·00
$4\frac{1}{2}$	0·32	0·1024	2·12
5	0·33	0·109	2·24
$5\frac{1}{2}$	0·35	0·1225	2·35
6	0·37	0·137	2·45

to show the variation of period with the weight of the mass and obtain a value for g, the acceleration due to gravity. The spring stiffness is 5 lb/in. Fig. 21.10 shows the plot of time T against weight W. A smooth curve has been drawn through the plotted points so that the points lie evenly about the curve. The point A has been disregarded when drawing the curve since the likelihood of a random error so much larger than the error in the other points is small. The plotted curve has not been drawn to pass through the origin since there is insufficient evidence to show that it should do so.

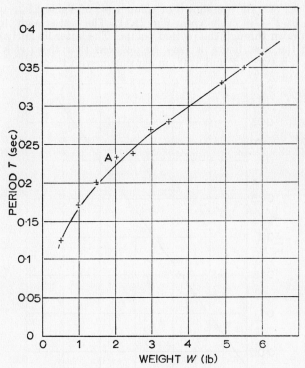

FIG. 21.10. VIBRATION OF SPRING-SUPPORTED MASS. GRAPH OF PERIOD
T AGAINST WEIGHT W

The variation of T with W is shown by the graph of Fig. 21.10, but as drawn, the graph does not allow us to obtain a mathematical relation between the quantities. The theoretical relation between T and W, however, is

$$T = 2\pi \sqrt{\left(\frac{W}{Sg}\right)}$$

where S is the spring stiffness (lb/ft) and g the acceleration due to gravity (ft/sec²). Thus

$$T = \frac{2\pi}{\sqrt{(Sg)}} \times \sqrt{W}$$

$$= k\sqrt{W}$$

where $\qquad k = \dfrac{2\pi}{\sqrt{Sg}}$, a constant

Hence if T is plotted against $\sqrt{W}$ a straight line should be obtained, and the constant k is given by the slope of the line.

Values of $\sqrt{W}$ are shown in column (4) of Table 21.3, and the graph of T-$\sqrt{W}$ is shown in Fig. 21.11. The best straight line has been drawn through the plotted points. The latter lie fairly evenly about the line, hence it may be deduced that there is a linear relation between T and $\sqrt{W}$, in agreement with theory.

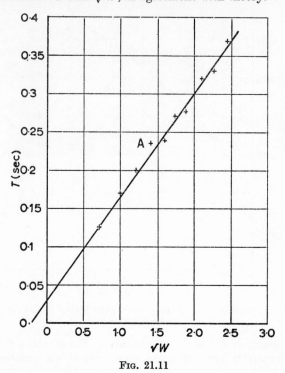

Fig. 21.11

The line cuts the $\sqrt{W}$ axis to the left of the zero point. The theory requires that the line should go through the origin. The discrepancy between theory and experiment is due to the (constant) error in not allowing for the mass of the spring. The "error" is of course in the theory. The value of W where the line cuts the horizontal axis represents the weight to be added to each value of W to allow for the mass of the spring.

A value for the acceleration due to gravity may be found as follows—

From
$$k = \frac{2\pi}{\sqrt{Sg}}$$

$$g = \frac{4\pi^2}{k^2 S}$$

Now $S = 5$ lb/in. $= 60$ lb/ft. From the graph, since k is given by the slope of the line—

$$k = \frac{0\cdot37}{2\cdot72} = 0\cdot136 \text{ sec/lb}^{\frac{1}{2}}$$

therefore

$$k^2 = 0\cdot0185 \text{ sec}^2/\text{lb}$$

hence

$$g = \frac{4\pi^2}{0\cdot0185 \times 60}$$

$$= \mathbf{35\cdot5 \text{ ft/sec}^2}$$

This estimate of g is not very good, so we try an alternative method. From

$$T = 2\pi \sqrt{\left(\frac{W}{Sg}\right)}$$

Squaring both sides

$$T^2 = \frac{4\pi^2}{Sg} \times W$$

$$= mW$$

where

$$m = \frac{4\pi^2}{Sg}, \text{ a constant}$$

Hence if we plot T^2 against W a straight line should result. The values of T^2 are given in column (3) of Table 21.3 and the resulting graph of T^2 against W is shown in Fig. 21.12.

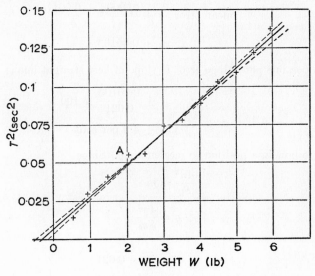

FIG. 21.12

The best straight line through the plotted points is shown as a full line on the figure. It is seen that the scatter about the line is greater than in the plot of Fig. 21.11. This method of plotting shows up the random errors. Point A has been disregarded when drawing the line since the likelihood of an error of the magnitude shown is probably small. By comparison with Fig. 21.11 it is seen that the points are more evenly spaced, i.e. at $\frac{1}{2}$-lb intervals. This method of plotting is therefore preferable.

In addition to the best straight line, drawn in full, two other broken lines have been drawn. These represent a fair estimate of the greatest and least slopes of a line through the plotted points. The possible error in the slope due to the method of plotting may be found as follows: From the graph

$$\text{maximum slope} = \frac{0\cdot136}{6\cdot2} = 0\cdot0219$$

$$\text{minimum slope} = \frac{0\cdot129}{6\cdot5} = 0\cdot01985$$

$$\text{slope of best straight line} = \frac{0\cdot1325}{6\cdot32} = 0\cdot021$$

$$\text{error of maximum slope} = 0\cdot0219 - 0\cdot021 = 0\cdot0009$$

$$\text{error of minimum slope} = 0\cdot01985 - 0\cdot021 = -0\cdot00115$$

$$\text{mean error} = \pm\ \frac{(0\cdot0009 + 0\cdot00115)}{2}$$

$$= \pm\ 0\cdot00103$$

Thus possible percentage error in slope of best straight line is

$$\pm\ \frac{0\cdot00103}{0\cdot021} \times 100$$

$$= \pm\ 4\cdot9 \text{ per cent}$$

We are now in a position to recalculate g. Since

$$\frac{4\pi^2}{Sg} = m$$

then

$$g = \frac{4\pi^2}{Sm}$$

$$= \frac{4\pi^2}{60 \times 0\cdot021}$$

$$= \mathbf{31\cdot3\ ft/sec^2}$$

The possible error in g is the same as the possible error in m, i.e. $\pm$ 4·9 per cent, or $\pm$ 1·53 ft/sec². Thus

$$g = 31·3 \pm 1·53 \text{ ft/sec}^2$$

The accepted value of g for London is 32·18 ft/sec². The error in our mean value is therefore

$$32·18 - 31·3 = 0·88 \text{ ft/sec}^2$$

which is well within the error involved in drawing the best straight line. Note, however, that the value 31·3 ft/sec² is much better than that obtained from the straight line of Fig. 21.11, i.e. 35·5 ft/sec².

Index

LOGARITHMS

	0	1	2	3	4	5	6	7	8	9	1	2	3	4	5	6	7	8	9
10	0000	0043	0086	0128	0170	0212	0253	0294	0334	0374	4	9	13	17	21	26	30	34	38
											4	8	12	16	20	24	28	32	37
11	0414	0453	0492	0531	0569	0607	0645	0682	0719	0755	4	8	12	15	19	23	27	31	35
											4	7	11	15	19	22	26	30	33
12	0792	0828	0864	0899	0934	0969	1004	1038	1072	1106	3	7	11	14	18	21	25	28	32
											3	7	10	14	17	20	24	27	31
13	1139	1173	1206	1239	1271	1303	1335	1367	1399	1430	3	7	10	13	16	20	23	26	30
											3	7	10	12	16	19	22	25	29
14	1461	1492	1523	1553	1584	1614	1644	1673	1703	1732	3	6	9	12	15	18	21	24	28
											3	6	9	12	15	17	20	23	26
15	1761	1790	1818	1847	1875	1903	1931	1959	1987	2014	3	6	9	11	14	17	20	23	26
											3	5	8	11	14	16	19	22	25
16	2041	2068	2095	2122	2148	2175	2201	2227	2253	2279	3	5	8	11	14	16	19	22	24
											3	5	8	10	13	15	18	21	23
17	2304	2330	2355	2380	2405	2430	2455	2480	2504	2529	3	5	8	10	13	15	18	20	23
											2	5	7	10	12	15	17	19	22
18	2553	2577	2601	2625	2648	2672	2695	2718	2742	2765	2	5	7	9	12	14	16	19	21
											2	5	7	9	11	14	16	18	21
19	2788	2810	2833	2856	2878	2900	2923	2945	2967	2989	2	4	7	9	11	13	16	18	20
											2	4	6	8	11	13	15	17	19
20	3010	3032	3054	3075	3096	3118	3139	3160	3181	3201	2	4	6	8	11	13	15	17	19
21	3222	3243	3263	3284	3304	3324	3345	3365	3385	3404	2	4	6	8	10	12	14	16	18
22	3424	3444	3464	3483	3502	3522	3541	3560	3579	3598	2	4	6	8	10	12	14	15	17
23	3617	3636	3655	3674	3692	3711	3729	3747	3766	3784	2	4	6	7	9	11	13	15	17
24	3802	3820	3838	3856	3874	3892	3909	3927	3945	3962	2	4	5	7	9	11	12	14	16
25	3979	3997	4014	4031	4048	4065	4082	4099	4116	4133	2	3	5	7	9	10	12	14	15
26	4150	4166	4183	4200	4216	4232	4249	4265	4281	4298	2	3	5	7	8	10	11	13	15
27	4314	4330	4346	4362	4378	4393	4409	4425	4440	4456	2	3	5	6	8	9	11	13	14
28	4472	4487	4502	4518	4533	4548	4564	4579	4594	4609	2	3	5	6	8	9	11	12	14
29	4624	4639	4654	4669	4683	4698	4713	4728	4742	4757	1	3	4	6	7	9	10	12	13
30	4771	4786	4800	4814	4829	4843	4857	4871	4886	4900	1	3	4	6	7	9	10	11	13
31	4914	4928	4942	4955	4969	4982	4997	5011	5024	5038	1	3	4	6	7	8	10	11	12
32	5051	5065	5079	5092	5105	5119	5132	5145	5159	5172	1	3	4	5	7	8	9	11	12
33	5185	5198	5211	5224	5237	5250	5263	5276	5289	5302	1	3	4	5	6	8	9	10	12
34	5315	5328	5340	5353	5366	5378	5391	5403	5416	5428	1	3	4	5	6	8	9	10	11
35	5441	5453	5465	5478	5490	5502	5514	5527	5539	5551	1	2	4	5	6	7	9	10	11
36	5563	5575	5587	5599	5611	5623	5635	5647	5658	5670	1	2	4	5	6	7	8	10	11
37	5682	5694	5705	5717	5729	5740	5752	5763	5775	5786	1	2	3	5	6	7	8	9	10
38	5798	5809	5821	5832	5843	5855	5866	5877	5888	5899	1	2	3	5	6	7	8	9	10
39	5911	5922	5933	5944	5955	5966	5977	5988	5999	6010	1	2	3	4	5	7	8	9	10
40	6021	6031	6042	6053	6064	6075	6085	6096	6107	6117	1	2	3	4	5	6	8	9	10
41	6128	6138	6149	6160	6170	6180	6191	6201	6212	6222	1	2	3	4	5	6	7	8	9
42	6232	6243	6253	6263	6274	6284	6294	6304	6314	6325	1	2	3	4	5	6	7	8	9
43	6335	6345	6355	6365	6375	6385	6395	6405	6415	6425	1	2	3	4	5	6	7	8	9
44	6435	6444	6454	6464	6474	6484	6493	6503	6513	6522	1	2	3	4	5	6	7	8	9
45	6532	6542	6551	6561	6571	6580	6590	6599	6609	6618	1	2	3	4	5	6	7	8	9
46	6628	6637	6646	6656	6665	6675	6684	6693	6702	6712	1	2	3	4	5	6	7	7	8
47	6721	6730	6739	6749	6758	6767	6776	6785	6794	6803	1	2	3	4	5	5	6	7	8
48	6812	6821	6830	6839	6848	6857	6866	6875	6884	6893	1	2	3	4	4	5	6	7	8
49	6902	6911	6920	6928	6937	6946	6955	6964	6972	6981	1	2	3	4	4	5	6	7	8

LOGARITHMS

	0	1	2	3	4	5	6	7	8	9	1	2	3	4	5	6	7	8	9
50	6990	6998	7007	7016	7024	7033	7042	7050	7059	7067	1	2	3	3	4	5	6	7	8
51	7076	7084	7093	7101	7110	7118	7126	7135	7143	7152	1	2	3	3	4	5	6	7	8
52	7160	7168	7177	7185	7193	7202	7210	7218	7226	7235	1	2	2	3	4	5	6	7	7
53	7243	7251	7259	7267	7275	7284	7292	7300	7308	7316	1	2	2	3	4	5	6	6	7
54	7324	7332	7340	7348	7356	7364	7372	7380	7388	7396	1	2	2	3	4	5	6	6	7
55	7404	7412	7419	7427	7435	7443	7451	7459	7466	7474	1	2	2	3	4	5	5	6	7
56	7482	7490	7497	7505	7513	7520	7528	7536	7543	7551	1	2	2	3	4	5	5	6	7
57	7559	7566	7574	7582	7589	7597	7604	7612	7619	7627	1	2	2	3	4	5	5	6	7
58	7634	7642	7649	7657	7664	7672	7679	7686	7694	7701	1	1	2	3	4	4	5	6	7
59	7709	7716	7723	7731	7738	7745	7752	7760	7767	7774	1	1	2	3	4	4	5	6	7
60	7782	7789	7796	7803	7810	7818	7825	7832	7839	7846	1	1	2	3	4	4	5	6	6
61	7853	7860	7868	7875	7882	7889	7896	7903	7910	7917	1	1	2	3	4	4	5	6	6
62	7924	7931	7938	7945	7952	7959	7966	7973	7980	7987	1	1	2	3	3	4	5	6	6
63	7993	8000	8007	8014	8021	8028	8035	8041	8048	8055	1	1	2	3	3	4	5	5	6
64	8062	8069	8075	8082	8089	8096	8102	8109	8116	8122	1	1	2	3	3	4	5	5	6
65	8129	8136	8142	8149	8156	8162	8169	8176	8182	8189	1	1	2	3	3	4	5	5	6
66	8195	8202	8209	8215	8222	8228	8235	8241	8248	8254	1	1	2	3	3	4	5	5	6
67	8261	8267	8274	8280	8287	8293	8299	8306	8312	8319	1	1	2	3	3	4	5	5	6
68	8325	8331	8338	8344	8351	8357	8363	8370	8376	8382	1	1	2	3	3	4	4	5	6
69	8388	8395	8401	8407	8414	8420	8426	8432	8439	8445	1	1	2	2	3	4	4	5	6
70	8451	8457	8463	8470	8476	8482	8488	8494	8500	8506	1	1	2	2	3	4	4	5	6
71	8513	8519	8525	8531	8537	8543	8549	8555	8561	8567	1	1	2	2	3	4	4	5	5
72	8573	8579	8585	8591	8597	8603	8609	8615	8621	8627	1	1	2	2	3	4	4	5	5
73	8633	8639	8645	8651	8657	8663	8669	8675	8681	8686	1	1	2	2	3	4	4	5	5
74	8692	8698	8704	8710	8716	8722	8727	8733	8739	8745	1	1	2	2	3	4	4	5	5
75	8751	8756	8762	8768	8774	8779	8785	8791	8797	8802	1	1	2	2	3	3	4	5	5
76	8808	8814	8820	8825	8831	8837	8842	8848	8854	8859	1	1	2	2	3	3	4	5	5
77	8865	8871	8876	8882	8887	8893	8899	8904	8910	8915	1	1	2	2	3	3	4	4	5
78	8921	8927	8932	8938	8943	8949	8954	8960	8965	8971	1	1	2	2	3	3	4	4	5
79	8976	8982	8987	8993	8998	9004	9009	9015	9020	9025	1	1	2	2	3	3	4	4	5
80	9031	9036	9042	9047	9053	9058	9063	9069	9074	9079	1	1	2	2	3	3	4	4	5
81	9085	9090	9096	9101	9106	9112	9117	9122	9128	9133	1	1	2	2	3	3	4	4	5
82	9138	9143	9149	9154	9159	9165	9170	9175	9180	9186	1	1	2	2	3	3	4	4	5
83	9191	9196	9201	9206	9212	9217	9222	9227	9232	9238	1	1	2	2	3	3	4	4	5
84	9243	9248	9253	9258	9263	9269	9274	9279	9284	9289	1	1	2	2	3	3	4	4	5
85	9294	9299	9304	9309	9315	9320	9325	9330	9335	9340	1	1	2	2	3	3	4	4	5
86	9345	9350	9355	9360	9365	9370	9375	9380	9385	9390	1	1	2	2	3	3	4	4	5
87	9395	9400	9405	9410	9415	9420	9425	9430	9435	9440	0	1	1	2	2	3	3	4	4
88	9445	9450	9455	9460	9465	9469	9474	9479	9484	9489	0	1	1	2	2	3	3	4	4
89	9494	9499	9504	9509	9513	9518	9523	9528	9533	9538	0	1	1	2	2	3	3	4	4
90	9542	9547	9552	9557	9562	9566	9571	9576	9581	9586	0	1	1	2	2	3	3	4	4
91	9590	9595	9600	9605	9609	9614	9619	9624	9628	9633	0	1	1	2	2	3	3	4	4
92	9638	9643	9647	9652	9657	9661	9666	9671	9675	9680	0	1	1	2	2	3	3	4	4
93	9685	9689	9694	9699	9703	9708	9713	9717	9722	9727	0	1	1	2	2	3	3	4	4
94	9731	9736	9741	9745	9750	9754	9759	9763	9768	9773	0	1	1	2	2	3	3	4	4
95	9777	9782	9786	9791	9795	9800	9805	9809	9814	9818	0	1	1	2	2	3	3	4	4
96	9823	9827	9832	9836	9841	9845	9850	9854	9859	9863	0	1	1	2	2	3	3	4	4
97	9868	9872	9877	9881	9886	9890	9894	9899	9903	9908	0	1	1	2	2	3	3	4	4
98	9912	9917	9921	9926	9930	9934	9939	9943	9948	9952	0	1	1	2	2	3	3	4	4
99	9956	9961	9965	9969	9974	9978	9983	9987	9991	9996	0	1	1	2	2	3	3	3	4

ANTILOGARITHMS

	0	**1**	**2**	**3**	**4**	**5**	**6**	**7**	**8**	**9**	**1**	**2**	**3**	**4**	**5**	**6**	**7**	**8**	**9**
·00	1000	1002	1005	1007	1009	1012	1014	1016	1019	1021	0	0	1	1	1	1	2	2	2
·01	1023	1026	1028	1030	1033	1035	1038	1040	1042	1045	0	0	1	1	1	1	2	2	2
·02	1047	1050	1052	1054	1057	1059	1062	1064	1067	1069	0	0	1	1	1	1	2	2	2
·03	1072	1074	1076	1079	1081	1084	1086	1089	1091	1094	0	0	1	1	1	1	2	2	2
·04	1096	1099	1102	1104	1107	1109	1112	1114	1117	1119	0	1	1	1	1	2	2	2	2
·05	1122	1125	1127	1130	1132	1135	1138	1140	1143	1146	0	1	1	1	1	2	2	2	2
·06	1148	1151	1153	1156	1159	1161	1164	1167	1169	1172	0	1	1	1	1	2	2	2	2
·07	1175	1178	1180	1183	1186	1189	1191	1194	1197	1199	0	1	1	1	1	2	2	2	2
·08	1202	1205	1208	1211	1213	1216	1219	1222	1225	1227	0	1	1	1	1	2	2	2	3
·09	1230	1233	1236	1239	1242	1245	1247	1250	1253	1256	0	1	1	1	1	2	2	2	3
·10	1259	1262	1265	1268	1271	1274	1276	1279	1282	1285	0	1	1	1	1	2	2	2	3
·11	1288	1291	1294	1297	1300	1303	1306	1309	1312	1315	0	1	1	1	2	2	2	2	3
·12	1318	1321	1324	1327	1330	1334	1337	1340	1343	1346	0	1	1	1	2	2	2	2	3
·13	1349	1352	1355	1358	1361	1365	1368	1371	1374	1377	0	1	1	1	2	2	2	3	3
·14	1380	1384	1387	1390	1393	1396	1400	1403	1406	1409	0	1	1	1	2	2	2	3	3
·15	1413	1416	1419	1422	1426	1429	1432	1435	1439	1442	0	1	1	1	2	2	2	3	3
·16	1445	1449	1452	1455	1459	1462	1466	1469	1472	1476	0	1	1	1	2	2	2	3	3
·17	1479	1483	1486	1489	1493	1496	1500	1503	1507	1510	0	1	1	1	2	2	2	3	3
·18	1514	1517	1521	1524	1528	1531	1535	1538	1542	1545	0	1	1	1	2	2	3	3	3
·19	1549	1552	1556	1560	1563	1567	1570	1574	1578	1581	0	1	1	1	2	2	3	3	3
·20	1585	1589	1592	1596	1600	1603	1607	1611	1614	1618	0	1	1	1	2	2	3	3	3
·21	1622	1626	1629	1633	1637	1641	1644	1648	1652	1656	0	1	1	2	2	2	3	3	3
·22	1660	1663	1667	1671	1675	1679	1683	1687	1690	1694	0	1	1	2	2	2	3	3	3
·23	1698	1702	1706	1710	1714	1718	1722	1726	1730	1734	0	1	1	2	2	2	3	3	4
·24	1738	1742	1746	1750	1754	1758	1762	1766	1770	1774	0	1	1	2	2	2	3	3	4
·25	1778	1782	1786	1791	1795	1799	1803	1807	1811	1816	0	1	1	2	2	2	3	3	4
·26	1820	1824	1828	1832	1837	1841	1845	1849	1854	1858	0	1	1	2	2	3	3	3	4
·27	1862	1866	1871	1875	1879	1884	1888	1892	1897	1901	0	1	1	2	2	3	3	3	4
·28	1905	1910	1914	1919	1923	1928	1932	1936	1941	1945	0	1	1	2	2	3	3	4	4
·29	1950	1954	1959	1963	1968	1972	1977	1982	1986	1991	0	1	1	2	2	3	3	4	4
·30	1995	2000	2004	2009	2014	2018	2023	2028	2032	2037	0	1	1	2	2	3	3	4	4
·31	2042	2046	2051	2056	2061	2065	2070	2075	2080	2084	0	1	1	2	2	3	3	4	4
·32	2089	2094	2099	2104	2109	2113	2118	2123	2128	2133	0	1	1	2	2	3	3	4	4
·33	2138	2143	2148	2153	2158	2163	2168	2173	2178	2183	0	1	1	2	2	3	3	4	4
·34	2188	2193	2198	2203	2208	2213	2218	2223	2228	2234	1	1	2	2	3	3	4	4	5
·35	2239	2244	2249	2254	2259	2265	2270	2275	2280	2286	1	1	2	2	3	3	4	4	5
·36	2291	2296	2301	2307	2312	2317	2323	2328	2333	2339	1	1	2	2	3	3	4	4	5
·37	2344	2350	2355	2360	2366	2371	2377	2382	2388	2393	1	1	2	2	3	3	4	4	5
·38	2399	2404	2410	2415	2421	2427	2432	2438	2443	2449	1	1	2	2	3	3	4	4	5
·39	2455	2460	2466	2472	2477	2483	2489	2495	2500	2506	1	1	2	2	3	3	4	5	5
·40	2512	2518	2523	2529	2535	2541	2547	2553	2559	2564	1	1	2	2	3	4	4	5	5
·41	2570	2576	2582	2588	2594	2600	2606	2612	2618	2624	1	1	2	2	3	4	4	5	5
·42	2630	2636	2642	2649	2655	2661	2667	2673	2679	2685	1	1	2	2	3	4	4	5	6
·43	2692	2698	2704	2710	2716	2723	2729	2735	2742	2748	1	1	2	3	3	4	4	5	6
·44	2754	2761	2767	2773	2780	2786	2793	2799	2805	2812	1	1	2	3	3	4	4	5	6
·45	2818	2825	2831	2838	2844	2851	2858	2864	2871	2877	1	1	2	3	3	4	5	5	6
·46	2884	2891	2897	2904	2911	2917	2924	2931	2938	2944	1	1	2	3	3	4	5	5	6
·47	2951	2958	2965	2972	2979	2985	2992	2999	3006	3013	1	1	2	3	3	4	5	5	6
·48	3020	3027	3034	3041	3048	3055	3062	3069	3076	3083	1	1	2	3	4	4	5	6	6
·49	3090	3097	3105	3112	3119	3126	3133	3141	3148	3155	1	1	2	3	4	4	5	6	6

ANTILOGARITHMS

	0	1	2	3	4	5	6	7	8	9	1	2	3	4	5	6	7	8	9
·50	3162	3170	3177	3184	3192	3199	3206	3214	3321	3228	1	1	2	3	4	4	5	6	7
·51	3236	3243	3251	3258	3266	3273	3281	3289	3296	3304	1	2	2	3	4	5	5	6	7
·52	3311	3319	3327	3334	3342	3350	3357	3365	3373	3381	1	2	2	3	4	5	5	6	7
·53	3388	3396	3404	3412	3420	3428	3436	3443	3451	3459	1	2	2	3	4	5	5	6	7
·54	3467	3475	3483	3491	3499	3508	3516	3524	3532	3540	1	2	2	3	4	5	6	6	7
·55	3548	3556	3565	3573	3581	3589	3597	3606	3614	3622	1	2	2	3	4	5	6	7	7
·56	3631	3639	3648	3656	3664	3673	3681	3690	3698	3707	1	2	3	3	4	5	6	7	8
·57	3715	3724	3733	3741	3750	3758	3767	3776	3784	3793	1	2	3	3	4	5	6	7	8
·58	3802	3811	3819	3828	3837	3846	3855	3864	3873	3882	1	2	3	4	4	5	6	7	8
·59	3890	3899	3908	3917	3926	3936	3945	3954	3963	3972	1	2	3	4	5	5	6	7	8
·60	3981	3990	3999	4009	4018	4027	4036	4046	4055	4064	1	2	3	4	5	6	6	7	8
·61	4074	4083	4093	4102	4111	4121	4130	4140	4150	4159	1	2	3	4	5	6	7	8	9
·62	4169	4178	4188	4198	4207	4217	4227	4236	4246	4256	1	2	3	4	5	6	7	8	9
·63	4266	4276	4285	4295	4305	4315	4325	4335	4345	4355	1	2	3	4	5	6	7	8	9
·64	4365	4375	4385	4395	4406	4416	4426	4436	4446	4457	1	2	3	4	5	6	7	8	9
·65	4467	4477	4487	4498	4508	4519	4529	4539	4550	4560	1	2	3	4	5	6	7	8	9
·66	4571	4581	4592	4603	4613	4624	4634	4645	4656	4667	1	2	3	4	5	6	7	9	10
·67	4677	4688	4699	4710	4721	4732	4742	4753	4764	4775	1	2	3	4	5	7	8	9	10
·68	4786	4797	4808	4819	4831	4842	4853	4864	4875	4887	1	2	3	4	6	7	8	9	10
·69	4898	4909	4920	4932	4943	4955	4966	4977	4989	5000	1	2	3	5	6	7	8	9	10
·70	5012	5023	5035	5047	5058	5070	5082	5093	5105	5117	1	2	4	5	6	7	8	9	11
·71	5129	5140	5152	5164	5176	5188	5200	5212	5224	5236	1	2	4	5	6	7	8	10	11
·72	5248	5260	5272	5284	5297	5309	5321	5333	5246	5358	1	2	4	5	6	7	9	10	11
·73	5370	5383	5395	5408	5420	5433	5445	5458	5470	5483	1	3	4	5	6	8	9	10	11
·74	5495	5508	5521	5534	5546	5559	5572	5585	5598	5610	1	3	4	5	6	8	9	10	11
·75	5623	5636	5649	5662	5675	5689	5702	5715	5728	5741	1	3	4	5	7	8	9	10	12
·76	5754	5768	5781	5794	5808	5821	5834	5848	5861	5875	1	3	4	5	7	8	9	11	12
·77	5888	5902	5916	5929	5943	5957	5970	5984	5998	6012	1	3	4	5	7	8	10	11	12
·78	6026	6039	6053	6067	6081	6095	6109	6124	6138	6152	1	3	4	6	7	8	10	11	13
·79	6166	6180	6194	6209	6223	6237	6252	6266	6281	6295	1	3	4	6	7	9	10	11	13
·80	6310	6324	6339	6353	6368	6383	6397	6412	6427	6442	1	3	4	6	7	9	10	12	13
·81	6457	6471	6486	6501	6516	6531	6546	6561	6577	6592	2	3	5	6	8	9	11	12	14
·82	6607	6622	6637	6653	6668	6683	6699	6714	6730	6745	2	3	5	6	8	9	11	12	14
·83	6761	6776	6792	6808	6823	6839	6855	6871	6887	6902	2	3	5	6	8	9	11	13	14
·84	6918	6934	6950	6966	6982	6998	7015	7031	7047	7063	2	3	5	6	8	10	11	13	15
·85	7079	7096	7112	7129	7145	7161	7178	7194	7211	7228	2	3	5	7	8	10	12	13	15
·86	7244	7261	7278	7295	7311	7328	7345	7362	7379	7396	2	3	5	7	8	10	12	13	15
·87	7413	7430	7447	7464	7482	7499	7516	7534	7551	7568	2	3	5	7	9	10	12	14	16
·88	7586	7603	7621	7638	7656	7674	7691	7709	7727	7745	2	4	5	7	9	11	12	14	16
·89	7762	7780	7798	7816	7834	7852	7870	7889	7907	7925	2	4	5	7	9	11	13	14	16
·90	7943	7962	7980	7998	8017	8035	8054	8072	8091	8110	2	4	6	7	9	11	13	15	17
·91	8128	8147	8166	8185	8204	8222	8241	8260	8279	8299	2	4	6	8	9	11	13	15	17
·92	8318	8337	8356	8375	8395	8414	8433	8453	8472	8492	2	4	6	8	10	12	14	15	17
·93	8511	8531	8551	8570	8590	8610	8630	8650	8670	8690	2	4	6	8	10	12	14	16	18
·94	8710	8730	8750	8770	8790	8810	8831	8851	8872	8892	2	4	6	8	10	12	14	16	18
·95	8913	8933	8954	8974	8995	9016	9036	9057	9078	9099	2	4	6	8	10	12	15	17	19
·96	9120	9141	9162	9183	9204	9226	9247	9268	9290	9311	2	4	6	8	11	13	15	17	19
·97	9333	9354	9376	9397	9419	9441	9462	9484	9506	9528	2	4	7	9	11	13	15	17	20
·98	9550	9572	9594	9616	9638	9661	9683	9705	9727	9750	2	4	7	9	11	13	16	18	20
·99	9772	9795	9817	9840	9863	9886	9908	9931	9954	9977	2	5	7	9	11	14	16	18	20

PLATE III. PENDULUM CAR
(*French National Railways*)

PLATE IV. PIPELINES ENTERING ABADAN
(*British Petroleum Co. Ltd.*)